My
Beanie
Baby™
Binder

Expressly for Casual to Compulsive Collectors

by Peg et. al.

Published by
Vine Street Publishing, Inc.

Third Edition

Dedication
To Joan, who started it

"My Beanie Baby™ Binder: Expressly for Casual to Compulsive Collectors":
Researched and written by Peg Fugal, PLBF, Inc.
Photography by Brian Twede, Twede Photography
Art Direction by Jayson Fugal, PLBF, Inc.
Design by Randall Smith, Randall Smith Associates

Special thanks:
to Joan Remund for allowing BBB to photograph her 1/1/97 and 5/11/97 Retireds
to Wes and Geraldine Dalley for allowing BBB to photograph their '95–'96 Retireds
and to Kathy and Collin Ainge for allowing BBB to photograph their 1/1/99 Beanie Buddies

Vine Street Publishing, Inc.
Box 97
Orem, UT 84059
(801) 222-9670; 222-9680 fax
www.mybeaniebabybinder.com

ISBN 0-9666105-0-4
First printing: August, 1998
Second printing: October, 1998
Third printing: February, 1999

Distributor & retailer inquiries welcome

First things first

1. Fill in your name, address & phone number on inside front cover with permanent ink pen or marker

2. Following the mini table of contents on each tab, collate tabs into pages (all intro, retired, and list pages are numbered for your convenience)

3. Find My Beanie Baby Binder Order Form located in the back of your binder and order your FREE Clubby page, Auto-Ship Service, additional books, and empty binders

4. Show off your BBB to all your friends and tell them where to buy it

5. Show off your BBB to all your favorite Beanie retailers and bookstores and then give them the phone number on the back of the binder to call for ordering

6. Compile and mail to us a list of the Beanie Baby retailers in your area (including name, address, phone & fax) and we'll send you a FREE gift!

Thanks for your business! Here's to a long, fun-filled Beanie buddy relationship!

Introduction

Welcome

Greetings, fellow Ty® Beanie Baby™ collector! Welcome to the Beanie Baby™ Binder—the first Beanie Baby™ publication designed expressly for casual to compulsive collectors. (Which are you?)

You've made a wise purchase. To amass the amount of information included in this one binder, you'd have to buy more than a dozen Beanie Baby™ publications—every one of which is out-dated before it is ever released—and totalling a cost that is ten times what you just paid for this Beanie Baby™ Binder.

The Beanie Baby™ Binder is the only Beanie Baby™ publication that never goes out of date—because it updates itself—as you will soon see.

The big difference

There are a handful of Beanie Baby™ publications available in the marketplace. Most are desk-top publishing efforts by amateurs. None contain the all-inclusive, detailed information necessary for casual to compulsive collectors.

The Beanie Baby™ Binder is the first Beanie Baby™ publication researched and written by a best-selling writer, photographed by an award-winning photographer, and designed by an award-winning designer. Compare the Beanie Baby™ Binder with other Beanie Baby™ publications and you'll see what we mean!

Chocolate® the moose:
1 of 9 original Beanie Babies®

More importantly, the Beanie Baby™ Binder is the last Beanie Baby™ publication you'll ever have to buy—because it never goes out of date!

With the binder-tab format, you can move pages from "New Releases" to "Currents" to "Retireds" as needed.

With our exclusive Auto-Ship Service, you'll automatically receive in the mail new tabs and individual Beanie Baby™ pages as Beanie Babies® are released and retired and new intro pages and lists as updated.

Also included are never-before-compiled Beanie Baby™ lists for your information and shopping/collecting convenience.

About Peg

I was born in Vermont and raised on a dairy farm in western New York, the first daughter and middle child of a southern mother and a New Englander father who met and married during the war.

For the past 28 years, I have lived in Utah, where I graduated with honors, a degree in communications, and a secondary teaching certificate from Brigham Young University—where I also met and married my husband Sherm (of Utah pioneer stock). Together we have raised four handsome, healthy, bright, witty, spiritual, accomplished sons: Jayson, Josh, Jake, and Jer. Together we have built three successful businesses.

I have spent a lifetime writing. I began writing and illustrating stories at the tender age of eight. I wrote my first book, a mystery, when I was ten. I began stringing for the local daily newspaper when I was 16. I wrote my first short story at 17. My writing earned me full scholarships to both prep school and college. I sold my first short story when I was a freshman in college. While in college, I wrote for the daily campus newspaper, spent a summer in southeast Alaska covering the clear-cut logging controversy for several regional newspapers and magazines, and worked as a radio and television personality. Just prior to graduating from college, I started my own advertising agency and marketing firm, where I have spent the past 24 years writing and producing award-winning advertising. I have taught writing at BYU; I have ghost-written two best-selling self-help books; I have co-authored two best-selling religious books and two best-selling pocket books; I have kept journals and scrapbooks my whole life.

The point is, I know how to write. The amazing thing is, I never thought I'd write a Beanie Baby™ book. It kind of snuck up on me.

Cubbie™ the bear:
1 of 9 original Beanie Babies®

A complete collection in 4 days

When Beanie Babies® first came out, I saw them in a store and thought, "Oh, these are cute; I ought to start collecting them." I didn't. And I never saw them again.

Christmas of '97, my oldest and dearest friend Joan gave to me "Peace™". By that point, I had forgotten all about Beanie Babies®, and had no idea what I had—or to where it would lead.

In late January of '98, I ran across the first big display of Beanie Babies® I had ever seen in one of my favorite gift shops. I called Joan on my cell phone to ask if she needed me to pick up anything for her. She had everything.

My youngest son Jeremy was with me. Together, we decided to buy seven jungle Beanie Babies®, which cost $9.99 each. On the way home, we discussed collecting all the Beanie Babies®, decided against it, and determined to collect only the jungle Beanie Babies®. We called and told Joan of our decision and she invited us to come see her collection. We were not prepared for what awaited us.

Joan has a seven-shelf, lighted curio cabinet filled with every current Beanie Baby™, as well as many of the retired Beanie Babies®. I was pea-green with envy. I didn't like Joan having something I did not.

I am a collector by nature. Because I am a writer, I am also a prolific reader and, hence, a prolific collector of books. In fact, I have a collection of children's books that rival most libraries. As a successful businesswoman decorating my dream home, I also started collecting original watercolors, as well as limited edition prints, not to mention Hummels and Lladro. My business has taken me all over the world. In my travels, I have collected art treasures from more than 20 countries, including music boxes, inlaid wood boxes, vases, baskets, trays, and figurines. Because my business requires me to dress up almost daily and to entertain regularly, I also collect dinner rings. Because I had no daughters for whom to buy dolls, I started collecting the American Girl dolls for myself. I collect two Department 56 Christmas villages: New England and North Pole, as well as mercury glass ornaments, and the Fontanini nativity. The point is, I didn't need another thing to collect.

While viewing Joan's collection, she gave me three more jungle Beanie Babies®. A few days later, she delivered an early birthday present—two more jungle Beanie Babies®. I now had 12.

A mutual friend, Melanie, commented, "Pretty soon, you'll have them all."

"Oh, no;" I assured her, "I'm collecting only the jungle Beanie Babies®." She laughed.

A snobby neighbor Nat commented, "Beanie Babies®! That's so beneath you."

I felt a little embarrassed.

That was on Tuesday.

Wednesday morning I was out running errands when I came across one Beanie Baby™ retailer after another. Funny I had never noticed them before. I found and bought several more jungle Beanie Babies®.

But the others beckoned—and, in less than an hour, I succumbed.

Throughout the day, I stopped at one Beanie Baby™ retailer after another until I had 17 more Beanie Babies® hidden in various sacks under a blanket in my car. I could not admit to myself, let alone to anyone else, what I had done. I agonized all night.

Thursday morning I decided to go for it. Business be darned, I spent the entire day in mad pursuit of Beanie Babies®, amassing 21 more that day, for a total of 50.

That evening, I confessed my compulsion to Joan. She said, "Well, as long as you have that many, you might as well collect them all." She then generously sold to me, from her own collection, at her cost, hard-to-find and retired Beanie Babies® I might not otherwise have found or afforded. (Everyone should have a friend as generous as Joan.)

I hunted Beanie Babies® all day Friday and Saturday.

By Saturday evening, I had more than 100 Beanie Babies®—all the new releases, all the currents, all the hard-to-finds, and the last two sets of retireds. When I showed my list to Joan that evening, she exclaimed, "You've collected in four days what it took me more than a year to collect!" My story spread like wildfire. Soon I was legend. And people expect something legendary of legends.

A seed is planted

During my four-day Beanie Baby™ hunt, I found myself too often confused and frustrated. Being new to Beanie Babies®, I had no idea how many there were, what kind there were, what their names were, what they looked like, which were new releases, which were current, which were hard-to-find, or which were retired and when. In fact, there was so little written information available at that time, that I began compiling my own on my computer, which I updated after each find. The seeds of the Beanie Baby™ Binder had been planted. What one would expect of a legend.

With a passion that borders on profession, I've decided to put my talents to work to produce the first-ever Beanie Baby™ Binder for casual to compulsive collectors just like me. There is nothing else like it in the marketplace. There is no easier or cheaper way to catalogue your collection. A more comprehensive compilation of facts has never been published. There have never been better pictures, design, or printing. As one would expect, the Beanie Baby™ Binder is already legend.

Flash™ the dolphin:
1 of 9 original Beanie Babies®

Content

Please note that your Beanie Baby™ Binder has 5 different kinds of pages:
1. Tabs
2. Intro pages
3. Individual Beanie Baby™ pages
4. Lists
5. Forms

Also note that there are 12 different tabs:
1. New Releases
2. Currents
3. 12/98 Retireds
4. 9/98 Retireds
5. 5/1/98 Retireds
6. 12/31/97 Retireds
7. 10/1/97 Retireds
8. 5/11/97 Retireds
9. 1/1/97 Retireds
10. '95–'96 Retireds

11. Teenies/Buddies
12. Lists & Forms

Note as well that each individual Beanie Baby™ page lists 17 facts:
1. Name
2. Picture
3. Type
4. Categories
5. Style no.
6. Birthday
7. Released
8. Retired
9. Position
10. Tags
11. Teenie
12. Description
13. Replaces
14. Variations
15. Oddities
16. Commentary
17. Poem

To amass this amount of information on your own would require you to buy more than a dozen different Beanie Baby™ publications—most of which are out-of-date before they're ever released—and totalling in cost ten times what you paid for this Beanie Baby™ Binder. Much of the information compiled here is available only in this Beanie Baby™ Binder. And none of this information is dated. In fact, the Beanie Baby™ Binder is the only Beanie Baby™ publication that updates itself, as you will see.

Using your Beanie Baby™ Binder (BBB)

12 TABS

When you open your BBB, you will note that it is only loosely collated. Half the fun of the BBB is collating it yourself. The following will help you do so.

1. New Releases
- Place under this tab New Release Beanie Babies®
- Because New Release Beanie Babies® are always the most difficult to find, we have segregated them into their own section
- When the next set of New Release Beanie Babies® comes out, move these pages to the appropriate section
- As is the case with all New Release Beanie Babies®, they are hard to find and often cost more than suggested retail; don't panic; eventually every retailer will receive their allotment that you can purchase for suggested retail

2. Currents
- Place under this tab Beanie Babies® currently in circulation
- When these Beanie Babies® retire, move these pages to the appropriate retired section
- Though current Beanie Babies® are usually readily available at suggested retail, some styles become so popular that they are hard-to-find and end up selling for more than suggested retail; however, all Beanie Babies® usually remain in the marketplace long enough for you to eventually find all of them at suggested retail

3. 12/98 Retireds
- Place under this tab the 26 Beanie Babies® that retired 12/98
- These pages will never move again
(Pages numbered 1-26)

4. 9/98 Retireds
- Place under this tab the 13 Beanie Babies® that retired 9/98
- These pages will never move again
(Pages numbered 1-13)

5. 5/1/98 Retireds
- Place under this tab the 28 Beanie Babies® that retired 5/1/98
- These pages will never move again
(Pages numbered 1-28)

6. 12/31/97 Retireds
- Place under this tab the 9 Beanie Babies® that retired 12/31/97
- These pages will never move again

(Pages numbered 1-9)

7. 10/1/97 Retireds
- Place under this tab the 11 Beanie Babies® that retired 10/1/97
- These pages will never move again

(Pages numbered 1-11)

8. 5/11/97 Retireds
- Place under this tab the 9 Beanie Babies® that retired 5/11/97
- These pages will never move again

(Pages numbered 1-9)

9. 1/1/97 Retireds
- Place under this tab the 9 Beanie Babies® that retired 1/1/97
- These pages will never move again

(Pages numbered 1-9)

Legs™ the frog:
1 of 9 original Beanie Babies®

10. '95–'96 Retireds
- Place under this tab the 23 Beanie Babies® that retired in '95–'96
- These pages will never move again

(Pages numbered 1-23)

(All retired Beanie Babies® are costly: the longer they have been retired, the costlier they become)

11. Teenies™/Buddies®
- Place under this tab all the McDonald's Teenie Beanie Babies™ pages and all the Beanie Buddies® pages
- These pages will never move again

(Teenie™ promotions last a week or two; thereafter, Teenies® are considered retired and re-sell accordingly)

(Beanie Buddies® were introduced 9/98; because they were new, gorgeous and in short supply, they immediately sky-rocketed in value and continue to do so, even before retirement)

12. Lists & Forms

Under this tab you will find:

- 5 comprehensive Beanie Baby™ lists for your information and shopping/collecting convenience:
  1. Current Beanie Babies®
  2. Retired Beanie Babies® & Values (prepared by antique dealer Kathy Ainge)
  3. Beanie Babies® by date of release
  4. Beanie Baby™ Multiples
  5. Beanie Baby™ Birthdays

- BBB Order Form to order:
  1. FREE Clubby™ page
  2. Auto-Ship Service
  3. Additional complete "My Beanie Baby™ Binder"s
  4. Empty "My Beanie Baby™ Binder"s

INDIVIDUAL BEANIE BABY™ PAGES

You will note that each individual Beanie Baby™ page lists 17 facts about that Beanie Baby™—the most comprehensive compilation of information ever available on that Beanie Baby™.

1. Name
Every Beanie Baby™ has a name given to it by Ty® Inc. Those names headline each individual Beanie Baby™ page. Note the 9 original Beanie Babies® have a special designation.

2. Picture
In all of Beaniedom, never have better pictures been taken of our beloved Beanie Babies®, thanks to the creativity (not to mention the patience and long-suffering) of photographer Brian Twede and art director Jayson Fugal. Please note that every picture contains a hand-carved wooden block containing the first letter in the name of that Beanie Baby™, as a means of helping you learn and remember that Beanie Baby's™ name.

3. Type
Because what each Beanie Baby™ is, is not always readily apparent, we list type here. Poems usually indicate gender of Beanie Baby™, also listed here. Some Beanie Babies® have no gender indicated. No other Beanie Baby™ publication lists type or gender.

4. Categories
Because there are so many Beanie Babies®, it sometimes helps to categorize them, for ease in remembering, as well as in collecting them. Some Beanie Babies® fit into more than one category. For instance, Gobbles™ the turkey fits into the bird category, as well as the farm animals category, as well as the woodland animals category. Feel free to write in the space provided any other categories that come to mind. No other Beanie Baby™ publication categorizes.

Patti® the platypus:
1 of 9 original Beanie Babies®

5. Style no.
Beanie Baby™ style numbers can be confusing because they are sometimes inconsistent. Sometimes you will find two or three different Beanie Babies®, each with the same style number. Sometimes you will find four or five variations of the same Beanie Baby™, each with the same style number. Sometimes, you will find Beanie Babies® with no style numbers.

6. & 7. Birthday & Released

Though every Beanie Baby™ has a birthday, few have ever been released on their birthdays, which might make you question the reason for birthdays. Who knows? Perhaps birthdays reflect the day Ty® determined to make that Beanie Baby™, or the day the design of that Beanie Baby™ was completed, or the day production of that Beanie Baby™ commenced. Some collectors get a kick out of knowing that a particular Beanie Baby™ was born on their birthday, or under their sign of the zodiac; sometimes, that Beanie Baby™ becomes their own personal mascot.

8. Retired

Those pages with dates have obviously been retired and belong under the appropriate tabs. Those pages without dates are either New Releases or Currents and belong under those tabs. When a New Release or Current retires, write in the retired date, and move to the appropriate retired tab. (If you are on Auto-Ship, you will automatically receive in the mail additional retired tabs as needed.)

9. Position

Some Beanie Babies® lay down; some sit up; some appear to be swimming; birds look like they are perched, ready to take flight; insects look like they are crawling; we indicate what each Beanie Baby™ is doing (not to be confused with pose of Beanie Baby™ in photo). No other Beanie Baby™ publication lists position.

10. Tags

Hang tags are usually attached at the ear with a plastic string. There are five generations of hang tags.

The Beanie Babies Collection
Humphrey ™ · Style 4060
© 1993 Ty Inc. Oakbrook, IL. USA
All Rights Reserved. Caution:
Remove this tag before giving
toy to a child. For ages 5 and up.
Handmade in China
Surface
Wash.

Generation 1 (1993)
(w/ 1st generation tush tag)

Generation 2 (mid 1994)
(w/ 1st generation tush tag)

Generation 3 (mid 1995)
(w/ 1st & 2nd generation tush tag)

Generation 4 (mid 1996)
(w/ 3rd generation tush tag)

Generation 5 (1998)
(w/ 4th-6th generation tush tag)
("original" & "surface" misspelled on 10 different styles of Beanie Babies®)

The dates indicate when that hang tag was introduced; you will also note which hang tags appeared with which tush tags.

Tush tags are usually sewn into a bottom seam. There are six generations of tush tags.

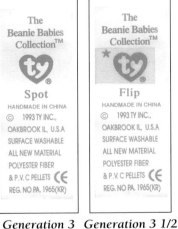

Generation 1   *Generation 2*   *Generation 3*   *Generation 3 1/2*
(1993 & '95)   *(1993 & '95)*   *(1993, '95, '96)*

Generation 4   *Generation 5*   *Generation 6*   *Generation 7*
(1993, '95, '96)   *(1993, '95-'97)*   *(1993-'98)*   *(1999)*
(w/ red stamp inside)

The dates indicate which copyright dates appeared on those tush tags. The 6th generation tush tag comes with a red stamp inside, which is one way to guard against counterfeits. The 7th generation tush tag is holographic to discourage counterfeits

Canadian Beanie Babies® come with two tush tags: one in English and one in French.

You will note on each individual Beanie Baby™ page how many generations of tags that particular Beanie Baby™ has been through. The longer the Beanie Baby™ has been in circulation, the more generations of tags it will have. More current releases are available in only the latest tags. The older the tags, the more valuable the Beanie Baby™. For future reference, indicate which generation your tags are.

11. Teenie
If a Teenie version of that Beanie Baby™ exists, we indicate such here. If and when a Teenie of that Beanie Baby™ is released, write the date of that release here.

12. Description
Each individual BBB page includes a detailed description of that particular Beanie Baby™, from the color and texture of its fabric, to its distinguishing characteristics, to the color of its thread whiskers and/or mouth. No other Beanie Baby™ publication offers this kind of detailed description.

13., 14., & 15. Replaces, Variations & Oddities
Some newer Beanie Babies® "replace" previous Beanie Babies®. For instance, Ewey™ the cream lamb "replaces" Fleece™ the white lamb; Luke™ the black lab "replaces" Fetch™ the golden lab; and Slippery™ the gray seal "replaces" Seamore the white seal.

There have been several "variations" of some Beanie Babies®. For instance, Inky™ the pink octopus appeared earlier as a tan octopus. The same holds true for Lucky™ the ladybug, who first appeared with felt spots and later with printed spots.

Inky™ the tan octopus has appeared with several "oddities": with a mouth, without a mouth, with seven legs, with eight legs.

The BBB is the only Beanie Baby™ publication that has compiled all of these facts on the same page.

16. Commentary
Interesting things we have learned about that particular Beanie Baby™ from our research and/or collecting experience.

17. Poem
Every single Beanie Baby™ poem is personally penned by Beanie Baby™ creator Ty Warner. Considering the fact that he releases as many as 30 new Beanie Babies® a year, that makes him one of the most prodigious poets in history!

Tips for casual to compulsive collectors

A little history

Ty Warner, the creator of Beanie Babies®, once worked for Dakin, the renowned plush toy manufacturer. Following that experience, Ty decided to start his own plush toy company, which manufactures several lines of plush toys, including Beanie Babies®.

Depending upon your age, you might remember that bean bag toys have been around since the early '70s. Though my sons would never admit to it now, they played as babies with bean bag dolls. But, for some reason, bean bag toys disappeared from the marketplace— probably due to some safety concern about the beans.

Pinchers™ the lobster: 1 of 9 original Beanie Babies®

Ty® Beanie Babies® didn't catch on immediately. Initially released in November of 1993, they didn't enjoy any real prominence until 1996—which is why the earliest Beanie Babies® are so rare and costly.

It was Ty®'s partnership with McDonald's (both headquartered in Oakbrook, Illinois) and the release of 10 Ty®/McDonald's Teenie Beanie Babies™ in April of 1997 that put Ty® Beanie Babies® in the spotlight. (McDonald's gave away more than 100 million Teenies that month, and twice that many the following May.) From then on America was hooked.

Today, Ty® Beanie Babies® are the hottest collectible in American collecting history. In fact, beanieologists claim there are more than 200 million Ty® Beanie Baby™ collectors worldwide.

Popularity contest

Five factors, in my opinion, contribute to the unprecedented popularity of Beanie Babies®:

1. They're so cute
2. They're well designed and made
3. Initially, they're readily available and affordable
4. After they retire, they sky-rocket in value
5. The fun of the hunt

Collectors know no bounds

Who's buying all the Beanie Babies®? My friend Joan. Me, who owns an ad agency. My son, who works for me. My girlfriend, who owns a floral shop. Her son, who is a lineman for a cable company. My neighbor, who is a 70-year-old grandma. Another neighbor, who quit her job as a grocery checker to buy and sell Beanie Babies® full time. That snobby neighbor I mentioned in the introduction. An old college chum, who is also a very wealthy woman. Another college chum, who is a Beanie Baby™ retailer. My niece and nephew, who are cute little kids. My Orkin man who admired my collection while spraying for spiders. Unlike most products, Beanie Babies® have no target market because all segments of the market collect them—a marketer's dream come true.

Crystal ball

Like all crazes, the Beanie Baby™ craze could end, but I doubt it will be in the near future. As long as Ty® keeps releasing new Beanie Babies®, everyone who has been collecting them, will continue to collect them— because true collectors do not like incomplete sets. As long as retired Beanie Babies® continue to escalate in value, people will continue collecting them as an investment they can later trade, sell, or gift.

Name that Beanie Baby™

You will note that Beanie Babies® in this binder are listed by name. Because Beanie Babies® are ordered, purchased, traded, and re-sold by name, rather than description, you need to familiarize yourself with the names of each Beanie Baby™. It's easier than you think. Begin by studying the pages in this binder. The hand-carved wooden letter blocks in each picture serve as a pneumonic device for aiding your recall of names.

Splash™ the whale:
1 of 9 original Beanie Babies®

You will quickly become so attached to your Beanie Babies® that you will know their names as well as you know the names of your friends, neighbors, relatives, and business associates—probably better.

People who do not know the names of their Beanie Babies® are not considered serious collectors— and have a very hard time communicating with other collectors.

Inspection

When buying New Release, Current, or Retired Beanie Babies®, always, always, always check the quality of the construction, as well as the state of the tags. Beanie Babies® with any flaws in their construction or tags have a reduced value when it comes to trading or re-selling. (I am glad to report that I have never found a flawed Beanie Baby™.)

Mis-tags

There have been some mis-tagged Beanie Babies® over the years. I have a "Pinky™" that is mis-tagged "Pugsly™". "Original" and "surface" were misspelled on ten different styles of Beanie Babies® with 5th generation hang tags (some "surface" corrected with stickers). When originally released, "Iggy™" the iguana and "Rainbow™" the chameleon were thought to be mis-tagged. (Actually the tags were correct: it was the fabrics that were mistakenly switched—since corrected.)

Though mis-tags are fun to find, they are of little value. Serious collectors want Beanie Babies® with correct tags. An extra set of mis-tagged Beanie Babies® might be a fun addition to your collection, but if you're collecting only one of each Beanie Baby™, make sure their tags are correct.

Spot™ the dog:
1 of 9 original Beanie Babies®

What to pay

New Release Beanie Babies® are in such demand that they often sell for more than suggested retail. I have paid as much as $30 for a New Release, for fear of not securing one before they disappear. It was a stupid thing to do. New Releases may be slow to reach retailers, but once they do, there are plenty to go around, at suggested retail. Be patient.

New Release bears are in such demand that they often sell for hundreds of dollars before readily available. Don't be sucked in. I paid $150 for my first Princess™ and Erin™, $75 and $90 for my second Princess™ and Erin™, $7 each for my third Princess™ and Erin™, and $30 each for my fourth Princess™ and Erin™. They may be slow in coming, but I am confident that Ty® will not retire a bear until it has had a fair and full run. In fact, Beanie Baby™ bears tend to remain in circulation longer than any other Beanie Babies®.

Escalating values

Beanie Baby™ values tend to follow this pattern:
    New Releases—$5 to $30
    Currents—$5 to $10
    Newly retireds—$10 to $25
    Retired for 1 to 3 months—$25 to $50
    Retired for 3 to 6 months—$50 to $75
    Retired for 6 to 12 months—$75 to $100
    Retired for more than a year—$100+
Hence, your collection of Beanie Babies® increases in value every day; collect and care for accordingly.

18

Stocking up

Knowing which Beanie Babies® to stock up on in anticipation of the next retirement is always a brain-teaser. A good rule of thumb: buy one Beanie Baby™ for your permanent collection and as many extra Beanie Babies® to later trade and/or re-sell as you can afford. I buy only one of the styles I don't like, three of the styles I do like (one for my permanent collection and two to trade and/or re-sell later), and six of the styles I think will be hot (bears, bunnies, cats, etc.).

Anticipating retireds

On May 1, 1998, Ty® did something no one expected: they retired 28 Beanie Babies® all at the same time. Ty® retired 26 Beanie Babies™ in December of '98. Previously Ty® had retired no more than 9 to 11 Beanie Babies® at a time; hence, 28 and then 26 more retireds caught most collectors off-guard—and in short supply! Beanie Babies® available for $5 one day were selling for as much as $25 the next day. Though the suggested retail for current Beanie Babies® is $5 to $7, Ty® has no control over the cost of retired Beanie Babies®.

Ty® has a history of retiring Beanie Babies® spring, fall, and winter. Before those seasons come around, make sure you have all the current Beanie Babies® you want in your permanent collection, as well as all the extras you want for later trading and/or re-selling.

Special edition Beanie Babies®

There have been several special edition Beanie Babies® with commemorative cards produced for various special events, promotions, and giveaways (e.g., Cubbie™ for a Chicago Cubs game, Maple™ for the Canadian Special Olympics, Snort® for a Chicago Bulls game, and Glory™ for the All-Star game). Initially such special editions with commemorative cards were rare and expensive. Now, due to the popularity of Beanie Babies®, there are more and more special edition Beanie Babies® with commemorative cards, making them less special, though no less valuable. Because there have been too many to track, we mention only a few of them here.

Squealer™ the pig:
1 of 9 original Beanie Babies®

Protecting, displaying & storing

Naturally, children like to play with and display their Beanie Babies® in their rooms—which means their Beanie Babies® will experience some wear and perhaps even become soiled—which is fine—Beanie Babies® were designed for children. Tag protectors and a special storage place will help prolong the lives of their Beanie Babies®.

More serious collectors should always use tag protectors, keep their Beanie Babies® out of direct sunlight, and enclosed to avoid dust damage. My girlfriend Joan keeps her Beanie Babies® in an enclosed, lighted curio cabinet. I keep mine in clear Rubbermaid® boxes in the master bedroom closet. (In fact, my collection occupies half my closet space: my husband moved his things to another closet). Some collectors store their Beanie Babies® in plexiglas® cases and stack them for display. Some collectors store their Beanie Babies® in Zip-Loc® bags. All of the aforementioned serves the purpose of protecting Beanie Babies® from wear. Use whatever system best suits your needs and budget.

Even though my Beanies Babies are in boxes in a closet, I get them out often to look at them, to take inventory, to share them with my family and fellow collectors, and to let neighborhood kids visit them. Sharing your Beanie Babies® is half the fun of collecting them.

Clubby

There is only one Beanie Baby™ missing from the BBB: Clubby™, the official Beanie Baby™ of the Beanie Babies® Official Club (BBOC). It is a royal blue plush sit-up bear with a button of the BBOC logo attached over its heart and a tie-dyed ribbon tied around its neck. To secure Clubby, one had to first purchase the BBOC kit and then fill in and mail the BBOC registration card. Six to eight weeks later, registered club members received information on how to special order Clubby. However, Clubby retired 2/15/99 and is no longer available. To secure the Clubby page for your BBB, fill in and mail the order form in the back of the binder. It's free!

Beanie Baby™ etiquette

Because I have several friends who retail Beanie Babies®, I have never had to stand in line and wait or fight with other collectors over new shipments of Beanie Babies®. I have, however, heard horror stories. When hunting for Beanie Babies®, keep this in mind: Beanie Babies® are for children. Make room for them, defer to them, let them have first dibs. There are plenty of Beanie Babies® to go around. And if there are not, then what few there are should rightfully go to the children.

To our readers

In using the Beanie Baby™ Binder, make note of what you like and dislike, what you would improve or change, and then let us hear from you. Though we have made a concerted effort to include every known fact about every Beanie Baby™, we are not perfect. If we missed an interesting fact you know, please share it with us. Thank you for your support.

The Authors
My Beanie Baby™ Binder

BEANIE BABY SHIPMENT
Thursday April 15th

For more info visit   NEW website
http://home.att.net/~BeanieHQ

LIMIT ONE   and   LIMIT ONE

Princess	Mystic	Mooch
Peace	Batty	Mac
Sammy	Luke	Butch
Hope	Nibbler	Goochy
Millennium	Hippie	Scat
Signature	Ewey	Tiny
Kicks	Prickles	Goatee
Valentina	Stilts	Slippery
Fuzz		

Also Available: Gigi-Whisper-Tracker-Loosy
Roam-Scorch-Derby-Beak-Canyon

LIMITS (as posted) are PER HOUSEHOLD
TIMES: Doors open at   10:00am
Random #drawings   9-9:30 am
No lining up before   8:00am
Anyone outside lining up before these times will be asked
to leave and will not be able to get a number.
EVERYONE wishing to purchase beanies during these
times MUST have a current identification with a picture
AND an address on same document.

1999 Signature Bear™

Type:	Bear	*Categories:*	Bears, heather	*Style no.:*	4228	

Birthday: None   *Released:* 1/1/99   *Retired:*

Position: Sitting up   *Tags:* 5th gen. hang, 7th gen. tush   *Teenie:*

Description: Brownish-gray heather plush body; red embroidered heart over heart w/ white lettering that reads: "1999 Ty"; wine-colored ribbon w/ white edging tied around neck; black plastic eyes & nose; hang tag left ear; tush tag left bottom

Replaces: None

Variations: Heather coloring varies

Oddities: No gender, birthday, or poem; first edged ribbon

Commentary: A very special Beanie Baby bear bearing the coveted signature of Beanie Baby creator, Ty Warner; a new fabric for Ty: heather; one of five heather & one of eight bears this release; destined to become the most popular and valuable Beanie bear of all time

Poem: None

My record

(Beanies are the #1 collectible in American collecting history. A complete, detailed record will vastly increase the value of this Beanie, if and when you ever appraise, trade, re-sell, gift, or bequeath it.)

Description *(which version do you have?):*

Gift from:

Date received/purchased:

Purchased from:

NAME OF PERSON OR RETAILER

ADDRESS

CITY/STATE/ZIP

PHONE

Qty. purchased: **Cost ea.**
(check one)   ❏ *Cash*   ❏ *Check*   ❏ *Charge*

Reason(s) for purchase(s):

Traded to:

NAME

ADDRESS

CITY/STATE/ZIP

PHONE

TRADED FOR

Re-sold to:

NAME

ADDRESS

CITY/STATE/ZIP

PHONE

PRICE RE-SOLD FOR

Your feelings about and/or experiences with this Beanie:

Butch™

Type:	Bull terrier	*Categories:* Dogs, spotted, white	*Style no.:* 4227

Birthday: October 2, 1998   *Released:* 1/1/99   *Retired:*

Position: Laying down   *Tags:* 5th gen. hang, 7th gen. tush   *Teenie:*

Description: White plush body w/ brown spots on left back & around right eye, pink plush inner ears, stubby tail, black plastic eyes, black plastic textured dog nose, black thread mouth, hang tag right ear, tush tag left back leg

Replaces: Spot the white dog w/ black spot, retired

Variations: None

Oddities: No gender indicated, poem written in first person human

Commentary: Released three months after birth, one of three dogs & one of three white Beanies this release, popular w/ bull terrier fans; could become as popular & valuable as Spot

Poem: Going to the pet shop to buy dog food
I ran into Butch in a good mood
"Come to the pet shop down the street
Be a good dog, I'll buy you a treat!"™"

My record

(Beanies are the #1 collectible in American collecting history. A complete, detailed record will vastly increase the value of this Beanie, if and when you ever appraise, trade, re-sell, gift, or bequeath it.)

Description *(which version do you have?):*

Gift from:

Date received/purchased: ✓ *4 - 19 — 99*

Purchased from: *ARMC Gift Shop*

NAME OF PERSON OR RETAILER

ADDRESS

CITY/STATE/ZIP *Auburn*

PHONE

Qty. purchased: *1*   **Cost ea.** *6⁵⁰* *incl.*
(check one)   ❏ *Cash*   ❏ *Check*   ❏ *Charge*

Reason(s) for purchase(s):

Traded to:

NAME

ADDRESS

CITY/STATE/ZIP

PHONE

TRADED FOR

Re-sold to:

NAME

ADDRESS

CITY/STATE/ZIP

PHONE

PRICE RE-SOLD FOR

Your feelings about and/or experiences with this Beanie:

Eggbert™

Type:	Female chick	**Categories:**	Birds, farm, white	**Style no.:**	4232

Birthday: April 10, 1998   **Released:** 1/1/99   **Retired:**

Position: Peeking   **Tags:** 5th gen. hang, 7th gen. tush   **Teenie:**

Description: Yellow napped chick peeking out of half white eggshell, orange beak w/ black thread nostrils, black plastic eyes, hang tag left side, tush tag bottom

Replaces: Quackers the yellow duck, retired

Variations: None

Oddities: First Beanie in a shell

Commentary: Released almost nine months after birth; one of three napped, one of three white, one of two farm Beanies this release; popular Easter decoration/gift; one of the cutest Beanies ever; could become as popular & valuable as other Easter Beanies

Poem: Cracking her shell taking a peek
Look, she's playing hide & seek
Ready or not, here I come
Take me home and have some fun!™

My record

(Beanies are the #1 collectible in American collecting history. A complete, detailed record will vastly increase the value of this Beanie, if and when you ever appraise, trade, re-sell, gift, or bequeath it.)

Description *(which version do you have?):*

Gift from:

Date received/purchased: 4 - 30 - 99

Purchased from: ARMC

NAME OF PERSON OR RETAILER

ADDRESS

CITY/STATE/ZIP

PHONE

Qty. purchased: **Cost ea.** 5⁹⁵ +tax ARMC
(check one) ❏ *Cash* ❏ *Check* ❏ *Charge*

Reason(s) for purchase(s):

Traded to:

NAME

ADDRESS

CITY/STATE/ZIP

PHONE

TRADED FOR

Re-sold to:

NAME

ADDRESS

CITY/STATE/ZIP

PHONE

PRICE RE-SOLD FOR

Your feelings about and/or experiences with this Beanie:

Ewey™

Type:	Female lamb	**Categories:** Farm, lambs, napped	**Style no.:** 4219

Birthday: March 1, 1998   **Released:** 1/1/99   **Retired:**

Position: Floppy   **Tags:** 5th gen. hang, 7th gen. tush   **Teenie:**

Description: Cream-colored napped body, flesh-colored plush face, light brown plush hooves, pink flannel inner ears, stubby tail, black plastic eyes, pink plastic nose, pink thread mouth, hang tag left ear, tush tag left back leg

Replaces: Chops the cream-colored plush lamb w/ black face, retired + Fleece the white napped lamb w/ cream-colored face, retired

Variations: None

Oddities: Long, floppy legs

Commentary: Released ten months after birth; one of three napped & one of three floppy-legged Beanies this release; will join retired lambs as well as retired & current Easter Beanies in popularity & value; along w/ Stilts the stork, popular baby decoration/gift

Poem: Needles and yarn, Ewey loves to knit
Making sweaters with perfect fit
Happy to make one for you and me
Showing off hers, for all to see!™

My record

(Beanies are the #1 collectible in American collecting history. A complete, detailed record will vastly increase the value of this Beanie, if and when you ever appraise, trade, re-sell, gift, or bequeath it.)

Description *(which version do you have?):* _Biege Tan / brown_

Gift from:

Date received/purchased:

Purchased from: _ARM @ 4-30-99_

NAME OF PERSON OR RETAILER

ADDRESS

CITY/STATE/ZIP

PHONE

Qty. purchased: _$5·95 +tax_ Cost ea. _6 ⁵⁰_

(check one) ❏ *Cash* ❏ *Check* ☑ *Charge*

Reason(s) for purchase(s):

Traded to:

NAME

ADDRESS

CITY/STATE/ZIP

PHONE

TRADED FOR

Re-sold to:

NAME

ADDRESS

CITY/STATE/ZIP

PHONE

PRICE RE-SOLD FOR

Your feelings about and/or experiences with this Beanie:

Goatee™

Type:	Female goat	*Categories:* Goat, heather	*Style no.:* 4235

Birthday: November 4, 1998   *Released:* 1/1/99   *Retired:*

Position: Laying down   *Tags:* 5th gen. hang, 7th gen. tush   *Teenie:*

Description: Brownish-gray heather plush body, dark brown plush hooves, lighter grayish-brown flannel horns & inner ears, lighter tannish-brown hairy beard & tail, black plastic eyes, black thread nose, hang tag left ear, tush tag left back

Replaces: None

Variations: Heather coloring varies

Oddities: None

Commentary: Released two months after birth; a new fabric for Ty: heather; one of five heather & one of two farm Beanies this release; one of the most detailed Beanies; popular w/ boys

Poem: Though she's hungry, she's in a good mood
Searching through garbage, tin cans for food
For Goatee the goat, it's not a big deal
Anything at all makes a fine meal!™

My record

(Beanies are the #1 collectible in American collecting history. A complete, detailed record will vastly increase the value of this Beanie, if and when you ever appraise, trade, re-sell, gift, or bequeath it.)

Description *(which version do you have?)*:

Biege with black paws

Gift from:

Date received/purchased: 4-19-99

Purchased from: ARMC gift shop

NAME OF PERSON OR RETAILER

ADDRESS

CITY/STATE/ZIP

PHONE

Qty. purchased: **Cost ea.** 6.50

(check one)   ❏ Cash   ❏ Check   ☑ Charge

Reason(s) for purchase(s):

Traded to:

NAME

ADDRESS

CITY/STATE/ZIP

PHONE

TRADED FOR

Re-sold to:

NAME

ADDRESS

CITY/STATE/ZIP

PHONE

PRICE RE-SOLD FOR

Your feelings about and/or experiences with this Beanie:

Goochy™

Type: Male jellyfish   **Categories:** Sea, tie-dyed   **Style no.:** 4230

Birthday: November 18, 1998   **Released:** 1/1/99   **Retired:**

Position: Floating   **Tags:** 5th gen. hang, 7th gen. tush   **Teenie:**

Description: Pastel tie-dyed iridescent plush head, skirt & legs; black embroidered eyes on white embroidered droopies; ten legs; hang tag left front; tush tag left back

Replaces: None

Variations: Tie-dye varies in colors

Oddities: So light-weight, almost airy; strange animal to turn into a Beanie

Commentary: Released almost two months after birth; one of three tie-dyes & one of two iridescent this release; just quirky enough to sky-rocket in popularity & value

Poem: Swirl, swish, squirm and wiggle
Listen closely, hear him giggle
The most ticklish jellyfish you'll ever meet
Even though he has no feet!™

My record

(Beanies are the #1 collectible in American collecting history. A complete, detailed record will vastly increase the value of this Beanie, if and when you ever appraise, trade, re-sell, gift, or bequeath it.)

Description *(which version do you have?):*

Gift from:

Date received/purchased: *5. - 3 -99*

Purchased from:

NAME OF PERSON OR RETAILER *A RMC - gift shop*

ADDRESS

CITY/STATE/ZIP

PHONE

Qty. purchased: **Cost ea.**
(check one)   ❏ *Cash*   ❏ *Check*   ❏ *Charge*

Reason(s) for purchase(s):

Traded to:

NAME

ADDRESS

CITY/STATE/ZIP

PHONE

TRADED FOR

Re-sold to:

NAME

ADDRESS

CITY/STATE/ZIP

PHONE

PRICE RE-SOLD FOR

Your feelings about and/or experiences with this Beanie:

Hippie™

Type:	Male bunny **Categories:** Bunnies, tie-dyed	**Style no.:** 4218
Birthday:	May 4, 1998 **Released:** 1/1/99	**Retired:**
Position:	Sitting up **Tags:** 5th gen. hang, 7th gen. tush	**Teenie:**

Description: Pastel tie-dyed plush body, pink flannel inner ears, white plush tail, black plastic eyes, pink plastic nose, pink thread whiskers, hang tag left ear, tush tag left back

Replaces: Four retired Beanie bunnies: Ears, Floppity, Hippity & Hoppity

Variations: Tie-dye colors vary

Oddities: None

Commentary: Released eight months after birth, one of three bunnies & one of three tie-dyed Beanies this release, destined to become as popular & valuable as four retired Beanie bunnies, popular Easter decoration/gift, popular w/ girls

Poem: Hippie fell into the dye, they say
While coloring eggs, one spring day
From the tips of his ears, down to his toes
Colors of springtime, he proudly shows!™

My record

(Beanies are the #1 collectible in American collecting history. A complete, detailed record will vastly increase the value of this Beanie, if and when you ever appraise, trade, re-sell, gift, or bequeath it.)

Description (which version do you have?):

Pastel pink, green blended

Gift from:

Date received/purchased:

Purchased from: *ARMC*

NAME OF PERSON OR RETAILER

ADDRESS

CITY/STATE/ZIP

PHONE

Qty. purchased: **Cost ea.** *6 50*
(check one)   ❑ Cash   ❑ Check   ☑ Charge

Reason(s) for purchase(s):

Traded to:

NAME

ADDRESS

CITY/STATE/ZIP

PHONE

TRADED FOR

Re-sold to:

NAME

ADDRESS

CITY/STATE/ZIP

PHONE

PRICE RE-SOLD FOR

Your feelings about and/or experiences with this Beanie:

Hope™

Type:	Bear	**Categories:** Bears, butterscotch	**Style no.:** 4213

Birthday: March 23, 1998   **Released:** 1/1/99   **Retired:**

Position: Praying   **Tags:** 5th gen. hang, 7th gen. tush   **Teenie:**

Description: Butterscotch plush body; cream plush snout, paws & feet bottoms; brown plush plastic nose; black thread closed eyes; brown thread mouth & detailing on paws; hang tag left ear; tush tag left back

Replaces: None

Variations: None

Oddities: No gender indicated, first bear w/ no eyes (closed), one of few bears w/ no ribbon

Commentary: Released almost ten months after birth; a new color for Ty: butterscotch; an interesting subject matter; hands & feet sewn into place; one of eight bears this release; popular w/ little children

Poem: Every night when it's time for bed
Fold your hands and bow your head
An angelic face, a heart that's true
You have a friend to pray with you!™

My record

(Beanies are the #1 collectible in American collecting history. A complete, detailed record will vastly increase the value of this Beanie, if and when you ever appraise, trade, re-sell, gift, or bequeath it.)

Description *(which version do you have?):*

Gift from:

Date received/purchased:

Purchased from: 99   A R M C

NAME OF PERSON OR RETAILER

ADDRESS

CITY/STATE/ZIP

PHONE

Qty. purchased: **Cost ea.**
(check one)   ❏ *Cash*   ❏ *Check*   ❏ *Charge*

Reason(s) for purchase(s):

Traded to:

NAME

ADDRESS

CITY/STATE/ZIP

PHONE

TRADED FOR

Re-sold to:

NAME

ADDRESS

CITY/STATE/ZIP

PHONE

PRICE RE-SOLD FOR

Your feelings about and/or experiences with this Beanie:

Kicks™

Type:	Male bear	**Categories:** Bears, green, sports	**Style no.:** 4229
Birthday:	August 16, 1998	**Released:** 1/1/99	**Retired:**
Position:	Sitting up	**Tags:** 5th gen. hang, 7th gen. tush	**Teenie:**

Description: Iridescent lime green plush body, black & white soccer ball embroidered over heart, black plastic eyes & nose, hang tag left ear, tush tag left bottom

Replaces: None

Variations: None

Oddities: Strange shade of green for soccer bear, one of few Beanies with sheen to fabric

Commentary: Released almost five months after birth; a new color for Ty: lime green; commemorates World Cup games: interesting subject matter that may lead to more sports bears; one of three sports, one of two iridescent, & one of eight bears this release; popular w/ soccer fans

Poem: The world cup is his dream
Kicks the bear is the best on his team
He hopes that one day he'll be the pick
First he needs to improve his kick!™

My record

(Beanies are the #1 collectible in American collecting history. A complete, detailed record will vastly increase the value of this Beanie, if and when you ever appraise, trade, re-sell, gift, or bequeath it.)

Description *(which version do you have?):*

Gift from:

Date received/purchased:

Purchased from:

NAME OF PERSON OR RETAILER

ADDRESS

CITY/STATE/ZIP

PHONE

Qty. purchased:　　**Cost ea.**
(check one)　　❏ *Cash*　　　　❏ *Check*　　　　❏ *Charge*

Reason(s) for purchase(s):

Traded to:

NAME

ADDRESS

CITY/STATE/ZIP

PHONE

TRADED FOR

Re-sold to:

NAME

ADDRESS

CITY/STATE/ZIP

PHONE

PRICE RE-SOLD FOR

Your feelings about and/or experiences with this Beanie:

Luke™

Type: Male lab   **Categories:** Black, dog   **Style no.:** 4214

Birthday: June 15, 1998   **Released:** 1/1/99   **Retired:**

Position: Floppy   **Tags:** 5th gen. hang, 7th gen. tush   **Teenie:**

Description: Black plush body, black & white checkered cotton ribbon tied around neck, big ears, long legs, stubby tail, black plastic eyes, black plastic textured dog nose, hang tag left ear, tush tag left bottom

Replaces: Fetch the golden lab, retired

Variations: None

Oddities: Long, floppy seamed legs; first cotton, first checkered ribbon; first dog w/ ribbon

Commentary: Released almost six months after birth; one of three dogs & one of three floppy-legged Beanies this release; like most Beanie dogs, will escalate in popularity & value

Poem: After chewing on your favorite shoes
Luke gets tired, takes a snooze
Who wouldn't love a puppy like this?
Give him a hug, he'll give you a kiss!™

My record

(Beanies are the #1 collectible in American collecting history. A complete, detailed record will vastly increase the value of this Beanie, if and when you ever appraise, trade, re-sell, gift, or bequeath it.)

Description *(which version do you have?):*
Black w black & white neck ribbon

Gift from:

Date received/purchased: *4 - 19 - 99*

Purchased from: *ARMC Gift Shop*

NAME OF PERSON OR RETAILER

ADDRESS

CITY/STATE/ZIP

PHONE

Qty. purchased: *1* **Cost ea.** *6⁵⁰ tax incl!*
(check one) ❏ *Cash* ❏ *Check* ☑ *Charge*

Reason(s) for purchase(s):

Traded to:

NAME

ADDRESS

CITY/STATE/ZIP

PHONE

TRADED FOR

Re-sold to:

NAME

ADDRESS

CITY/STATE/ZIP

PHONE

PRICE RE-SOLD FOR

Your feelings about and/or experiences with this Beanie:

Mac™

Type:	Male cardinal	***Categories:***	Birds, red	***Style no.:***	4225	

Birthday: June 10, 1998   ***Released:*** 1/1/99   ***Retired:***

Position: Perching   ***Tags:*** 5th gen. hang, 7th gen. tush   ***Teenie:***

Description: Bright red plush body; red hairy crown; black plush mask; red felt beak, under tail & under wings; black felt feet; long, three-pronged tail; black plastic eyes, ringed w/ gold; hang tag left wing; tush tag bottom

Replaces: None

Variations: None

Oddities: One of few Beanies w/ companion (Sammy the bear, commemorating home-run king Sammy Sosa)

Commentary: Released almost six months after birth; brilliant red color; commemorates home-run king Mark Mcgwire: interesting subject matter that may lead to more sports Beanies; one of three birds & one of three sports Beanies this release; popular w/ baseball fans

Poem: Mac tries hard to prove he's the best
Swinging his bat harder than the rest
Breaking records, enjoying the game
Hitting home runs is his claim to fame!™

My record

(Beanies are the #1 collectible in American collecting history. A complete, detailed record will vastly increase the value of this Beanie, if and when you ever appraise, trade, re-sell, gift, or bequeath it.)

Description *(which version do you have?):*

Gift from:

Date received/purchased:

Purchased from: A R M C

NAME OF PERSON OR RETAILER

ADDRESS

CITY/STATE/ZIP

PHONE

Qty. purchased: **Cost ea.**
(check one)   ❏ *Cash*   ❏ *Check*   ❏ *Charge*

Reason(s) for purchase(s):

Traded to:

NAME

ADDRESS

CITY/STATE/ZIP

PHONE

TRADED FOR

Re-sold to:

NAME

ADDRESS

CITY/STATE/ZIP

PHONE

PRICE RE-SOLD FOR

Your feelings about and/or experiences with this Beanie:

Millenium™

Can't get ✓

Type: Bear **Categories:** Bears, magenta **Style no.:** 4226

Birthday: January 1, 1999 **Released:** 1/1/99 **Retired:**

Position: Sitting up **Tags:** 5th gen. hang, 7th gen. tush **Teenie:**

Description: Magenta plush body, globe w/ rising sun and "2000" embroidered over heart, copper metallic ribbon tied around neck, black plastic eyes & nose, hang tag left ear, tush tag left bottom

Replaces: None

Variations: None

Oddities: One of few Beanies born and released same day, no gender indicated, first metallic ribbon

Commentary: A very special Beanie Baby bear commemorating the new century; brilliant, eye-catching color; one of eight bears this release due to theme, destined to become one of the most popular and valuable Beanie bears ever

Poem: A brand new century has come to call
Health and happiness to one and all
Bring on the fireworks and all the fun
Let's keep the party going 'til 2001!™

My record

(Beanies are the #1 collectible in American collecting history. A complete, detailed record will vastly increase the value of this Beanie, if and when you ever appraise, trade, re-sell, gift, or bequeath it.)

Description *(which version do you have?):*

Gift from:

Date received/purchased:

Purchased from:

NAME OF PERSON OR RETAILER

ADDRESS

CITY/STATE/ZIP

PHONE

Qty. purchased: **Cost ea.**
(check one) ❏ *Cash* ❏ *Check* ❏ *Charge*

Reason(s) for purchase(s):

Traded to:

NAME

ADDRESS

CITY/STATE/ZIP

PHONE

TRADED FOR

Re-sold to:

NAME

ADDRESS

CITY/STATE/ZIP

PHONE

PRICE RE-SOLD FOR

Your feelings about and/or experiences with this Beanie:

Mooch™

Type:	Male spider monkey	**Categories:** Black, jungle	**Style no.:**	4224

Birthday: August 1, 1998   **Released:** 1/1/99   **Retired:**

Position: Hanging   **Tags:** 5th gen. hang, 7th gen. tush   **Teenie:**

Description: Black plush body; tan face, ears, hands & feet; cream-colored hairy beard around face; big, black plastic eyes, ringed w/ brown; black thread eyebrows, nostrils & mouth; long arms & legs w/ thumbs; long curled tail; hang tag left ear; tush tag bottom

Replaces: Nana w/ brown tail + Bongo w/ brown tail + Bongo w/ tan tail + Congo—all retired

Variations: None

Oddities: Hairy beard around face; long arms, legs & tail

Commentary: Released five months after birth; only jungle & one of two black Beanies this release; will join Bongo in popularity & value; great wrap-around Beanie w/ long arms, legs & tail

Poem:
Look in the treetops, up towards the sky
Swinging from branches way up high
Tempt him with a banana or fruit
When he's hungry, he acts so cute!™

My record

(Beanies are the #1 collectible in American collecting history. A complete, detailed record will vastly increase the value of this Beanie, if and when you ever appraise, trade, re-sell, gift, or bequeath it.)

Description *(which version do you have?):* *M*

Gift from:

Date received/purchased: 4 – 19 – 99

Purchased from: ARM c

NAME OF PERSON OR RETAILER

ADDRESS

CITY/STATE/ZIP

PHONE

Qty. purchased: **Cost ea.**
(check one) ❏ *Cash* ❏ *Check* ❏ *Charge*

Reason(s) for purchase(s):

Traded to:

NAME

ADDRESS

CITY/STATE/ZIP

PHONE

TRADED FOR

Re-sold to:

NAME

ADDRESS

CITY/STATE/ZIP

PHONE

PRICE RE-SOLD FOR

Your feelings about and/or experiences with this Beanie:

Nibbler™

Type:	Female bunny	**Categories:**	Bunnies, cream	**Style no.:**	4216

Birthday: April 6, 1998   **Released:** 1/1/99   **Retired:**

Position: Squatting   **Tags:** 5th gen. hang, 7th gen. tush   **Teenie:**

Description: Cream-colored plush body, pink flannel inner ears, cream hairy tail, black plastic eyes, pink plastic nose, pink thread mouth & whiskers, hang tag left ear, tush tag left back leg

Replaces: Four retired Beanie bunnies: Ears, Floppity, Hippity & Hoppity

Variations: None

Oddities: None

Commentary: Released nine months after birth; a new breed of bunny for Ty: squatting; one of three bunnies this release; destined to become as popular & valuable as four retired Beanie bunnies; popular Easter decoration/gift; popular w/ girls

Poem: Twitching her nose, she looks so sweet
Small in size, she's very petite
Soft and furry, hopping with grace
She'll visit your garden, her favorite place!™

My record

(Beanies are the #1 collectible in American collecting history. A complete, detailed record will vastly increase the value of this Beanie, if and when you ever appraise, trade, re-sell, gift, or bequeath it.)

Description *(which version do you have?)*: _____

_____

_____

_____

Gift from: _____

Date received/purchased: *4-19-99* *4-6-98*

Purchased from: *A R M C*

NAME OF PERSON OR RETAILER _____

ADDRESS _____

CITY/STATE/ZIP _____

PHONE _____

Qty. purchased: *1*   Cost ea. *5.95 + tax*
(check one)   ❏ *Cash*   ❏ *Check*   ❏ *Charge*

Reason(s) for purchase(s): _____

_____

_____

_____

Traded to:

NAME _____

ADDRESS _____

CITY/STATE/ZIP _____

PHONE _____

TRADED FOR _____

Re-sold to:

NAME _____

ADDRESS _____

CITY/STATE/ZIP _____

PHONE _____

PRICE RE-SOLD FOR _____

Your feelings about and/or experiences with this Beanie: _____

_____

_____

_____

Nibbly™

Type:	Bunny **Categories:** Bunnies, heather	**Style no.:** 4217
Birthday:	May 7, 1998 **Released:** 1/1/99	**Retired:**
Position:	Squatting **Tags:** 5th gen. hang, 7th gen. tush	**Teenie:**

Description: Brownish-green heather plush body, cream plush chin, cream flannel inner ears, cream hairy tail, black plastic eyes, pink plastic nose, pink thread mouth & whiskers, hang tag left ear, tush tag left back leg

Replaces: Four retired Beanie bunnies: Ears, Floppity, Hippity & Hoppity

Variations: Heather coloring varies

Oddities: No gender indicated

Commentary: Released eight months after birth; a new breed of bunny for Ty: squatting; a new fabric for Ty: heather; one of five heather Beanies & one of three bunnies this release; destined to become as popular & valuable as four retired Beanie bunnies; popular Easter decoration/gift; popular w/ girls

Poem: Wonderful ways to spend a day
Bight and sunny in the month of May
Hopping around as trees sway
Looking for friends, out to play!™

My record

(Beanies are the #1 collectible in American collecting history. A complete, detailed record will vastly increase the value of this Beanie, if and when you ever appraise, trade, re-sell, gift, or bequeath it.)

Description *(which version do you have?):*

_____

_____

_____

Gift from:

Date received/purchased: *5 - 28,99*

Purchased from: *A R M C*

NAME OF PERSON OR RETAILER

ADDRESS

CITY/STATE/ZIP

PHONE

Qty. purchased: **Cost ea.** *5⁹⁵*
(check one) ❑ *Cash* ❑ *Check* ❑ *Charge*

Reason(s) for purchase(s):

_____

_____

_____

Traded to:

NAME

ADDRESS

CITY/STATE/ZIP

PHONE

TRADED FOR

Re-sold to:

NAME

ADDRESS

CITY/STATE/ZIP

PHONE

PRICE RE-SOLD FOR

Your feelings about and/or experiences with this Beanie:

_____

_____

_____

_____

Prickles™

Type: Female hedgehog   **Categories:** Brown, napped   **Style no.:** 4220

Birthday: February 19, 1998   **Released:** 1/1/99   **Retired:**

Position: Standing   **Tags:** 5th gen. hang, 7th gen. tush   **Teenie:**

Description: Brown napped back; light brown face & underside; light brown flannel ears; big, black plastic eyes, ringed w/ brown; big, black, round nose; thick, black thread whiskers; short, fat & long snout

Replaces: None

Variations: None

Oddities: Odd animal to turn into a Beanie, big eyes & nose

Commentary: Released almost eleven months after birth, one of three napped Beanies this release, just quirky enough to sky-rocket in popularity & value

Poem: Prickles the hedgehog loves to play
She rolls around the meadow all day
Tucking under her feet and head
Suddenly she looks like a ball instead!™

My record

(Beanies are the #1 collectible in American collecting history. A complete, detailed record will vastly increase the value of this Beanie, if and when you ever appraise, trade, re-sell, gift, or bequeath it.)

Description *(which version do you have?):*

Brown Back; Beige Underneath

Gift from:

Date received/purchased: _4 — 19 — 99_

Purchased from:

ARMC Gift Shop
NAME OF PERSON OR RETAILER
ADDRESS
CITY/STATE/ZIP
PHONE

Qty. purchased: **Cost ea.**   _6.50 incl Tax_
(check one) ✓   ❏ *Cash*   ❏ *Check*   ☑ *Charge*

Reason(s) for purchase(s):
to complete my collection

Traded to:

NAME
ADDRESS
CITY/STATE/ZIP
PHONE
TRADED FOR

Re-sold to:

NAME
ADDRESS
CITY/STATE/ZIP
PHONE
PRICE RE-SOLD FOR

Your feelings about and/or experiences with this Beanie:

Sammy™

Type:	Male bear	**Categories:** Bear, sports, tie-dyed	**Style no.:** 4215	

Birthday: June 23, 1998   **Released:** 1/1/99   **Retired:**

Position: Laying down   **Tags:** 5th gen. hang, 7th gen. tush   **Teenie:**

Description: Bright tie-dyed plush body, black shiny plastic eyes, black matte nose, hang tag left ear, tush tag left back leg

Replaces: None

Variations: Tie-dye colors vary

Oddities: One of few Beanies w/ companion (Mac the cardinal, commemorating home-run king Mark Macgwire)

Commentary: Released almost six months after birth; commemorates home-run king Sammy Sosa: interesting subject matter that may lead to more sports bears; one of three sports bears, one of eight bears, only lay-down bear this release; one of three tie-dyed Beanies in this release; popular w/ baseball fans

Poem: As Sammy steps up to the plate
The crowd gets excited, can hardly wait
We know Sammy won't let us down
He makes us the happiest fans in town!™

My record

(Beanies are the #1 collectible in American collecting history. A complete, detailed record will vastly increase the value of this Beanie, if and when you ever appraise, trade, re-sell, gift, or bequeath it.)

Description *(which version do you have?):*

Gift from:

Date received/purchased: *3 – 22-99*

Purchased from: *A Rmc*

NAME OF PERSON OR RETAILER

ADDRESS

CITY/STATE/ZIP

PHONE

Qty. purchased: **Cost ea.** *5 95 +tnf*
(check one)   ❏ *Cash*   ❏ *Check*   ❏ *Charge*

Reason(s) for purchase(s):

Traded to:

NAME

ADDRESS

CITY/STATE/ZIP

PHONE

TRADED FOR

Re-sold to:

NAME

ADDRESS

CITY/STATE/ZIP

PHONE

PRICE RE-SOLD FOR

Your feelings about and/or experiences with this Beanie:

Scat™

Type:	Female cat	***Categories:*** Cats, heather	***Style no.:*** 4231

Birthday: May 27, 1998   ***Released:*** 1/1/99   ***Retired:***

Position: Floppy   ***Tags:*** 5th gen. hang, 7th gen. tush   ***Teenie:***

Description: Greenish-brown heather plush body; beige plush inner ears & feetpads; black plastic eyes, ringed w/ gold; pink plastic nose; pink thread mouth & whiskers; hang tag left ear; tush tag left back

Replaces: Seven Beanie cats before it: Nip, Zip, Flip, Chip & Snip (all retired) and Chip, Pounce & Prance (all current)

Variations: Heather coloring varies

Oddities: All the seams: down leg fronts & backs, back of head, back & belly

Commentary: Released eight months after birth; a new fabric for Ty: heather; one of five heather Beanies & one of three floppy-legged Beanies this release; unlike other Beanie cats, not particularly cute: must be an ally cat! like all cats will escalate in popularity & value

Poem: Newborn kittens require lots of sleep
Shhh...it's naptime, don't make a peep
Touch her fur, it feels like silk
Wake her up to drink mother's milk!™

My record

(Beanies are the #1 collectible in American collecting history. A complete, detailed record will vastly increase the value of this Beanie, if and when you ever appraise, trade, re-sell, gift, or bequeath it.)

Description *(which version do you have?):*

Gift from:

Date received/purchased: 4 - 19 - 99

Purchased from: A R M C

NAME OF PERSON OR RETAILER

ADDRESS

CITY/STATE/ZIP

PHONE

Qty. purchased: 1 **Cost ea.** 6 ^{50} tax incl.
(check one) ❏ *Cash* ❏ *Check* ☑ *Charge*

Reason(s) for purchase(s):

Traded to:

NAME

ADDRESS

CITY/STATE/ZIP

PHONE

TRADED FOR

Re-sold to:

NAME

ADDRESS

CITY/STATE/ZIP

PHONE

PRICE RE-SOLD FOR

Your feelings about and/or experiences with this Beanie:

Slippery™

Type:	Male seal	**Categories:**	Heather, sea	**Style no.:**	4222

Birthday: January 17, 1998   **Released:** 1/1/99   **Retired:**

Position: Floating   **Tags:** 5th gen. hang, 7th gen. tush   **Teenie:**

Description: Grayish-white heather plush body, two fins, split tail, black plastic eyes & nose, black thread eyebrows & whiskers, hang tag left fin, tush tag back

Replaces: Seamore the white seal

Variations: Heather coloring varies

Oddities: One of few Beanies w/ eyebrows

Commentary: Released one year after birth; a new fabric for Ty: heather; one of five heather Beanies this release; one of the cutest Beanies ever; similar in style to Seamore the white seal and Seaweed the brown otter: destined to become as popular & valuable as both

Poem: In the ocean, near a breaking wave
Slippery the seal acts very brave
On his surfboard, he sees a swell
He's riding the wave! Oooops...he fell!™

My record

(Beanies are the #1 collectible in American collecting history. A complete, detailed record will vastly increase the value of this Beanie, if and when you ever appraise, trade, re-sell, gift, or bequeath it.)

Description *(which version do you have?)*:

Gift from:

Date received/purchased: *4 – 19 – 99*

Purchased from: *A R M c*

NAME OF PERSON OR RETAILER

ADDRESS

CITY/STATE/ZIP

PHONE

Qty. purchased: *1* **Cost ea.** *6⁵⁰ tax incl.*
(check one) ❑ *Cash* ❑ *Check* ☑ *Charge*

Reason(s) for purchase(s):

Traded to:

NAME

ADDRESS

CITY/STATE/ZIP

PHONE

TRADED FOR

Re-sold to:

NAME

ADDRESS

CITY/STATE/ZIP

PHONE

PRICE RE-SOLD FOR

Your feelings about and/or experiences with this Beanie:

Stilts™

Type:	Stork	**Categories:** Birds, white	**Style no.:** 4221

Birthday: June 16, 1998   **Released:** 1/1/99   **Retired:**

Position: Standing   **Tags:** 5th gen. hang, 7th gen. tush   **Teenie:**

Description: White plush body; bright orange beak, legs & feet; black tail & wingtips; long beak & legs; black plastic eyes; hang tag left wing; tush tag left bottom

Replaces: Pinky the flamingo, retired

Variations: None

Oddities: No gender indicated

Commentary: Released almost six months after birth; fun subject for Beanies; will join Fleece in popularity as baby gift; one of three birds & three white Beanies this release

Poem: Flying high over mountains and streams
Fulfilling wishes, hopes and dreams
The stork brings parents bundles of joy
The greatest gift, a girl or boy!™

My record

(Beanies are the #1 collectible in American collecting history. A complete, detailed record will vastly increase the value of this Beanie, if and when you ever appraise, trade, re-sell, gift, or bequeath it.)

Description *(which version do you have?):*

White, orange beak & legs, black wing tips & tail

Gift from:

Date received/purchased: ✓ *A R M C Gift Shop* 4/19/99

Purchased from:

NAME OF PERSON OR RETAILER

ADDRESS

CITY/STATE/ZIP

PHONE

Qty. purchased: **Cost ea.**
(check one)   ❏ *Cash*   ❏ *Check*   ❏ *Charge*

Reason(s) for purchase(s):

Traded to:

NAME

ADDRESS

CITY/STATE/ZIP

PHONE

TRADED FOR

Re-sold to:

NAME

ADDRESS

CITY/STATE/ZIP

PHONE

PRICE RE-SOLD FOR

Your feelings about and/or experiences with this Beanie:

Tiny™

Type: Chihuahua   **Categories:** Brown, dogs   **Style no.:** ✓4234

Birthday: September 8, 1998   **Released:** 1/1/99   **Retired:**

Position: Standing up   **Tags:** 5th gen. hang, 7th gen. tush   **Teenie:**

Description: Light brown plush body; big ears; stubby tail; big, black plastic eyes ringed w/ brown & surrounded by black plastic rings; black plastic textured dog nose; black thread mouth; hang tag left ear; tush tag left back leg

Replaces: None

Variations: None

Oddities: No gender indicated, released during height of popularity of Taco Bell® chihuahua

Commentary: Released almost four months after birth; one of three dogs this release; one of cutest Beanie dogs ever; like most Beanie dogs, will escalate in popularity & value

Poem: South of the border, in the sun
Tiny the chihuahua is having fun
Attending fiestas, breaking pinatas
Eating a taco, or some enchiladas!™

My record

(Beanies are the #1 collectible in American collecting history. A complete, detailed record will vastly increase the value of this Beanie, if and when you ever appraise, trade, re-sell, gift, or bequeath it.)

Description *(which version do you have?):*

Gift from:

Date received/purchased: A 9-8-98

Purchased from: ARMc (9-8-98 Birthdate)

NAME OF PERSON OR RETAILER

ADDRESS

CITY/STATE/ZIP

PHONE

Qty. purchased: **Cost ea.** 5⁹⁵ + tax
(check one)   ❏ *Cash*   ❏ *Check*   ❏ *Charge*

Reason(s) for purchase(s):

Traded to:

NAME

ADDRESS

CITY/STATE/ZIP

PHONE

TRADED FOR

Re-sold to:

NAME

ADDRESS

CITY/STATE/ZIP

PHONE

PRICE RE-SOLD FOR

Your feelings about and/or experiences with this Beanie:

Valentina™

Type: Bear	*Categories:* Bears, pink	*Style no.:* 4233
Birthday: February 14, 1998	*Released:* 1/1/99	*Retired:*
Position: Sitting up	*Tags:* 5th gen. hang, 7th gen. tush	*Teenie:*

Description: Hot pink plush body, white embroidered heart over heart, hot pink satin ribbon tied around neck, black plastic eyes & nose, hang tag left ear, tush tag left bottom

Replaces: None

Variations: None

Oddities: First hot pink Beanie; one of few Beanies w/ companion; no gender indicated, though obvious female companion to Valentino

Commentary: Released eleven months after birth; brilliant hot pink color makes it a stand-out among Beanie bears, one of eight bears this release, popular Valentine decoration/gift, destined to become as popular & valuable as companion, very popular w/ girls

Poem: Flowers, candy and hearts galore
Sweet words of love for those you adore
With this bear comes love that's true
On Valentine's Day and all year through!™

My record

(Beanies are the #1 collectible in American collecting history. A complete, detailed record will vastly increase the value of this Beanie, if and when you ever appraise, trade, re-sell, gift, or bequeath it.)

Description *(which version do you have?):*

_____

_____

_____

Gift from: _____

Date received/purchased: _____

Purchased from: _____

NAME OF PERSON OR RETAILER

ADDRESS

CITY/STATE/ZIP

PHONE

Qty. purchased: **Cost ea.**
(check one)   ❑ *Cash*   ❑ *Check*   ❑ *Charge*

Reason(s) for purchase(s): _____

_____

_____

Traded to:

NAME

ADDRESS

CITY/STATE/ZIP

PHONE

TRADED FOR

Re-sold to:

NAME

ADDRESS

CITY/STATE/ZIP

PHONE

PRICE RE-SOLD FOR

Your feelings about and/or experiences with this Beanie: _____

_____

_____

_____

Batty™

Type:	Bat	***Categories:*** Creepie crawlie, tie-dyed	***Style no.:*** 4035

Birthday: October 29, 1996   ***Released:*** 10/1/97   ***Retired:***

Position: Flying   ***Tags:*** 5th generation   ***Teenie:***

Description: Tie-dyed blue to brown plush body; dark brown felt ears, hands & feet; black plastic eyes; brown plastic nose & thread mouth; thread detailing on wings; velcro closures on wings; hang tag left wing; tush tag back

Replaces: Radar the black bat, style no. 4091, birthday 10/30/95, released 9/1/95, retired 5/11/97, rare & expensive; brown Batty

Variations: Tie dye varies in colors

Oddities: No gender; only Beanie w/ velcro

Commentary: Released nearly one year after birth, special Halloween release, popular Halloween decoration/gift, very popular with boys

Poem: Bats may make some people jitter
Please don't be scared of this critter
If you're lonely or have nothing to do
This Beanie Baby would love to hug you!™

My record

(Beanies are the #1 collectible in American collecting history. A complete, detailed record will vastly increase the value of this Beanie, if and when you ever appraise, trade, re-sell, gift, or bequeath it.)

Description *(which version do you have?):*

Gift from:

Date received/purchased:

Purchased from:

NAME OF PERSON OR RETAILER

ADDRESS

CITY/STATE/ZIP

PHONE

Qty. purchased: **Cost ea.**
(check one) ❏ *Cash* ❏ *Check* ❏ *Charge*

Reason(s) for purchase(s):

Traded to:

NAME

ADDRESS

CITY/STATE/ZIP

PHONE

TRADED FOR

Re-sold to:

NAME

ADDRESS

CITY/STATE/ZIP

PHONE

PRICE RE-SOLD FOR

Your feelings about and/or experiences with this Beanie:

Beak™

Type:	Female kiwi	**Categories:** Birds, napped, tie-dyed	**Style no.:** 4211

Birthday: February 3,1998   **Released:** 9/30/98   **Retired:**

Position: Squatting   **Tags:** 5th generation   **Teenie:**

Description: Brown, gold, rust tie-dyed, coarse napped body; brown flannel under wings & feet; lighter brown, extra-long beak w/ black thread nostrils; black plastic eyes ringed w/ gold; hang tag left wing; tush tag left bottom

Replaces: None

Variations: Tie-dye varies in colors

Oddities: None

Commentary: Released seven months after birth; new tie-dyed, coarse napped fabric; one of three napped Beanies released simultaneously; first New Zealand Beanie

Poem: Isn't this just the funniest bird?
When we saw her, we said "how absurd"
Looks aren't everything, this we know
Her love for you, she's sure to show!™

My record

(Beanies are the #1 collectible in American collecting history. A complete, detailed record will vastly increase the value of this Beanie, if and when you ever appraise, trade, re-sell, gift, or bequeath it.)

Description *(which version do you have?):*

Gift from:

Date received/purchased: ✓ 5 - 24 - 99

Purchased from: ARMC Gift Shop

NAME OF PERSON OR RETAILER

ADDRESS

CITY/STATE/ZIP

PHONE 253 - 833 - 7711

Qty. purchased: **Cost ea.**
(check one) 1 ☑ Cash   ☐ Check   ☑ Charge 5⁹⁵ + tx

Reason(s) for purchase(s):
Because I have visited Australia and saw the Bird - Kiwi. They are Nocturnal. Only saw those in cages

Traded to:

NAME

ADDRESS

CITY/STATE/ZIP

PHONE

TRADED FOR

Re-sold to:

NAME

ADDRESS

CITY/STATE/ZIP

PHONE

PRICE RE-SOLD FOR

Your feelings about and/or experiences with this Beanie:

Britannia™

unable to get here

Type:	Female bear ***Categories:*** Bear, brown, flag ***Style no.:*** 4601	
Birthday:	December 15, 1997 ***Released:*** 12/31/97 ***Retired:***	
Position:	Sitting up ***Tags:*** 5th generation ***Teenie:***	

Description: Brown plush body; black plastic eyes & nose; red satin ribbon tied around neck; red, white & blue British flag inset over heart; hang tag left ear; tush tag left bottom

Replaces: None

Variations: Flag inset in fabric, flag stitched on fabric

Oddities: One of few Beanies born & released same month; along w/ Maple, one of only two exclusive foreign releases

Commentary: Released exclusively in Great Britain, making it nearly impossible to obtain in the U.S.; one of the most sought-after Beanies ever; initially sold for $500-$800 on the secondary market; like all Beanie bears, will sky-rocket in value upon retirement

Poem: Britannia the bear will sail the seas
So she can be with you and me
She's always sure to catch the tide
And wear the Union Flag with pride!™

My record

(Beanies are the #1 collectible in American collecting history. A complete, detailed record will vastly increase the value of this Beanie, if and when you ever appraise, trade, re-sell, gift, or bequeath it.)

Description *(which version do you have?):*

_____
_____
_____

Gift from:

Date received/purchased:

Purchased from:

NAME OF PERSON OR RETAILER
ADDRESS
CITY/STATE/ZIP
PHONE

Qty. purchased: **Cost ea.**
(check one)   ❏ *Cash*   ❏ *Check*   ❏ *Charge*

Reason(s) for purchase(s):

_____
_____
_____

Traded to:

NAME
ADDRESS
CITY/STATE/ZIP
PHONE
TRADED FOR

Re-sold to:

NAME
ADDRESS
CITY/STATE/ZIP
PHONE
PRICE RE-SOLD FOR

Your feelings about and/or experiences with this Beanie:

_____
_____
_____
_____

Canyon™

Type:	Cougar	*Categories:*	Big cats, brown	*Style no.:*	4212
Birthday:	May 28, 1998	*Released:*	9/30/98	*Retired:*	
Position:	Laying down	*Tags:*	5th generation	*Teenie:*	

Description: Cool brown plush body & tail; cream inner ears, snout, throat & belly; black outer ears & markings on snout; black plastic eyes ringed w/ gold; flesh plastic nose; black thread whiskers & mouth; hang tag left ear; tush tag left back leg

Replaces: None

Variations: None

Oddities: No gender, poem in first person

Commentary: Released four months after birth, proud big cat of the American mountains, one of few big cat Beanies, very popular w/ boys

Poem: I climb rocks and run really fast
Try to catch me, it's a blast
Through the mountains, I used to roam
Now in your room, I'll call it home!™

My record

(Beanies are the #1 collectible in American collecting history. A complete, detailed record will vastly increase the value of this Beanie, if and when you ever appraise, trade, re-sell, gift, or bequeath it.)

Description (which version do you have?):

Brown plush, white tummy,
Black +
long tail,

Gift from:

Date received/purchased:

Purchased from: 4 -19-99

NAME OF PERSON OR RETAILER A R M C gift Shp

ADDRESS

CITY/STATE/ZIP

PHONE

Qty. purchased: 1 **Cost ea.** 6⁵⁰
(check one) ❏ Cash   ❏ Check   ❏ Charge

Reason(s) for purchase(s):

Traded to:

NAME

ADDRESS

CITY/STATE/ZIP

PHONE

TRADED FOR

Re-sold to:

NAME

ADDRESS

CITY/STATE/ZIP

PHONE

PRICE RE-SOLD FOR

Your feelings about and/or experiences with this Beanie:

Chip™

Type: Female calico cat **Categories:** Cat, multi-colored **Style no.:** 4121

Birthday: January 26, 1996 **Released:** 5/11/97 **Retired:**

Position: Laying down **Tags:** 4th & 5th generation **Teenie:**

Description: Reddish brown plush head, left side & tail; black left side of face, back side of left ear & right side; white inner ears, belly & socks; black plastic eyes ringed w/ gold; pink plastic nose; white thread whiskers & mouth; long tail; hang tag left ear; tush tag left back leg

Replaces: None

Variations: None

Oddities: None

Commentary: Released 16 months after birth; one of the most detailed Beanies; like all Beanie cats, very popular, which means it will become scarce & pricey upon retirement

Poem: Black and gold, brown and white
The shades of her coat are quite a sight
At mixing her colors she was a master
On anyone else it would be a disaster!™

My record

(Beanies are the #1 collectible in American collecting history. A complete, detailed record will vastly increase the value of this Beanie, if and when you ever appraise, trade, re-sell, gift, or bequeath it.)

Description *(which version do you have?):*

Gift from:

Date received/purchased:

Purchased from:

NAME OF PERSON OR RETAILER

ADDRESS

CITY/STATE/ZIP

PHONE

Qty. purchased: **Cost ea.**
(check one)   ❏ *Cash*   ❏ *Check*   ❏ *Charge*

Reason(s) for purchase(s):

Traded to:

NAME

ADDRESS

CITY/STATE/ZIP

PHONE

TRADED FOR

Re-sold to:

NAME

ADDRESS

CITY/STATE/ZIP

PHONE

PRICE RE-SOLD FOR

Your feelings about and/or experiences with this Beanie:

Derby™

Type:	Male horse **Categories:** Brown, farm	**Style no.:** 4008
Birthday:	September 16, 1995 **Released:** 1/99	**Retired:**
Position:	Laying down **Tags:** 5th generation	**Teenie:**

Description: Light brown plush body, white diamond on forehead, dark brown inner ears, dark brown hairy mane & tail, black plastic eyes, black thread nostrils, hang tag left ear, tush tag left back leg

Replaces: Derby w/ fine yarn mane & tail & no diamond + Derby w/ coarse brown mane & tail & no diamond + Derby w/ coarse brown mane & tail & diamond

Variations: Forehead: w/o & w/ diamond; mane & tail: fine yarn, coarse yarn, hairy

Oddities: All variations share same style no. & birthday; previous variation always retires same day new variation released

Commentary: Released nearly 40 months after original birth; more variations than any other Beanie except Mystic; one of the most popular Beanies ever

Poem: All the other horses used to tattle
Because Derby never wore his saddle
He left the stables and the horses, too
Just so Derby can be with you!™

My record

(Beanies are the #1 collectible in American collecting history. A complete, detailed record will vastly increase the value of this Beanie, if and when you ever appraise, trade, re-sell, gift, or bequeath it.)

Description (which version do you have?):
tan. w/ brown main & tail. white diamond shaped spot in forehead.

Gift from:

Date received/purchased: 4 - 19 - 99

Purchased from: A R Mc Aufelary Hospital .
NAME OF PERSON OR RETAILER
ADDRESS 2 202 Division St. N.
CITY/STATE/ZIP auburn, Wa. 98002
PHONE 833 - 7711

Qty. purchased: **Cost ea.** 6 to 5o
(check one) ❏ Cash ❏ Check ☒ Charge

Reason(s) for purchase(s): to complete groups

Traded to:

NAME
ADDRESS
CITY/STATE/ZIP
PHONE
TRADED FOR

Re-sold to:

NAME
ADDRESS
CITY/STATE/ZIP
PHONE
PRICE RE-SOLD FOR

Your feelings about and/or experiences with this Beanie:

Early™

Type:	Male robin	*Categories:*	Bird, brown, tie-dyed	*Style no.:*	4190

Birthday: March 20, 1997   *Released:* 5/30/98   *Retired:*

Position: Perching   *Tags:* 5th generation   *Teenie:*

Description: Brown tie-dyed plush body, bright red breast, cream underside, cream flannel under wings & under tail, gold felt beak, brown felt feet, black plastic eyes, hang tag left wing, tush tag left back

Replaces: None

Variations: None

Oddities: Similar to Pounce, tie-dyed nature of brown plush body barely noticeable

Commentary: Released 14 months after birth; one of the most recognizable and popular of all birds, which will make Early very popular and very much in demand; one of six birds released simultaneously

Poem: Early is a red-breasted robin
For a worm he'll soon be bobbin'
Always known as a sign of spring
The happy robin loves to sing!™

My record

(Beanies are the #1 collectible in American collecting history. A complete, detailed record will vastly increase the value of this Beanie, if and when you ever appraise, trade, re-sell, gift, or bequeath it.)

Description *(which version do you have?):*

Gift from:

Date received/purchased:

Purchased from: *Peckenpaugh*

NAME OF PERSON OR RETAILER

ADDRESS

CITY/STATE/ZIP

PHONE

Qty. purchased: Cost ea. *5.99 + tax*
(check one)   ☑ *Cash*   ❏ *Check*   ❏ *Charge*
3 – 2 2 - 9 9
Reason(s) for purchase(s):

Traded to:

NAME

ADDRESS

CITY/STATE/ZIP

PHONE

TRADED FOR

Re-sold to:

NAME

ADDRESS

CITY/STATE/ZIP

PHONE

PRICE RE-SOLD FOR

Your feelings about and/or experiences with this Beanie:

Erin™

Type: Bear **Categories:** Bear, green **Style no.:** 4186

Birthday: March 17, 1997 **Released:** 1/31/98 **Retired:**

Position: Sitting up **Tags:** 5th generation **Teenie:**

Description: Emerald green plush body, white shamrock embroidered over heart, black plastic eyes & nose, hang tag left ear, tush tag left bottom

Replaces: None

Variations: None

Oddities: One of few Beanies w/ no gender indicated; one of few Beanies bears w/ no ribbon tied around neck; one of few holiday Beanies

Commentary: Released 10 months after birth; special St. Patrick's Day release; one of the most anticipated and sought-after Beanies ever; still hard to find & pricey; initially sold for $150-250 on secondary market; one of the most beautiful Beanies ever; like all Beanie bears, it will skyrocket in value upon retirement

Poem: Named after the beautiful Emerald Isle
This Beanie Baby will make you smile
A bit of luck, a pot of gold
Light up the faces, both young and old!™

My record

(Beanies are the #1 collectible in American collecting history. A complete, detailed record will vastly increase the value of this Beanie, if and when you ever appraise, trade, re-sell, gift, or bequeath it.)

Description *(which version do you have?)*:

Gift from:

Date received/purchased:

Purchased from:

NAME OF PERSON OR RETAILER

ADDRESS

CITY/STATE/ZIP

PHONE

Qty. purchased: Cost ea.
(check one)   ❏ *Cash*   ❏ *Check*   ❏ *Charge*

Reason(s) for purchase(s):

Traded to:

NAME

ADDRESS

CITY/STATE/ZIP

PHONE

TRADED FOR

Re-sold to:

NAME

ADDRESS

CITY/STATE/ZIP

PHONE

PRICE RE-SOLD FOR

Your feelings about and/or experiences with this Beanie:

Fortune™

Type:	Panda bear	**Categories:** Bear, black & white	**Style no.:** 4196
Birthday:	December 6, 1997	**Released:** 5/30/98	**Retired:**
Position:	Sitting up	**Tags:** 5th generation	**Teenie:**

Description: White plush head & body; black ears, arms & legs; black plastic eyes encircled in black; red satin ribbon tied around neck; hang tag left ear; tush tag left bottom

Replaces: Peking the original panda bear, style no. 4013, birthday unknown, released 6/25/94, retired 1/7/96, extremely rare & expensive

Variations: None

Oddities: One of few Beanies w/ no gender indicated

Commentary: Released five months after birth; like disappearing pandas in the wild, very scarce, hence, very expensive; like all Beanie bears, very popular; will sky rocket in value upon retirement; one of two bears released simultaneously

Poem: Nibbling on a bamboo tree
This little panda is hard to see
You're so lucky with this one you found
Only a few are still around!™

My record

(Beanies are the #1 collectible in American collecting history. A complete, detailed record will vastly increase the value of this Beanie, if and when you ever appraise, trade, re-sell, gift, or bequeath it.)

Description *(which version do you have?):* *Panda*
Black + white

Gift from:

Date received/purchased: *Monday 4 - 12 - 99*

Purchased from:

NAME OF PERSON OR RETAILER *Homespun Elegance*
ADDRESS *102 E. Main St.*
CITY/STATE/ZIP *Auburn, Wa, 98002*
PHONE *253 - 833-2070 ; 1-888-733-207*

Qty. purchased: *1* Cost ea. *6.99 + tax 0.60 - total 7.59*
(check one) ☒ *Cash* ❏ *Check* ❏ *Charge*

Reason(s) for purchase(s): *Wanted it.*

Traded to:

NAME
ADDRESS
CITY/STATE/ZIP
PHONE
TRADED FOR

Re-sold to:

NAME
ADDRESS
CITY/STATE/ZIP
PHONE
PRICE RE-SOLD FOR

Your feelings about and/or experiences with this Beanie:

Gigi™

Type: Female poodle **Categories:** Black, dog, napped **Style no.:** 4191

Birthday: April 7, 1997 **Released:** 5/30/98 **Retired:**

Position: Standing **Tags:** 5th generation **Teenie:**

Description: Napped black body; shaved back, neck & chin; black eyes & nose; droopy ears & stubby tail; red tied bows on ears; hang tag left ear; tush tag left back leg

Replaces: None

Variations: None

Oddities: None

Commentary: Like all well-groomed poodles, natural curly hair w/ some areas shaved smooth & be-ribboned ears; like all Beanie dogs, very popular & very much in demand; one of three dogs released simultaneously

Poem:
Prancing and dancing all down the street
Thinking her hairdo is oh so neat
Always so careful in the wind and rain
She's a dog that is anything but plain!™

My record

(Beanies are the #1 collectible in American collecting history. A complete, detailed record will vastly increase the value of this Beanie, if and when you ever appraise, trade, re-sell, gift, or bequeath it.)

Description *(which version do you have?):*

Gift from:

Date received/purchased: May 98

Purchased from: A RMC Gift Shop

NAME OF PERSON OR RETAILER

ADDRESS

CITY/STATE/ZIP

PHONE

Qty. purchased: **Cost ea.** 5-98 + 6¢

(check one)   ☑ *Cash*   ❑ *Check*   ❑ *Charge*

Reason(s) for purchase(s):

Traded to:

NAME

ADDRESS

CITY/STATE/ZIP

PHONE

TRADED FOR

Re-sold to:

NAME

ADDRESS

CITY/STATE/ZIP

PHONE

PRICE RE-SOLD FOR

Your feelings about and/or experiences with this Beanie:

Gobbles™

Type: Female turkey **Categories:** Bird, farm, woodland **Style no.:** 4034

Birthday: November 27, 1996 **Released:** 10/1/97 **Retired:**

Position: Strutting **Tags:** 4th & 5th generation **Teenie:**

Description: Brown plush body; red head; brown & red plush wings w/ thread detailing; gold flannel under wings; gold beak & feet; red felt wattle; brown, red & white fanned out tail feathers w/ red thread detailing; black plastic eyes; black thread nostrils; hang tag left wing; tush tag left side of tail feathers

Replaces: None

Variations: None

Oddities: Born on Thanksgiving; one of few holiday Beanies; female turkeys don't have wattle or fanned tail feathers

Commentary: Released eleven months after birth; special Thanksgiving release; one of the most detailed Beanies; popular Thanksgiving decoration/gift; like all holiday Beanies, it will become scarce & pricey upon retirement

Poem: Gobbles the turkey loves to eat
Once a year she has a feast
I have a secret I'd like to divulge
If she eats too much her tummy will bulge!™

My record

(Beanies are the #1 collectible in American collecting history. A complete, detailed record will vastly increase the value of this Beanie, if and when you ever appraise, trade, re-sell, gift, or bequeath it.)

Description *(which version do you have?):*

Gift from: Linda Elliott   11-98

Date received/purchased:

Purchased from:

NAME OF PERSON OR RETAILER

ADDRESS

CITY/STATE/ZIP

PHONE

Qty. purchased: **Cost ea.**
(check one)   ❏ *Cash*   ❏ *Check*   ❏ *Charge*

Reason(s) for purchase(s):

Traded to:

NAME

ADDRESS

CITY/STATE/ZIP

PHONE

TRADED FOR

Re-sold to:

NAME

ADDRESS

CITY/STATE/ZIP

PHONE

PRICE RE-SOLD FOR

Your feelings about and/or experiences with this Beanie:

Halo™

Type: Bear   **Categories:** Bear, white   **Style no.:** 4208

Birthday: August 31, 1998   **Released:** 9/30/98   **Retired:**

Position: Sitting up   **Tags:** 5th generation   **Teenie:**

Description: Iridescent white plush body, iridescent wings & halo in crinkle fabric, pale pink sheer ribbon w/ gold trim tied around neck, black plastic eyes, brown plastic nose, hang tag left ear, tush tag left bottom

Replaces: None

Variations: None

Oddities: No gender, poem in first person

Commentary: Released one month after birth; first Beanie w/ iridescent plush fabric & sheer ribbon; born on day Princess Diana died; one of the most beautiful Beanies ever; like all Beanie bears, will skyrocket in value upon retirement; one of few fantasy & holiday Beanies

Poem: When you sleep, I'm always here
Don't be afraid, I am near
Watching over you with lots of love
Your guardian angel from up above!™

My record

(Beanies are the #1 collectible in American collecting history. A complete, detailed record will vastly increase the value of this Beanie, if and when you ever appraise, trade, re-sell, gift, or bequeath it.)

Description *(which version do you have?):*

Gift from:

Date received/purchased:

Purchased from:

NAME OF PERSON OR RETAILER

ADDRESS

CITY/STATE/ZIP

PHONE

Qty. purchased: **Cost ea.**
(check one)   ❑ *Cash*   ❑ *Check*   ❑ *Charge*

Reason(s) for purchase(s):

Traded to:

NAME

ADDRESS

CITY/STATE/ZIP

PHONE

TRADED FOR

Re-sold to:

NAME

ADDRESS

CITY/STATE/ZIP

PHONE

PRICE RE-SOLD FOR

Your feelings about and/or experiences with this Beanie:

Hissy™

Type: Male snake   **Categories:** Jungle, reptile, tie-dyed   **Style no.:** 4185

Birthday: April 4, 1997   **Released:** 12/31/97   **Retired:**

Position: Coiled   **Tags:** 5th generation   **Teenie:**

Description: Blue-green tie-dyed plush back; yellow-green belly; big black plastic eyes; red velveteen forked tongue; wide, flat head; long, elasticized body that coils; hang tag top; tush tag bottom

Replaces: Slither, style no. 4031, birthday none, released 6/25/94, retired 6/15/95, one of the rarest & most expensive Beanies ever

Variations: Tie-dye varies in colors from cool to warm

Oddities: Biggest Beanie eyes ever

Commentary: Released eight months after birth; one of the newer releases, so readily available; like all jungle animals, very popular, which means it will become scarce & pricey upon retirement; very popular w/ boys

Poem: Curled and coiled and ready to play
He waits for you patiently every day
He'll keep his best friend, but not his skin
And stay with you through thick and thin!™

My record

(Beanies are the #1 collectible in American collecting history. A complete, detailed record will vastly increase the value of this Beanie, if and when you ever appraise, trade, re-sell, gift, or bequeath it.)

Description *(which version do you have?):*

Gift from:

Date received/purchased:

Purchased from:

NAME OF PERSON OR RETAILER

ADDRESS

CITY/STATE/ZIP

PHONE

Qty. purchased: **Cost ea.**
(check one) ❏ *Cash* ❏ *Check* ❏ *Charge*

Reason(s) for purchase(s):

Traded to:

NAME

ADDRESS

CITY/STATE/ZIP

PHONE

TRADED FOR

Re-sold to:

NAME

ADDRESS

CITY/STATE/ZIP

PHONE

PRICE RE-SOLD FOR

Your feelings about and/or experiences with this Beanie:

Iggy™

Type:	Male iguana	**Categories:** Reptile, tie-dyed	**Style no.:** 4038
Birthday:	August 12, 1997	**Released:** 12/31/97	**Retired:**
Position:	Crawling	**Tags:** 5th generation	**Teenie:**

Description: Blue-green tie-dyed plush body, moss green felt scales, protruding plush eyes w/ yellow plastic centers, fluorescent green felt mouth, curled tail, hang tag on scales, tush tag left back

Replaces: Pastel Iggy w/o tongue & pastel Iggy w/ tongue

Variations: Tie-dye varies in colors; hang tag on foot, hang tag on scales

Oddities: Originally released w/ Rainbow's fabric

Commentary: Released four months after birth; very popular with boys; earlier version in wrong fabric very valuable

Poem: Sitting on a rock, basking in the sun
Is this Iguana's idea of fun
Towel and glasses, book and beach chair
His life is so perfect without a care!™

My record

(Beanies are the #1 collectible in American collecting history. A complete, detailed record will vastly increase the value of this Beanie, if and when you ever appraise, trade, re-sell, gift, or bequeath it.)

Description *(which version do you have?)*:

Gift from:

Date received/purchased:

Purchased from:

NAME OF PERSON OR RETAILER

ADDRESS

CITY/STATE/ZIP

PHONE

Qty. purchased: **Cost ea.**
(check one)   ❏ *Cash*   ❏ *Check*   ❏ *Charge*

Reason(s) for purchase(s):

Traded to:

NAME

ADDRESS

CITY/STATE/ZIP

PHONE

TRADED FOR

Re-sold to:

NAME

ADDRESS

CITY/STATE/ZIP

PHONE

PRICE RE-SOLD FOR

Your feelings about and/or experiences with this Beanie:

Jabber™

Type:	Male parrot	*Categories:*	Bird, jungle	*Style no.:*	4197
Birthday:	October 10, 1997	*Released:*	5/30/98	*Retired:*	
Position:	Perching	*Tags:*	5th generation	*Teenie:*	

Description: Red plush body; gold & black beak, under wings & feet; blue accents on head, wings & tail; black plastic eyes ringed w/ gold & surrounded by white circles w/ black stripes; hang tag left wing; tush tag bottom

Replaces: None

Variations: None

Oddities: None

Commentary: Released seven months after birth; bar none, the most colorful, detailed Beanie to date, which will make it very popular & very much in demand; one of six birds released simultaneously

Poem: Teaching Jabber to move his beak
A large vocabulary he can now speak
Jabber will repeat what you say
Teach him a new word every day!™

My record

(Beanies are the #1 collectible in American collecting history. A complete, detailed record will vastly increase the value of this Beanie, if and when you ever appraise, trade, re-sell, gift, or bequeath it.)

Description *(which version do you have?):*

Gift from:

Date received/purchased:

Purchased from:

NAME OF PERSON OR RETAILER

ADDRESS

CITY/STATE/ZIP

PHONE

Qty. purchased: **Cost ea.**
(check one)   ❏ *Cash*   ❏ *Check*   ❏ *Charge*

Reason(s) for purchase(s):

Traded to:

NAME

ADDRESS

CITY/STATE/ZIP

PHONE

TRADED FOR

Re-sold to:

NAME

ADDRESS

CITY/STATE/ZIP

PHONE

PRICE RE-SOLD FOR

Your feelings about and/or experiences with this Beanie:

Jake™

Type:	Male mallard	**Categories:** Bird, woodland	**Style no.:** 4199
Birthday:	April 16, 1997	**Released:** 5/30/98	**Retired:**
Position:	Perching	**Tags:** 5th generation	**Teenie:**

Description: Teal head; light brown beak & webbed feet; tan ringed neck; gray topside w/ brown underside; gray wings topside, tan underside; teal tail; tan bottom; black plastic eyes; black thread nostrils; hang tag left wing; tush tag left bottom

Replaces: None

Variations: None

Oddities: None

Commentary: Released 13 months after birth; one of the most colorful, detailed Beanies to date, which will make it very popular & very much in demand; one of six birds released simultaneously

Poem: Jake the drake likes to splash in a puddle
Take him home and give him a cuddle
Quack, quack, quack, he will say
He's so glad you're here to play!™

My record

(Beanies are the #1 collectible in American collecting history. A complete, detailed record will vastly increase the value of this Beanie, if and when you ever appraise, trade, re-sell, gift, or bequeath it.)

Description *(which version do you have?):*

Gift from:

Date received/purchased:

Purchased from:

NAME OF PERSON OR RETAILER

ADDRESS

CITY/STATE/ZIP

PHONE

Qty. purchased: **Cost ea.**
(check one)   ❏ *Cash*   ❏ *Check*   ❏ *Charge*

Reason(s) for purchase(s):

Traded to:

NAME

ADDRESS

CITY/STATE/ZIP

PHONE

TRADED FOR

Re-sold to:

NAME

ADDRESS

CITY/STATE/ZIP

PHONE

PRICE RE-SOLD FOR

Your feelings about and/or experiences with this Beanie:

Kuku™

Type:	Male cockatoo	**Categories:**	Bird, white	**Style no.:**	4192
Birthday:	January 5, 1997	**Released:**	5/30/98	**Retired:**	
Position:	Perching	**Tags:**	5th generation	**Teenie:**	

Description: White plush body, pink tuft of hair on top of head, gray beak & feet, pink flannel under wings & under tail, black plastic eyes ringed w/ gold, hang tag left wing, tush tag bottom

Replaces: None

Variations: None

Oddities: None

Commentary: Released 16 months after birth; one of the most beautiful Beanies, which will make it very popular & very much in demand; one of six birds released simultaneously

Poem: This fancy bird loves to converse
He talks in poems, rhythms and verse
So take him home and give him some time
You'll be surprised how he can rhyme!™

My record

(Beanies are the #1 collectible in American collecting history. A complete, detailed record will vastly increase the value of this Beanie, if and when you ever appraise, trade, re-sell, gift, or bequeath it.)

Description *(which version do you have?):*

Gift from:

Date received/purchased:

Purchased from: A R m c

NAME OF PERSON OR RETAILER

ADDRESS

CITY/STATE/ZIP

PHONE

Qty. purchased: Cost ea. 5 95

(check one)   ❏ *Cash*   ❏ *Check*   ❏ *Charge*

Reason(s) for purchase(s):

Traded to:

NAME

ADDRESS

CITY/STATE/ZIP

PHONE

TRADED FOR

Re-sold to:

NAME

ADDRESS

CITY/STATE/ZIP

PHONE

PRICE RE-SOLD FOR

Your feelings about and/or experiences with this Beanie:

Loosy™

Type:	Female goose	**Categories:**	Birds, black, gray	**Style no.:**	4206
Birthday:	March 29, 1998	**Released:**	9/30/98	**Retired:**	
Position:	Squatting	**Tags:**	5th generation	**Teenie:**	

Description: Black, white & gray plush body w/ markings of traditional Canadian goose; black flannel beak & feet; wine-colored satin ribbon tied around neck; black plastic eyes; hang tag left wing; tush tag left bottom

Replaces: None

Variations: None

Oddities: None

Commentary: Released six months after birth; grand Canadian goose, harbinger of autumn in both Canada & America; could be considered holiday Beanie; very popular w/ girls

Poem: A tale has been told
Of a goose that laid gold
But try as she might
Loosy's eggs are just white!™

My record

(Beanies are the #1 collectible in American collecting history. A complete, detailed record will vastly increase the value of this Beanie, if and when you ever appraise, trade, re-sell, gift, or bequeath it.)

Description *(which version do you have?):*

Loosy - female goose

Gift from:

Date received/purchased: 8-28-99

Purchased from: *Peckenpaugh Drug*

NAME OF PERSON OR RETAILER

ADDRESS *Auburn, Wa*

CITY/STATE/ZIP

PHONE

Qty. purchased: **Cost ea.**

(check one)   ❏ *Cash*   ❏ *Check*   ❏ *Charge*

Reason(s) for purchase(s):

Traded to:

NAME

ADDRESS

CITY/STATE/ZIP

PHONE

TRADED FOR

Re-sold to:

NAME

ADDRESS

CITY/STATE/ZIP

PHONE

PRICE RE-SOLD FOR

Your feelings about and/or experiences with this Beanie:

Maple™

Unable to get here

Type:	Male bear	**Categories:** Bear, flag, white	**Style no.:** 4600
Birthday:	July 1, 1996	**Released:** 1/1/97	**Retired:**
Position:	Sitting up	**Tags:** 4th & 5th generation	**Teenie:**

Description: White plush body, red & white Canadian flag stitched w/ white thread over heart, black plastic eyes, brown plastic nose, red satin ribbon tied around neck, hang tag left ear, tush tag left bottom, second tush tag in French

Replaces: Originally named Pride, extremely rare & expensive

Variations: Canadian Special Olympics edition w/ commemorative card, extremely rare & expensive

Oddities: Along w/ Britannia, one of only two exclusive foreign releases; Maple shares same birthday w/ Scoop

Commentary: Released six months after birth; released exclusively in Canada to commemorate Federation Day, making it nearly impossible to obtain in the U.S.; one of the most sought-after Beanies ever; initially sold for $150-$300 on the secondary market; like all Beanie bears, will sky-rocket in value upon retirement

Poem: Maple the bear likes to ski
With his friends, he plays hockey.
He loves his pancakes and eats every crumb,
Can you guess which country he's from?™

My record

(Beanies are the #1 collectible in American collecting history. A complete, detailed record will vastly increase the value of this Beanie, if and when you ever appraise, trade, re-sell, gift, or bequeath it.)

Description *(which version do you have?):*

Gift from:

Date received/purchased:

Purchased from:

NAME OF PERSON OR RETAILER

ADDRESS

CITY/STATE/ZIP

PHONE

Qty. purchased: **Cost ea.**
(check one)   ❏ *Cash*   ❏ *Check*   ❏ *Charge*

Reason(s) for purchase(s):

Traded to:

NAME

ADDRESS

CITY/STATE/ZIP

PHONE

TRADED FOR

Re-sold to:

NAME

ADDRESS

CITY/STATE/ZIP

PHONE

PRICE RE-SOLD FOR

Your feelings about and/or experiences with this Beanie:

Mel™

Type: Male koala   **Categories:** Aussie, bear, gray   **Style no.:** 4162

Birthday: January 15, 1996   **Released:** 1/1/97   **Retired:**

Position: Laying down   **Tags:** 4th & 5th generation   **Teenie:** 5/98

Description: Gray plush body; white belly & inner ears; black plastic eyes; big, black, plastic, oval-shaped nose; black thread mouth; hang tag left ear; tush tag left back leg

Replaces: None

Variations: None

Oddities: Obviously named after Australian actor Mel Gibson who, unlike other entities, has not sued manufacturer for unauthorized use of his name; one of few Beanies w/ authentic-looking nose

Commentary: Released one year after birth; one of only three Australian Beanies; like all Beanie bears, very popular, which means it will sky-rocket in value upon retirement

Poem: How do you name a Koala bear?
It's rather tough, I do declare!
It confuses me, I get into a funk
I'll name him Mel, after my favorite hunk!™

My record

(Beanies are the #1 collectible in American collecting history. A complete, detailed record will vastly increase the value of this Beanie, if and when you ever appraise, trade, re-sell, gift, or bequeath it.)

Description *(which version do you have?)*:

Gift from:

Date received/purchased:

Purchased from:

NAME OF PERSON OR RETAILER

ADDRESS

CITY/STATE/ZIP

PHONE

Qty. purchased: **Cost ea.**
(check one)   ❏ *Cash*   ❏ *Check*   ❏ *Charge*

Reason(s) for purchase(s):

Traded to:

NAME

ADDRESS

CITY/STATE/ZIP

PHONE

TRADED FOR

Re-sold to:

NAME

ADDRESS

CITY/STATE/ZIP

PHONE

PRICE RE-SOLD FOR

Your feelings about and/or experiences with this Beanie:

Mystic™

Type: Female unicorn **Categories:** Fantasy, white **Style no.:** 4007

Birthday: May 21, 1994 **Released:** 1/99 **Retired:**

Position: Laying down **Tags:** 5th generation **Teenie:**

Description: White plush body, rainbow-colored hairy mane & tail, iridescent horn w/ pink stitching, black plastic eyes ringed w/ blue, black thread nostrils, hang tag left ear, tush tag left back leg

Replaces: Mystic with brown horn & white yarn mane + Mystic w/ iridescent horn and & white yarn mane

Variations: Mane has appeared in fine yarn, coarse yarn, and now rainbow-colored hairy mane; horn has appeared in brown and iridescent, in varying lengths, w/ and w/o stitching

Oddities: All variations share same style no. & birthday; previous variation always retires same day new variation released

Commentary: Released nearly five years after original birth; more variations than any other Beanie except Derby; one of the most beautiful, popular Beanies ever

Poem: Once upon a time so far away
A unicorn was born one day in May
Keep Mystic with you, she's a prize
You'll see the magic in her blue eyes!™

My record

(Beanies are the #1 collectible in American collecting history. A complete, detailed record will vastly increase the value of this Beanie, if and when you ever appraise, trade, re-sell, gift, or bequeath it.)

Description *(which version do you have?):* White

Gift from:

Date received/purchased: 4 - 19 - 99

Purchased from: A R M C Gift Shop
NAME OF PERSON OR RETAILER

ADDRESS

CITY/STATE/ZIP

PHONE

Qty. purchased: **Cost ea.** 1 @ 6 50 incl tax
(check one) ❑ Cash ❑ Check ☑ Charge

Reason(s) for purchase(s): to complete

Traded to:

NAME

ADDRESS

CITY/STATE/ZIP

PHONE

TRADED FOR

Re-sold to:

NAME

ADDRESS

CITY/STATE/ZIP

PHONE

PRICE RE-SOLD FOR

Your feelings about and/or experiences with this Beanie:

Nanook™

Type:	Male husky **Categories:** Arctic, dog, gray	**Style no.:** 4104
Birthday:	November 21, 1996 **Released:** 5/11/97	**Retired:**
Position:	Laying down **Tags:** 4th & 5th generation	**Teenie:**

Description: Dark gray body; white face, inner ears, bottom side, socks & tip of tail; black plastic eyes ringed w/ blue; black plastic nose; black thread mouth; hang tag left ear; tush tag left back leg

Replaces: None

Variations: Shape of mouth

Oddities: None

Commentary: Released six months after birth; like all Beanie dogs, very popular, which means it will become scarce & pricey upon retirement

Poem:
Nanook is a dog that loves cold weather
To him a sled is light as a feather
Over the snow and through the slush
He runs at hearing the cry of "mush"!™

My record

(Beanies are the #1 collectible in American collecting history. A complete, detailed record will vastly increase the value of this Beanie, if and when you ever appraise, trade, re-sell, gift, or bequeath it.)

Description *(which version do you have?):*

Gift from:

Date received/purchased:

Purchased from:

NAME OF PERSON OR RETAILER

ADDRESS

CITY/STATE/ZIP

PHONE

Qty. purchased: **Cost ea.**
(check one)   ❏ *Cash*   ❏ *Check*   ❏ *Charge*

Reason(s) for purchase(s):

Traded to:

NAME

ADDRESS

CITY/STATE/ZIP

PHONE

TRADED FOR

Re-sold to:

NAME

ADDRESS

CITY/STATE/ZIP

PHONE

PRICE RE-SOLD FOR

Your feelings about and/or experiences with this Beanie:

Peace™

Type:	Bear	*Categories:* Bear, tie-dyed	*Style no.:* 4053
Birthday:	February 1, 1996	*Released:* 5/11/97	*Retired:*
Position:	Sitting up	*Tags:* 4th & 5th generation	*Teenie:*

Description: Tie-dyed plush body in pastel colors, multi-colored peace symbol embroidered over heart, black plastic eyes & nose, hang tag left ear, tush tag left bottom

Replaces: Garcia, style no. 4051, birthday 8/1/95, released 1/7/96, retired 5/11/97, very hard to find & very expensive; Peace in brighter colors

Variations: Tie-dye varies in colors

Oddities: No gender; Peace released same day Garcia retired

Commentary: Released 15 months after birth; like all Beanie bears, very popular (particularly w/ Baby Boomers); hard to find & pricey; like all Beanie bears, will skyrocket in value upon retirement

Poem: All races, all colors, under the sun
Join hands together and have some fun
Dance to the music, rock and roll is the sound
Symbols of peace and love abound!™

My record

(Beanies are the #1 collectible in American collecting history. A complete, detailed record will vastly increase the value of this Beanie, if and when you ever appraise, trade, re-sell, gift, or bequeath it.)

Description *(which version do you have?):*

Gift from: *ARmc*

Date received/purchased: *5/98*

Purchased from: *A Rmc*

NAME OF PERSON OR RETAILER

ADDRESS

CITY/STATE/ZIP

PHONE

Qty. purchased: **Cost ea.**
(check one)   ❏ *Cash*   ❏ *Check*   ❏ *Charge*

Reason(s) for purchase(s):

Traded to:

NAME

ADDRESS

CITY/STATE/ZIP

PHONE

TRADED FOR

Re-sold to:

NAME

ADDRESS

CITY/STATE/ZIP

PHONE

PRICE RE-SOLD FOR

Your feelings about and/or experiences with this Beanie:

Pouch™

Type:	Female kangaroo	**Categories:** Aussie, brown	**Style no.:** 4161
Birthday:	November 6, 1996	**Released:** 1/1/97	**Retired:**
Position:	Standing up	**Tags:** 4th & 5th generation	**Teenie:**

Description: Brown plush body; cream belly, chin & inner ears; black plastic eyes & nose; big feet; long tail; hang tag left ear; tush tag left side of tail; pouch w/ joey peeking out; joey has dark brown ears & black thread eyes; joey is a head only, attached by thread to mother

Replaces: None

Variations: None

Oddities: Only Beanie w/ baby

Commentary: Released two months after birth; one of the most detailed Beanies; one of only three Australian Beanies, hence, very popular, which means it will become scarce & pricey upon retirement; very popular w/ girls

Poem: My little pouch is handy I've found
It helps me carry my baby around
I hop up and down without any fear
Knowing my baby is safe and near.™

My record

(Beanies are the #1 collectible in American collecting history. A complete, detailed record will vastly increase the value of this Beanie, if and when you ever appraise, trade, re-sell, gift, or bequeath it.)

Description *(which version do you have?):*

Gift from:

Date received/purchased: 4 - 20 - 99

Purchased from: Fred Meyer

NAME OF PERSON OR RETAILER

ADDRESS

CITY/STATE/ZIP

PHONE

Qty. purchased: **Cost ea.** 6 99 + tax
(check one)   ☑ *Cash*   ❑ *Check*   ❑ *Charge*

Reason(s) for purchase(s):

Traded to:

NAME

ADDRESS

CITY/STATE/ZIP

PHONE

TRADED FOR

Re-sold to:

NAME

ADDRESS

CITY/STATE/ZIP

PHONE

PRICE RE-SOLD FOR

Your feelings about and/or experiences with this Beanie:

Pounce™

Type:	Cat	**Categories:** Brown, cat, tie-dyed	**Style no.:** 4122	

Birthday: August 28, 1997   **Released:** 12/31/97   **Retired:**

Position: Laying down   **Tags:** 5th generation   **Teenie:**

Description: Brown tie-dyed plush body; cream snout, inner ears & socks; black plastic eyes ringed w/ gold; pink plastic nose; brown thread whiskers & mouth; long tail; hang tag left ear; tush tag left back leg

Replaces: None

Variations: Tie-dye varies in colors from light to dark brown

Oddities: One of few Beanies w/ no gender indicated; tie-dye barely noticeable

Commentary: Released four months after birth; one of newer releases, so readily available; like all Beanie cats, very popular, which means it will become scarce & pricey upon retirement

Poem: Sneaking and slinking down the hall
To pounce upon a fluffy yarn ball
Under the tables, under the chairs
Through the rooms and down the stairs!™

My record

(Beanies are the #1 collectible in American collecting history. A complete, detailed record will vastly increase the value of this Beanie, if and when you ever appraise, trade, re-sell, gift, or bequeath it.)

Description *(which version do you have?):*

Gift from: *Linda Elliott*

Date received/purchased: 7 - 25 - 99

Purchased from:

NAME OF PERSON OR RETAILER

ADDRESS

CITY/STATE/ZIP

PHONE

Qty. purchased: **Cost ea.**
(check one)   ❑ *Cash*   ❑ *Check*   ❑ *Charge*

Reason(s) for purchase(s):

Traded to:

NAME

ADDRESS

CITY/STATE/ZIP

PHONE

TRADED FOR

Re-sold to:

NAME

ADDRESS

CITY/STATE/ZIP

PHONE

PRICE RE-SOLD FOR

Your feelings about and/or experiences with this Beanie:

Prance™

Type:	Female tiger cat	**Categories:**	Cat, gray, striped	**Style no.:**	4123
Birthday:	November 20, 1997	**Released:**	12/31/97	**Retired:**	
Position:	Laying down	**Tags:**	5th generation	**Teenie:**	

Description: Light gray plush body w/ dark gray stripes; white forehead, inner ears & socks; black plastic eyes ringed w/ blue; pink plastic nose; pink thread whiskers & mouth; long tail; hang tag left ear; tush tag left back leg

Replaces: None

Variations: None

Oddities: None

Commentary: Released one month after birth; one of the newer releases, so readily available; like all Beanie cats, very popular, which means it will become scarce & pricey upon retirement

Poem: She darts around and swats the air
Then looks confused when nothing's there
Pick her up and pet her soft fur
Listen closely, and you'll hear her purr!™

My record

(Beanies are the #1 collectible in American collecting history. A complete, detailed record will vastly increase the value of this Beanie, if and when you ever appraise, trade, re-sell, gift, or bequeath it.)

Description *(which version do you have?):*

Gift from: *Linda Elliott*

Date received/purchased: 7 - 25 - 99

Purchased from:

NAME OF PERSON OR RETAILER

ADDRESS

CITY/STATE/ZIP

PHONE

Qty. purchased: **Cost ea.**
(check one)   ❏ *Cash*   ❏ *Check*   ❏ *Charge*

Reason(s) for purchase(s):

Traded to:

NAME

ADDRESS

CITY/STATE/ZIP

PHONE

TRADED FOR

Re-sold to:

NAME

ADDRESS

CITY/STATE/ZIP

PHONE

PRICE RE-SOLD FOR

Your feelings about and/or experiences with this Beanie:

Princess™

Type:	Female bear	***Categories:***	Bear, purple	***Style no.:***	4300

Birthday: None   ***Released:*** 10/29/97   ***Retired:***

Position: Sitting up   ***Tags:*** 4th & 5th generation   ***Teenie:***

Description: Royal purple plush body, white rose w/ green leaves & stem embroidered over heart, black plastic eyes & nose, royal purple satin ribbon tied around neck, hang tag left ear, tush tag left bottom

Replaces: None

Variations: 1st version, PVC pellets; 2nd, PE

Oddities: Only Beanie specifically designed to commemorate a person—the late, beloved Diana, Princess of Wales; only later Beanie w/ no birthday indicated; only Beanie w/ poem in script typeface; all profits donated to Diana, Princess of Wales Memorial Fund; some stems green, some silver

Commentary: The most beautiful, meaningful, sought-after Beanie ever; initially sold for $250-$500 on the secondary market; still hard to find & pricey; like all Beanie bears, will sky-rocket in value upon retirement; early retirement anticipated; favorite of girls

Poem: Like an angel, she came from heaven above
She shared her compassion, her pain, her love
She only stayed with us long enough to teach
The world to share, to give, to reach.™

(crown added)

My record

(Beanies are the #1 collectible in American collecting history. A complete, detailed record will vastly increase the value of this Beanie, if and when you ever appraise, trade, re-sell, gift, or bequeath it.)

Description *(which version do you have?):*

Gift from:

Date received/purchased:

Purchased from:

NAME OF PERSON OR RETAILER

ADDRESS

CITY/STATE/ZIP

PHONE

Qty. purchased: **Cost ea.**
(check one)   ❑ *Cash*   ❑ *Check*   ❑ *Charge*

Reason(s) for purchase(s):

Traded to:

NAME

ADDRESS

CITY/STATE/ZIP

PHONE

TRADED FOR

Re-sold to:

NAME

ADDRESS

CITY/STATE/ZIP

PHONE

PRICE RE-SOLD FOR

Your feelings about and/or experiences with this Beanie:

Pugsly™

Type:	Male pug	*Categories:* Brown, dog *Style no.:* 4106
Birthday:	May 2, 1996	*Released:* 5/11/97 *Retired:*
Position:	Laying down	*Tags:* 4th & 5th generation *Teenie:*
Description:	Tan plush body; black snout, chin & ears; black plastic eyes & nose; curled tail; hang tag left ear; tush tag left back leg	
Replaces:	None	
Variations:	None	
Oddities:	None	
Commentary:	Released one year after birth; like all Beanie dogs, very popular, which means it will become scarce & pricey upon retirement	
Poem:	Pugsly is picky about what he will wear Never a spot, a stain or a tear Image is something of which he'll gloat Until he noticed his wrinkled coat!™	

My record

(Beanies are the #1 collectible in American collecting history. A complete, detailed record will vastly increase the value of this Beanie, if and when you ever appraise, trade, re-sell, gift, or bequeath it.)

Description *(which version do you have?):*

Gift from:

Date received/purchased:

Purchased from:

NAME OF PERSON OR RETAILER

ADDRESS

CITY/STATE/ZIP

PHONE

Qty. purchased: **Cost ea.**
(check one)   ❏ *Cash*   ❏ *Check*   ❏ *Charge*

Reason(s) for purchase(s):

Traded to:

NAME

ADDRESS

CITY/STATE/ZIP

PHONE

TRADED FOR

Re-sold to:

NAME

ADDRESS

CITY/STATE/ZIP

PHONE

PRICE RE-SOLD FOR

Your feelings about and/or experiences with this Beanie:

Rainbow™

Type: Male chameleon   **Categories:** Reptile, tie-dyed   **Style no.:** 4037

Birthday: October 14, 1997   **Released:** 12/31/97   **Retired:**

Position: Crawling   **Tags:** 5th generation   **Teenie:**

Description: Rainbow tie-dyed plush body, protruding plush eyes w/ red centers, red felt mouth, mauve forked ribbon tongue, hood, curled tail, hang tag left front leg, tush tag left back side

Replaces: Blue tie-dyed Rainbow

Variations: Tie-dye varies in colors

Oddities: Originally released w/ Iggy's fabric

Commentary: Released two months after birth; very popular w/ boys; earlier version in wrong fabric very valuable

Poem:
Red, green, blue and yellow
This chameleon is a colorful fellow
A blend of colors, his own unique hue
Rainbow was made especially for you!™

My record

(Beanies are the #1 collectible in American collecting history. A complete, detailed record will vastly increase the value of this Beanie, if and when you ever appraise, trade, re-sell, gift, or bequeath it.)

Description *(which version do you have?):*

Gift from:

Date received/purchased:

Purchased from:

NAME OF PERSON OR RETAILER

ADDRESS

CITY/STATE/ZIP

PHONE

Qty. purchased: **Cost ea.**
(check one)   ❑ *Cash*   ❑ *Check*   ❑ *Charge*

Reason(s) for purchase(s):

Traded to:

NAME

ADDRESS

CITY/STATE/ZIP

PHONE

TRADED FOR

Re-sold to:

NAME

ADDRESS

CITY/STATE/ZIP

PHONE

PRICE RE-SOLD FOR

Your feelings about and/or experiences with this Beanie:

Roam™

Type:	Male buffalo	**Categories:** Brown, napped	**Style no.:** 4209
Birthday:	September 27, 1998	**Released:** 9/30/98	**Retired:**
Position:	Standing	**Tags:** 5th generation	**Teenie:**

Description: Chocolate brown napped head, shoulders, front legs & tip of tail; plush snout, outer ears, belly, rear, tail & hooves; lighter brown flannel horns; chocolate brown flannel inner ears; black plastic eyes; thread nostrils; hang tag left ear; tush tag left back

Replaces: None

Variations: None

Oddities: None

Commentary: Released three days after birth, majestic symbol of the American west, one of the most realistic Beanies, one of three napped Beanies released simultaneously, very popular w/ boys

Poem:
Once roaming wild on the America land
Tall and strong, wooly and grand
So rare and special is this guy
Find him quickly, he's quite a buy!™

My record

(Beanies are the #1 collectible in American collecting history. A complete, detailed record will vastly increase the value of this Beanie, if and when you ever appraise, trade, re-sell, gift, or bequeath it.)

Description *(which version do you have?):*

Gift from:

Date received/purchased:

Purchased from:

NAME OF PERSON OR RETAILER

ADDRESS

CITY/STATE/ZIP

PHONE

Qty. purchased: **Cost ea.**
(check one)   ❏ *Cash*   ❏ *Check*   ❏ *Charge*

Reason(s) for purchase(s):

Traded to:

NAME

ADDRESS

CITY/STATE/ZIP

PHONE

TRADED FOR

Re-sold to:

NAME

ADDRESS

CITY/STATE/ZIP

PHONE

PRICE RE-SOLD FOR

Your feelings about and/or experiences with this Beanie:

Rocket™

Type: Male blue jay   **Categories:** Blue, bird, woodland   **Style no.:** 4202

Birthday: March 12, 1997   **Released:** 5/30/98   **Retired:**

Position: Perching   **Tags:** 5th generation   **Teenie:**

Description: Bright sky blue plush body; white face, underside & under wings; black beak & feet; black plastic eyes; crown & three-pronged tail; hang tag left wing; tush tag bottom

Replaces: None

Variations: None

Oddities: None

Commentary: Released 14 months after birth; one of the most beautiful shades of blue ever; one of the prettiest Beanie birds ever, which will make it very popular & very much in demand; one of six birds released simultaneously

Poem: Rocket is the fastest blue jay ever
He flies in all sorts of weather
Aerial tricks are his specialty
He's so entertaining for you and me!™

My record

(Beanies are the #1 collectible in American collecting history. A complete, detailed record will vastly increase the value of this Beanie, if and when you ever appraise, trade, re-sell, gift, or bequeath it.)

Description *(which version do you have?):*

Gift from:

Date received/purchased:

Purchased from:

NAME OF PERSON OR RETAILER

ADDRESS

CITY/STATE/ZIP

PHONE

Qty. purchased: **Cost ea.**
(check one)   ❏ *Cash*   ❏ *Check*   ❏ *Charge*

Reason(s) for purchase(s):

Traded to:

NAME

ADDRESS

CITY/STATE/ZIP

PHONE

TRADED FOR

Re-sold to:

NAME

ADDRESS

CITY/STATE/ZIP

PHONE

PRICE RE-SOLD FOR

Your feelings about and/or experiences with this Beanie:

Scorch™

Type:	Dragon	***Categories:*** Fantasy, napped, tie-dyed	***Style no.:*** 4210
Birthday:	July 31, 1998	***Released:*** 9/30/98	***Retired:***
Position:	Standing	***Tags:*** 5th generation	***Teenie:***

Description: Brown, green, purple tie-dyed, napped body; moss green felt scales & claws; red iridescent wings in crinkle fabric; black plastic eyes; red thread nostrils; pink flannel mouth w/ red forked ribbon tongue; curly tail; hang tag left ear; tush tag left bottom

Replaces: Magic, style no. 4088, birthday 9/5/95, released 6/3/95, retired 12/31/97, hard to find & pricey

Variations: Tie-dye varies in colors

Oddities: No gender; only Beanie w/ mouth that opens

Commentary: Released two months after birth; new tie-dyed, napped fabric; one of three napped Beanies released simultaneously; one of few fantasy Beanies; one of most detailed Beanies; very popular w/ kids

Poem: A magical mystery with glowing wings
Made by wizards and other things
Known to breathe fire with lots of smoke
Scorch is really a friendly ol' bloke!™

My record

(Beanies are the #1 collectible in American collecting history. A complete, detailed record will vastly increase the value of this Beanie, if and when you ever appraise, trade, re-sell, gift, or bequeath it.)

Description *(which version do you have?):*

Gift from:

Date received/purchased: 5 - 3 - 99

Purchased from: A R M C - Gift Shop

NAME OF PERSON OR RETAILER

ADDRESS

CITY/STATE/ZIP

PHONE

Qty. purchased: l   **Cost ea.** 5 95 + tax
(check one)   ❏ *Cash*   ❏ *Check*   ❏ *Charge*

Reason(s) for purchase(s):

Traded to:

NAME

ADDRESS

CITY/STATE/ZIP

PHONE

TRADED FOR

Re-sold to:

NAME

ADDRESS

CITY/STATE/ZIP

PHONE

PRICE RE-SOLD FOR

Your feelings about and/or experiences with this Beanie:

Smoochy™

Type:	Male frog	**Categories:**	Green, reptile	**Style no.:**	4039
Birthday:	October 1, 1997	**Released:**	12/31/97	**Retired:**	
Position:	Laying down	**Tags:**	5th generation	**Teenie:**	

Description: Bright green plush body; gold belly, chin & feet; protruding gold & green plush eyes w/ black plastic centers ringed w/ green; webbed feet; hang tag left front foot; tush tag left back leg

Replaces: Legs, style no. 4020, birthday 4/25/93, released 1/8/94, retired 10/1/97, somewhat available for a reasonable price

Variations: Red string mouth, red felt mouth

Oddities: None

Commentary: Released two months after birth; one of the newer releases, so readily available; one of the most colorful Beanies; very popular w/ boys

Poem: Is he a frog or maybe a prince?
This confusion makes him wince
Find the answer, help him with this
Be the one to give him a kiss!™

My record

(Beanies are the #1 collectible in American collecting history. A complete, detailed record will vastly increase the value of this Beanie, if and when you ever appraise, trade, re-sell, gift, or bequeath it.)

Description *(which version do you have?)*:

Gift from:

Date received/purchased: *4 - 20 - 99*

Purchased from:

Fred Meyer

NAME OF PERSON OR RETAILER

ADDRESS

CITY/STATE/ZIP

PHONE

Qty. purchased: **Cost ea.** *6 99 + tax*
(check one)   ☑ *Cash*   ❏ *Check*   ❏ *Charge*

Reason(s) for purchase(s):

Traded to:

NAME

ADDRESS

CITY/STATE/ZIP

PHONE

TRADED FOR

Re-sold to:

NAME

ADDRESS

CITY/STATE/ZIP

PHONE

PRICE RE-SOLD FOR

Your feelings about and/or experiences with this Beanie:

Spunky™

Type: Male cocker spaniel   **Categories:** Brown, dog   **Style no.:** 4184

Birthday: January 14, 1997   **Released:** 12/31/97   **Retired:**

Position: Laying down   **Tags:** 5th generation   **Teenie:**

Description: Light brown plush body; long, curly ears; black plastic eyes & nose; black thread mouth; stubby tail; hang tag left ear; tush tag left back leg

Replaces: None

Variations: None

Oddities: Only Beanie w/ curls

Commentary: Released 11 months after birth; one of the newer releases, so readily available; one of the cutest Beanies ever; like all Beanie dogs, very popular, which will make it scarce & pricey upon retirement

Poem: Bouncing around without much grace
To jump on your lap and lick your face
But watch him closely, he has no fears
He'll run so fast, he'll trip over his ears!™

My record

(Beanies are the #1 collectible in American collecting history. A complete, detailed record will vastly increase the value of this Beanie, if and when you ever appraise, trade, re-sell, gift, or bequeath it.)

Description *(which version do you have?):*
tan all over w/fuzzy ears

Gift from:

Date received/purchased: 4 ~ 19 ~ 99

Purchased from:

NAME OF PERSON OR RETAILER   A R M C Gift Shop
ADDRESS
CITY/STATE/ZIP
PHONE

Qty. purchased: 1   **Cost ea.** 5 95 F/C4X
(check one)   ❏ *Cash*   ❏ *Check*   ❏ *Charge*

Reason(s) for purchase(s):
I liked him

Traded to:

NAME
ADDRESS
CITY/STATE/ZIP
PHONE
TRADED FOR

Re-sold to:

NAME
ADDRESS
CITY/STATE/ZIP
PHONE
PRICE RE-SOLD FOR

Your feelings about and/or experiences with this Beanie:

Stretch™

Type: Female ostrich **Categories:** Bird, brown, jungle **Style no.:** 4182

Birthday: September 21, 1997 **Released:** 12/31/97 **Retired:**

Position: Standing up **Tags:** 5th generation **Teenie:**

Description: Dark brown plush body & upper wing fronts; tan head, under wings & legs; white lower wing fronts & tail feathers; tan felt beak w/ thread detailing; white hairy collar; black plastic eyes ringed w/ gold; black thread nostrils; long legs & big feet; hang tag left wing; tush tag left bottom

Replaces: None

Variations: None

Oddities: Odd animal to turn into a Beanie

Commentary: Released three months after birth; one of the newer releases, so readily available; one of the most detailed Beanies; like all jungle Beanies, very popular, which will make it scarce & pricey upon retirement

Poem: She thinks when her head is underground
The rest of her body can't be found
The Beanie Babies think it's absurd
To play hide and seek with this bird!™

My record

(Beanies are the #1 collectible in American collecting history. A complete, detailed record will vastly
increase the value of this Beanie, if and when you ever appraise, trade, re-sell, gift, or bequeath it.)

Description *(which version do you have?):*

Gift from: *Linda Elliott*

Date received/purchased: 7 - 25 - 99

Purchased from:

NAME OF PERSON OR RETAILER

ADDRESS

CITY/STATE/ZIP

PHONE

Qty. purchased: **Cost ea.**
(check one)   ❏ *Cash*   ❏ *Check*   ❏ *Charge*

Reason(s) for purchase(s):

Traded to:

NAME

ADDRESS

CITY/STATE/ZIP

PHONE

TRADED FOR

Re-sold to:

NAME

ADDRESS

CITY/STATE/ZIP

PHONE

PRICE RE-SOLD FOR

Your feelings about and/or experiences with this Beanie:

Strut®

Type:	Rooster **Categories:** Bird, farm, tie-dyed	**Style no.:** 4171	

Birthday: March 8, 1996 **Released:** 7/12/97 **Retired:**

Position: Strutting **Tags:** 4th & 5th generation **Teenie:**

Description: Tie-dyed plush body in wide range of colors, red wings & tail feathers, gold beak & feet, red felt comb & wattle, black plastic eyes ringed w/ gold, hang tag left wing, tush tag left bottom

Replaces: None

Variations: Formerly named Doodle, name changed due to flack from Chick-Fil-A whose mascot is named Doodle, very hard to find & expensive; tie-dye varies in colors from cool to warm

Oddities: One of few renamed Beanies; one of few Beanies w/ no gender indicated, though all roosters are males; one of few tie-dyed Beanies with such a wide range of colors

Commentary: Released 16 months after birth; one of the most colorful & detailed Beanies; like all farm Beanies, very popular, which means it will become scarce & pricey upon retirement

Poem: Listen closely to "Cock-a-doodle-doo"
What's the rooster saying to you?
Hurry, wake up sleepy head
We have lots to do, get out of bed!™

My record

(Beanies are the #1 collectible in American collecting history. A complete, detailed record will vastly increase the value of this Beanie, if and when you ever appraise, trade, re-sell, gift, or bequeath it.)

Description *(which version do you have?):*

Gift from:

Date received/purchased:

Purchased from:

NAME OF PERSON OR RETAILER

ADDRESS

CITY/STATE/ZIP

PHONE

Qty. purchased: **Cost ea.**
(check one)   ❏ *Cash*   ❏ *Check*   ❏ *Charge*

Reason(s) for purchase(s):

Traded to:

NAME

ADDRESS

CITY/STATE/ZIP

PHONE

TRADED FOR

Re-sold to:

NAME

ADDRESS

CITY/STATE/ZIP

PHONE

PRICE RE-SOLD FOR

Your feelings about and/or experiences with this Beanie:

Tracker™

Type:	Male basset hound	**Categories:** Brown, dog **Style no.:** 4198
Birthday:	June 5, 1997 **Released:** 5/30/98 **Retired:**	
Position:	Standing **Tags:** 5th generation **Teenie:**	

Description: Brown plush body; tan face, neck, underside & tip of tail; short legs & long ears; black plastic eyes ringed w/ brown & white felt droopies; black plastic nose; black thread mouth; hang tag left ear; tush tag left bottom

Replaces: None

Variations: None

Oddities: None

Commentary: Released nearly one year after birth; one of the most detailed Beanie dogs, which will make it very popular & very much in demand; one of three dogs released simultaneously

Poem: Sniffing and tracking and following trails
Tracker the basset always wags his tail
It doesn't matter what you do
He's always happy when he's with you!™

My record

(Beanies are the #1 collectible in American collecting history. A complete, detailed record will vastly increase the value of this Beanie, if and when you ever appraise, trade, re-sell, gift, or bequeath it.)

Description *(which version do you have?):*

Gift from:

Date received/purchased:

Purchased from:

NAME OF PERSON OR RETAILER

ADDRESS

CITY/STATE/ZIP

PHONE

Qty. purchased: **Cost ea.**
(check one)   ❑ *Cash*   ❑ *Check*   ❑ *Charge*

Reason(s) for purchase(s):

Traded to:

NAME

ADDRESS

CITY/STATE/ZIP

PHONE

TRADED FOR

Re-sold to:

NAME

ADDRESS

CITY/STATE/ZIP

PHONE

PRICE RE-SOLD FOR

Your feelings about and/or experiences with this Beanie:

Whisper™

Type:	Female fawn	**Categories:** Spotted, woodland	**Style no.:** 4194
Birthday:	April 5, 1997	**Released:** 5/30/98	**Retired:**
Position:	Laying down	**Tags:** 5th generation	**Teenie:**

Description: Golden brown plush body w/ inset white spotted back; white inner ears, under side & under tail; dark brown hooves; black plastic eyes; brown plastic nose; hang tag left ear; tush tag left bottom

Replaces: None

Variations: None

Oddities: Brown plush body different shade of brown from inset white spotted back

Commentary: Released 13 months after birth; one of the cutest Beanies, which will make it very popular & very much in demand; very popular w/ girls

Poem: She's very shy as you can see
When she hides behind a tree
With big brown eyes and soft to touch
This little fawn will love you so much!™

My record

(Beanies are the #1 collectible in American collecting history. A complete, detailed record will vastly increase the value of this Beanie, if and when you ever appraise, trade, re-sell, gift, or bequeath it.)

Description *(which version do you have?):*

Gift from:

Date received/purchased:

Purchased from: A R M c

NAME OF PERSON OR RETAILER

ADDRESS

CITY/STATE/ZIP

PHONE

Qty. purchased: **Cost ea.**
(check one)   ❑ *Cash*   ❑ *Check*   ❑ *Charge*

Reason(s) for purchase(s):

Traded to:

NAME

ADDRESS

CITY/STATE/ZIP

PHONE

TRADED FOR

Re-sold to:

NAME

ADDRESS

CITY/STATE/ZIP

PHONE

PRICE RE-SOLD FOR

Your feelings about and/or experiences with this Beanie:

Teenies™ '97

The first set of 10 McDonald's Teenie Beanie Babies™ were released & retired in April, 1997; during that time, McDonald's gave away more than 100 million Teenies w/ Happy Meals, spawning what has become a nationwide passion for Beanie Babies®; all have matching full-sized moms; while full-sized Beanie Babies® are made of plush, Teenies are made of velour; because they were released & retired simultaneously, all are very hard to find & very expensive; the McDonald's in-store Teenies displays are extremely rare & expensive.

Teenie Chocolate® the moose
Brown velour body, orange velour antlers, black thread eyes, stubby tail, hang tag left ear, tush tag left back leg

Teenie Chops® the lamb
Cream velour body, black velour face & inner ears, blue thread eyes, pink thread nose & mouth, stubby tail, hang tag left ear, tush tag left back leg

Teenie Goldie™ the goldfish
Orange velour body, orange thread detailing on front & top fins, black thread eyes, hang tag left front fin, tush tag bottom back fin

Teenie Lizz the lizard
Blue velour topside w/ black spots, orange velour bottom side, red velour tongue, black thread eyes, long tail, hang tag left front foot, tush tag left back leg, mom named Lizzy™

Teenie Patti® the platypus
Magenta velour body, gold velour feet, gold felt bill w/ gold thread detailing, black thread eyes, hang tag left front foot, tush tag back

Teenie Pinky™ the flamingo
Hot pink velour body, hot pink furry wings w/ pink flannel under side, lighter pink velour legs, orange velour beak, black thread eyes, long legs, hang tag left wing, tush tag bottom

Teenie Quacks™ the duck
Yellow velour body, yellow furry wings w/ yellow velour under side, orange velour bill w/ orange thread detailing, orange velour webbed feet, black thread eyes & eyebrows, hang tag left wing, tush tag bottom, mom named Quackers™

Teenie Seamore the seal
White velour body; black thread eyes, eyebrows & nose; hang tag left front fin; tush tag back left fin

Teenie Snort® the bull
Red velour body; cream velour snout, inner ears & hooves; cream felt horns; black thread eyes & nostrils; knotted tail; hang tag left ear; tush tag left back leg

Teenie Speedy® the turtle
Moss green velour body, brown velour shell w/ flocked brown spots, black thread eyes, hang tag left front foot, tush tag back left foot

Teenies™ '98

The second set of 12 McDonald's Teenie Beanie Babies™ were released &
retired in May, 1998; during that time, McDonald's gave away more than 200
million Teenies w/ Happy Meals, further fueling America's obsession with
Beanies while spawning tens of thousands of new collectors; all have matching full-sized moms; interestingly, eight of the moms were retired before their
Teenies were released; while full-sized Beanie Babies® are made of plush,
Teenies are made of velour; because they were released & retired simultaneously, all are hard to find & expensive; the McDonald's in-store Teenies displays are extremely rare & expensive.

Teenie Bones™ the hound dog
Brown velour body, darker brown ears & tail, black thread eyes & eyebrows,
long ears & tail, hang tag left ear, tush tag left back leg, mom retired before
Teenie released

Teenie Bongo™ the monkey
Reddish brown velour body; tan face, ears, hands, feet & tail; black thread
eyes & nostrils; curled tail; hang tag left ear; tush tag left bottom; one of the
most popular Teenies & the first released in this set; one of only four Teenies
in this set whose mom was not retired at the time of release

Teenie Doby™ the doberman
Black velour body; brown velour eyebrows, inner ears, under side & socks;
brown thread eyes; black thread nose & mouth; hang tag left ear; tush tag left
back leg; one of only four Teenies in this set whose mom was not retired at
the time of release

Teenie Happy™ the hippo
Purple velour body, black thread eyes, hang tag left ear, tush tag left back leg, the least detailed Teenie, the least attractive Teenie, mom retired before Teenie released

Teenie Inch™ the inchworm
Yellow, orange, green, blue, purple velour sectioned body, black thread eyes & antennae, hang tag left front side, tush tag left back side, mom retired before Teenie released

Teenie Mel™ the koala
Gray velour body; white velour inner ears & under side; black thread eyes, nose & mouth; hang tag left ear; tush tag left back leg; one of only four Teenies in this set whose mom not retired at the time of release

Teenie Peanut™ the elephant
Baby blue velour body, pink flannel inner ears, black thread eyes, trunk, knotted tail, hang tag left ear, tush tag left back leg, mom retired before Teenie released

Teenie Pinchers™ the lobster
Red velour body, two pinchers, fan tail w/ red thread detailing, black thread eyes & antennae, hang tag left pincher, tush tag left back side, mom retired before Teenie released

Teenie Scoop™ the pelican
Marine blue velour body, orange velour beak & feet, black thread eyes & nostrils, hang tag left wing, tush tag left bottom, one of only four Teenies in this set whose mom was not retired at the time of release

Teenie Twigs™ the giraffe
Pale yellow flannel body w/ orange spots; brown velour inner ears, mane & hooves; black thread eyes; hang tag left ear; tush tag left back leg; the only Teenie w/ a flannel body; mom retired before Teenie released

Teenie Waddle™ the penguin
Black velour body, white velour belly & under wings, orange velour beak & feet, yellow velour collar, blue thread eyes, hang tag left wing, tush tag bottom, one of the most detailed Teenies, mom retired before Teenie released

Teenie Zip™ the cat
Black velour body, white velour inner ears & socks, green thread eyes, pink thread nose, white thread whiskers & mouth, long tail, hang tag left ear, tush tag left back leg, one of the most detailed Teenies, mom retired before Teenie released.

Buddies®

The first nine Beanie Buddies® were originally released 9/30/98 to tremendous demand—so much so that they never really hit the retailers before they were sold out—and then Twigs™ retired 12/31/98! The remaining eight reappeared in January of '99, but remain hard to find and costly.

Beanie Buddies® represent the resurrection of once popular, rare, and/or valuable Beanie Babies®. If you never secured Peanut™ the royal blue Beanie Baby™ elephant in its day, then you can now own its cousin, Peanut™ the royal blue Beanie Buddy™ elephant.

Most Beanie Buddies® are made of a new lush, plush fabric created by Ty Warner expressly for Beanie Buddies®—surely the softest, most petable plush ever made—called tylon, after its creator.

Beak™

Beak was the first Ty creature ever to be released as both a Beanie Baby and a Beanie Buddy at the same time—9/30/98! Beak the tie-dyed, napped Beanie Baby kiwi bird introduced a new fabric from Ty—a heavy, knobby nap that feels good to the touch—while Beak the golden brown, hairy Beanie Buddy introduced a second new fabric from Ty—a long-haired, hairy fabric that is almost shocking in appearance, but really fun to touch!

Date/Place purchased_____ Amount paid_____

Humphrey™

Humphrey the camel-colored Beanie Baby camel was originally released 6/25/94 and retired one year later. Included in both the second batch of Beanie Babies ever released and the second batch of Beanie Babies ever retired, Humphrey's circulation was so limited that it now commands one of the highest resale values ever (approx. $3,000)—which is surely what qualified it to return as an equally sought-after Beanie Buddy.

Date/Place purchased_____ Amount paid_____

Jake™
Jake the multi-colored Beanie Baby mallard duck was originally released 5/30/98. With its colorful markings unique to mallard ducks (which means it was hard to manufacture), Jake immediately took flight and is today one of the most popular current Beanie Babies, qualifying it for Beanie Buddy status at a very early age.

Date/Place purchased_4–16–97_ _ARMC_ Amount paid_5⁹⁵_/+x
-- any

Peanut™
Peanut the royal blue Beanie Baby elephant was originally released 6/3/95 and retired a short four months later. Due to its dramatic color and extremely limited circulation, Peanut the royal blue elephant has become the most valuable Beanie Baby of all time (currently valued at $5,000+). As such, it seems only right to resurrect it as a Beanie Buddy.

Date/Place purchased_____ Amount paid_____

Quackers™
Quackers the sunshine yellow Beanie Baby duck was originally released 1/7/95 and retired 40 months later, making it one of the longest-running Beanie Babies ever. Quackers also made an appearance as a Teenie in April of '97. Now it has a third life as a Beanie Buddy. One of the most sought-after Beanie Babies of all time with its cheery yellow fluff and popularity as an Easter decoration/gift (not to mention its wingless/wing history), Quackers the Beanie Buddy is a welcome return.

Date/Place purchased_____ Amount paid_____

Rover™
Rover the red Beanie Baby hound dog was originally released 6/15/96 and retired 23 months later. Rover enjoyed the distinction of being the first non-breed Beanie Baby dog ever released. That, plus its cheerful, bright red color and cartoon-like features surely qualified it to return as a Beanie Buddy.

Date/Place purchased_____ Amount paid_____

Stretch™
Stretch the brown Beanie Baby ostrich was originally released 12/31/97. With its long neck and legs and numerous parts, Stretch is one of the most difficult

Beanie Babies ever to manufacture—qualifying it to reappear as a Beanie Buddy. Like Beak, Beanie Baby Stretch is entirely different from Beanie Buddy Stretch. While Baby Stretch is made of plush and felt, Buddy Stretch is made of Ty's new, softer plush with a napped head and neck as well as napped legs!

Date/Place purchased_____ Amount paid_____

Teddy Cranberry™
The original, special edition Teddy Cranberry Beanie Baby with green satin ribbon was presented by Ty to employees for Christmas—a very limited circulation—which explains its resurrection as a Beanie Buddy.

Date/Place purchased_____ Amount paid_____

Twigs™—retired 12/31/98
Twigs the yellow and orange Beanie Baby giraffe was originally released 1/7/96 and retired 28 months later. It also made an appearance as a Teenie in May of '98. Now it has a third life as a Beanie Buddy—perhaps so honored because it was the first Beanie Baby ever to appear in a custom fabric exclusive to Ty— perhaps because it was one of the most popular Beanie Babies of all times. Because it was one of the first Beanie Buddies ever released as well as the first Beanie Buddy to retire (due to production difficulties), Twigs the Beanie Buddy will surely become one of the most valuable Beanie Buddies of all time.

Date/Place purchased_____ Amount paid_____

1st generation hang & tush tags

Buddies®

Not yet available at press time: Hippity, the mint green Beanie Buddy

The second 14 Beanie Buddies® were released 1/1/99—again, to such tremendous demand that they were scarce and pricey before they were ever readily available.

The second release of Beanie Buddies® introduced both new hang tags and new tush tags, illustrated below.

Bongo™

Bongo, the brown Beanie Baby monkey, was originally released 8/17/95 and retired 40 months later. It also made an appearance as a Teenie in May of '98. Originally named Nana, Ty, the creator of Beanie Babies and Buddies, changed the name to Bongo because he plays the bongos. One of the oldest Beanie Babies with many variations, Bongo is also one of the most popular Beanie Babies ever—qualifying it to be reborn as a Beanie Buddy.

Date/Place purchased_____ Amount paid_____

Bubbles™

Bubbles, the yellow and black Beanie Baby fish, was originally released 6/3/95 and retired nearly two years later. One of the most beautiful Beanie Babies ever, it was also one of the hardest to manufacture because of its swimming position—a good reason to replace it with Bubbles the Beanie Buddy.

Date/Place purchased_____ Amount paid_____

Chilly™
Chilly, the white Beanie Baby polar bear, was originally released 6/25/94 and retired 19 months later, making it one of the shortest-lived Beanie Babies ever, hence, one of the most sought-after and pricey. Re-released as a Beanie Buddy, now everyone can own Chilly.

Date/Place purchased_____ Amount paid_____

Chip™
Chip, the calico Beanie Baby cat, was originally released 5/11/97. One of the most colorful Beanie Baby cats, it is also one of the most difficult to manufacture, requiring 20 separate pieces—which surely qualifies it to be resurrected as a Beanie Buddy.

Date/Place purchased_____ Amount paid_____

Erin™
A special St. Patrick's Day release, Erin the green Beanie Baby sit-up bear was originally released 1/31/98, though it never reached retailers until well after the holiday. One of the most anticipated, sought-after Beanie Baby bears ever, it is also the first Beanie Baby bear to represent a country without a flag insignia. It seems only right to re-introduce Erin as a Beanie Buddy.

Date/Place purchased_____ Amount paid_____

Hippity™
One of three pastel, sit-up Beanie Baby bunnies originally released 1/1/97 and retired 16 months later, Hippity the mint green bunny, along with his pastel friends, were some of the most popular, sought-after Beanie Babies ever. Greatly missed upon retirement, Hippity is a welcome Beanie Buddy.

Date/Place purchased_____ Amount paid_____

Patti®
Patti, one of the original nine Beanie Babies, was originally released 2/28/95 and retired 39 months later. It also made an appearance as a Teenie in April of '97. Because it was an original and an unusual animal in a brilliant color, it was one of the most popular Beanie Babies ever—earning it the right to be re-released as a Beanie Buddy.

Date/Place purchased_____ Amount paid_____

Peking™
Like Chilly, Peking the black and white Beanie Baby panda bear was originally released 6/25/94 and retired 19 months later, making it one of the shortest-lived Beanie Babies ever, hence, one of the most sought-after and pricey. Re-released as a Beanie Buddy, now everyone can own Peking.

Date/Place purchased_____ Amount paid_____

Pinky™
Pinky, the pink Beanie Baby flamingo, was originally released 6/3/95 and retired three and a half years later, making it one of the longest-running Beanie Babies ever. It also made an appearance as a Teenie in April of '97. One of the most colorful and one of the most difficult to manufacture with its long neck and legs, Pinky was also one of the most popular Beanie Babies ever— reason enough to resurrect it as a Beanie Buddy.

Date/Place purchased_____ Amount paid_____

Smoochy™
Smoochy, the green and gold Beanie Baby frog, was originally released 12/31/97, replacing Legs the original Beanie Baby frog. Popular with girls in search of their Prince, Smoochy is a popular Beanie Buddy, too.

Date/Place purchased_____ Amount paid_____

Snort®
Snort, the red Beanie Baby bull, was originally released 1/1/97, replacing Tabasco the red bull without hooves, and retired 20 months later. It also made an appearance as a Teenie in April of '97. Popular with Chicago Bulls fans, it was sorely missed when retired and welcomed back as a Beanie Buddy.

Date/Place purchased_____ Amount paid_____

Squealer™
Squealer, one of the original nine Beanie Babies, was originally released 1/8/94 and retired 52 months later, making it one of the longest-running Beanie Babies ever. A favorite farm animal with its baby pink color, Squealer was one of the most popular Beanie Babies ever—reason enough to re-release it as a Beanie Buddy.

Date/Place purchased_____ Amount paid_____

Tracker™

Tracker, the brown and tan Beanie Baby basset hound, was originally released 5/30/98. Boasting the most expressive eyes of all Beanie Baby dogs, Tracker is also one of the most difficult to manufacture, limiting its production—a good reason to release it as a Beanie Buddy as well.

Date/Place purchased_____ Amount paid_____

Waddle™

Waddle, the black and white Beanie Baby penguin, was originally released 6/3/95 and retired nearly three years later. It also made an appearance as a Teenie in May of '98. One of two Beanie Baby penguins, Waddle enjoyed great popularity as a Beanie Baby that it will surely repeat as a Beanie Buddy.

Date/Place purchased_____ Amount paid_____

2nd generation hang & tush tags

List #1:
Current Beanie Babies®

Following is a list of all Current Beanie Babies® to date, listed alphabetically by name, with descriptions, for your information and shopping/collecting convenience.

New Releases (12/98)

(1) 1999 Signature Bear (heather w/ Ty insignia)
(2) Butch (brown/white bull terrier)
(3) Eggbert (yellow chick in white shell)
(4) Ewey (cream, napped lamb)
(5) Fuzz (brown, napped bear)
(6) Germania (bear w/ German flag – *German exclusive*)
(7) Goatee (heather goat)
(8) Goochy (tie-dyed, iridescent jellyfish)
(9) Hippie (tie dyed, sit up bunny)
(10) Hope (butterscotch praying bear)
(11) Kicks (lime green bear w/ soccer ball insignia
(12) Luke (black lab w/ b+w checkered ribbon)
(13) Mac (red cardinal)
(14) Millennium (magenta bear w/ globe insignia)
(15) Mooch (spider monkey)
(16) Nibbler (cream bunny)
(17) Nibbly (heather bunny)
(18) Prickles (brown hedgehog)
(19) Sammy (tie- dyed, lay down bear)
(20) Scat (heather cat)
(21) Slippery (gray seal)
(22) Stilts (white stork)
(23) Tiny (brown chihuahua)
(24) Valentina hot pink bear w/ white heart)

Currents

(1) Batty (bat, brown & tie-dyed)
(2) Beak (brown, napped kiwi)
(3) Britannia (brown bear w/ British flag)
(4) Canyon (brown cougar)
(5) Chip (calico cat)
(6) Derby (brown horse, yarn & hairy)
(7) Early (brown robin w/ red breast)
(8) Erin (green bear w/ white shamrock)
(9) Fortune (black & white panda)
(10) Gigi (black, napped poodle)
(11) Gobbles (multi-colored turkey)
(12) Halo (white bear w/ iridescent halo & wings)
(13) Hissy (blue coiled snake)
(14) Iggy (tie-dyed blue iguana)
(15) Jabber (parrot)
(16) Jake (mallard duck)
(17) Kuku (white cockatoo)
(18) Loosy (black & white Canadian goose)
(19) Maple (white bear w/ Canadian flag)
(20) Mel (gray koala bear)
(21) Mystic (white unicorn w/ iridescent horn, yarn & hairy)
(22) Nanook (gray & white huskie)
(23) Peace (tie-dyed bear w/ peace symbol, bright & pastel)
(24) Pouch (brown kangaroo)
(25) Pounce (brown cat)

(26) Prance (tiger cat)
(27) Princess (royal purple bear w/ white rose)
(28) Pugsly (tan pug)
(29) Rainbow (tie-dyed chameleon)
(30) Roam (brown napped buffalo)
(31) Rocket (bluejay)
(32) Scorch (brown dragon w/ red iridescent wings)
(33) Smoochy (green & gold frog)
(34) Spunky (brown cockerspaniel)
(35) Stretch (brown ostrich)
(36) Strut (tie-dyed rooster)
(37) Tracker (brown basset hound)
(38) Whisper (brown deer)

(62 total New Releases & Currents to date)

List #2:

Retired Beanie Babies® & values

Following is a list of all Retired Beanie Babies® to date, followed by their current value, per Kathy Ainge of Olde Acquaintances

2/15/98
(1) Clubby (royal blue bear, BBOC mascot) **$40**

12/10/98
(1) Chocolate (brown moose) **$12**
(2) Roary (brown lion) **$15**
(3) Glory (white bear w/ red & blue stars) **$25**

12/9/98
(1) Bongo (brown monkey) **$12**
(2) Freckles (spotted leopard) **$15**

12/8/98
(1) Congo (black gorilla) **$12**
(2) Pinky (pink flamingo) **$12**
(3) Spike (gray rhino) **$15**

12/7/98
(1) Fleece (white, napped lamb) **$12**
(2) Snip (Siamese cat) **$12**

12/6/98
(1) Curly (brown, napped bear) **$20**

12/5/98
(1) Ants (gray anteater) **$12**
(2) Doby (doberman) **$12**
(3) Dotty (dalmatian) **$12**
(4) Nuts (brown squirrel) **$12**
(5) Tuffy (brown, napped terrier) **$15**

12/4/98
(1) Claude (tie-dyed crab) **$12**
(2) Pumkin (w/ green arms & legs) **$30**
(3) Wise (brown owl w/ mortarboard & tassel) **$20**

12/3/98
(1) Valentino (white bear w/ red heart) **$20**

12/2/98
(1) Fetch (golden lab) **$12**
(2) Scoop (blue pelican) **$12**
(3) Stinger (gray scorpion) **$12**

12/1/98
(1) 1998 Holiday Teddy (white bear w/ holly & berries) **$60**
(2) Santa (w/ green mittens) **$30**
(3) Zero (penguin w/ red cap) **$25**

9/28/98
(1) Stinky (black & white skunk) **$12**

9/24/98
(1) Crunch (blue shark) **$12**

9/22/98
(1) Bernie (St. Bernard) **$12**
(2) Sly (brown fox) **$15**
(3) Wrinkles (tan bulldog) **$12**

9/19/98
(1) Seaweed (brown otter) **$18**
(2) Spinner (black & brown spider) **$12**

9/18/98
(1) Bruno (brown & white bull terrier) **$12**
(2) Puffer (puffin) **$12**

9/16/98
(1) Ringo (raccoon) **$12**

9/15/98
(1) Blackie (black bear) **$15**
(2) Daisy (black & white cow) **$12**
(3) Snort (red bull) **$12**

5/1/98
(1) Baldy (eagle) **$25**
(2) Blizzard (white tiger) **$25**
(3) Bones (brown hound dog) **$25**
(4) Ears (brown bunny) **$25**
(5) Echo (blue dolphin) **$30**
(6) Floppity (lavender bunny) **$25**
(7) Gracie (white swan) **$25**
(8) Happy (purple hippo) **$35**
(9) Hippity (mint green bunny) **$25**
(10) Hoppity (pink bunny) **$25**
(11) Inch (multi-colored inch worm) **$30**
(12) Inky (pink octopus) **$30**
(13) Jolly (brown walrus) **$35**
(14) Lucky (ladybug) **$35**
(15) Patti (magenta platypus) **$25**
(16) Peanut (blue elephant) **$35**
(17) Pinchers (red lobster) **$35**
(18) Quackers (yellow duck) **$25**
(19) Rover (red hound dog) **$35**
(20) Scottie (black, napped terrier) **$40**

(21) Squealer (pink pig) **$30**
(22) Stripes (gold tiger) **$35**
(23) Twigs (giraffe) **$35**
(24) Waddle (penguin) **$35**
(25) Waves (black & white whale) **$30**
(26) Weenie (brown dachshund) **$35**
(27) Ziggy (zebra) **$30**
(28) Zip (black cat) **$35**

12/31/97
(1) 1997 Holiday Teddy (brown bear w/ red hat & scarf) **$55**
(2) Bucky (brown beaver) **$40**
(3) Cubbie (brown bear) **$30**
(4) Goldie (goldfish) **$50**
(5) Lizzy (multi-colored lizard) **$30**
(6) Magic (white dragon) **$55**
(7) Nip (gold cat) **$30**
(8) Snowball (snowman) **$45**
(9) Spooky (ghost) **$45**

12/15/97
(1) Derby (brown horse w/o diamond) $40

10/23/97
(1) Mystic (w/ brown horn) $65

10/15/97
(1) Inch (w/ felt antennae) **$225**

10/1/97
(1) Ally (alligator) **$55**
(2) Bessie (brown & white cow) **$65**
(3) Flip (white cat) **$35**
(4) Hoot (owl) **$55**
(5) Legs (green frog) **$25**
(6) Seamore (white seal) **$150**
(7) Speedy (turtle) **$35**
(8) Spot (white dog, black spot) **$60**

(9) Tank (gray armadillo) **$80**
(10) Teddy Brown (new face) **$100**
(11) Velvet (black panther) **$40**

5/11/97
(1) Bubbles (yellow & black fish) **$150**
(2) Digger (red crab) **$125**
(3) Flash (gray & white dolphin) **$110**
(4) Garcia (tie-dyed bear) **$175**
(5) Grunt (red razorback hog) **$165**
(6) Manny (gray manatee) **$150**
(7) Radar (black bat) **$160**
(8) Sparky (dalmatian) **$150**
(9) Splash (black & white whale) **$110**

1/1/97
(1) Chops (cream lamb) **$160**
(2) Coral (tie-dyed fish) **$175**
(3) Kiwi (toucan) **$175**
(4) Lefty (blue Democratic donkey w/ U.S. flag) **$250**
(5) Libearty (white bear w/ U.S. flag) **$350**
(6) Righty (gray Republican elephant w/ U.S. flag) **$250**
(7) Sting (tie-dyed manta ray) **$175**
(8) Tabasco (red bull) **$160**
(9) Tusk (brown walrus) **$140**

8/6/96
(1) Sly (brown-bellied fox) **$295**

6/29/96
(1) Bongo (brown monkey w/ brown tail) **$95**

6/15/96
(1) Bronty (tie-dyed brontosaurus) **$900**
(2) Bumble (bumblebee) **$500**

(3) Caw (crow) **$600**
(4) Flutter (tie-dyed butterfly) **$1,000**
(5) Rex (tie-dyed tyrannosaurus rex) **$800**
(6) Steg (tie-dyed stegosaurus) **$900**
(7) Web (black spider) **$1,400**

6/3/96
(1) Stripes (tiger w/ thin stripes) **$650**

3/10/96
(1) Nip (all gold cat) **$1,900**
(2) Zip (all black cat) **$2,200**

2/27/96
(1) Lucky (lady bug w/ felt spots) **$295**

1/7/96
(1) Chilly (polar bear) **$2,000**
(2) Lizzy (tie-dyed lizard) **$1,450**
(3) Nip (gold cat w/ white face) **$535**
(4) Peking (panda) **$1,800**
(5) Tank (w/o shell) **$350**
(6) Teddy Cranberry (new face) **$1,700**
(7) Teddy Jade (new face) **$1,700**
(8) Teddy Magenta (new face) **$2,000**
(9) Teddy Teal (new face) **$2,000**
(10) Teddy Violet (new face) **$2,000**
(11) Zip (black cat w/ white face) **$650**

10/2/95
(1) Peanut (royal blue elephant) **$5,000**

6/15/95
(1) Humphrey (camel) **$2,000**

(2) Slither (multi-colored snake)
$1,800
(3) Trap (gray mouse) **$1,400**

6/3/95
(1) Digger (orange crab) **$895**
(2) Happy (gray hippo) **$795**
(3) Inky (tan octopus w/ mouth)
$850

2/28/95
(1) Patti (maroon platypus)
$1,500

1/7/95
(1) Quackers (wingless duck)
$4,000
(2) Teddy Brown (old face)
$2,500
(3) Teddy Cranberry (old face)
$2,000
(4) Teddy Jade (old face) **$1,800**
(5) Teddy Magenta (old face)
$1,800
(6) Teddy Teal (old face) **$1,800**
(7) Teddy Violet (old face)
$1,800

9/12/94
(1) Inky (octopus w/o mouth)
$900

4/13/94
(1) Spot (dog w/o spot) **$4,500**

(150 total Retireds to date)

Beanie Babies® by date of release

Following is a list of all Beanie Babies® to date, listed first by date of release and then alphabetically, for your information and shopping/collecting convenience. You can tell by the length of each list which were regular releases and which were special releases.

1/8/94—original 9 Beanie Babies®
(1) Chocolate
(2) Brownie, renamed Cubbie
(3) Flash
(4) Legs
(5) Patti (maroon)
(6) Puncher, renamed Pinchers
(7) Splash
(8) Spot (w/o spot)
(9) Squealer

4/13/94—replacement
(1) Spot (w/ spot)

6/25/94
(1) Ally
(2) Blackie
(3) Bones
(4) Chilly
(5) Daisy ✓
(6) Digger (orange)
(7) Goldie
(8) Happy (gray)
(9) Humphrey
(10) Inky (tan w/o mouth)
(11) Lucky (w/ felt spots)
(12) Mystic (w/ gold horn)
(13) Peking
(14) Quackers (w/o wings)
(15) Seamore
(16) Slither
(17) Speedy
(18) Teddy Brown (old)
(19) Teddy Cranberry (old)
(20) Teddy Jade (old)
(21) Teddy Magenta (old)
(22) Teddy Teal (old)
(23) Teddy Violet (old)
(24) Trap
(25) Web

9/12/94—replacement
(1) Inky (tan w/ mouth)

1/7/95
(1) Nip (w/ white face)
(2) Quackers (w/ wings)
(3) Tank (w/o shell)
(4) Teddy Brown (new)
(5) Teddy Cranberry (new)
(6) Teddy Jade (new)
(7) Teddy Magenta (new)
(8) Teddy Teal (new)
(9) Teddy Violet (new)
(10) Tusk
(11) Valentino
(12) Zip (w/ white face)

2/28/95—replacement
(1) Patti (magenta)

6/3/95
(1) Bessie
(2) Bongo (w/ tan tail)
(3) Bronty
(4) Bubbles
(5) Bumble
(6) Caw
(7) Coral
(8) Derby (w/o diamond)
(9) Digger (red)
(10) Flutter

(11) Happy (purple)
(12) Inch (w/ felt antennae)
(13) Inky (pink)
(14) Kiwi
(15) Lizzy (tie-dyed)
(16) Magic
(17) Peanut (royal blue)
(18) Pinky
(19) Rex
(20) Steg
(21) Sting
(22) Stinky
(23) Tabasco
(24) Velvet
(25) Waddle
(26) Ziggy

9/1/95—special Halloween release
(1) Radar
(2) Spooky

10/2/95—replacement
(1) Peanut (light blue)

1/7/96
(1) Bucky
(2) Chops
(3) Ears
(4) Flip
(5) Garcia
(6) Grunt
(7) Hoot
(8) Lizzy (blue)
(9) Manny
(10) Nip (all gold)
(11) Ringo
(12) Seaweed
(13) Stripes (w/ thin stripes)
(14) Tank (w/ shell)
(15) Twigs
(16) Weenie
(17) Zip (all black)

2/6/96—replacement
(1) Bongo (w/ brown tail)

2/27/96—replacement
(1) Lucky (w/ printed spots)

3/10/96—replacements
(1) Nip (w/ white socks)
(2) Zip (w/ white socks)

6/3/96—replacement
(1) Stripes (w/ wide stripes)

6/15/96
(1) Congo
(2) Curly
(3) Freckles
(4) Lefty
(5) Libearty
(6) Righty
(7) Rover
(8) Scoop
(9) Scottie
(10) Sly (w/ brown belly)
(11) Sparky
(12) Spike
(13) Wrinkles

8/6/96—replacement
(1) Sly (w/ white belly)

1/1/97
(1) Bernie
(2) Crunch
(3) Doby
(4) Fleece
(5) Floppity
(6) Gracie
(7) Hippity
(8) Hoppity
(9) Maple
(10) Mel
(11) Nuts
(12) Pouch
(13) Snip
(14) Snort

5/11/97
(1) Baldy
(2) Blizzard
(3) Chip
(4) Claude
(5) Dotty
(6) Echo
(7) Jolly
(8) Nanook ✓
(9) Pugsly
(10) Peace ✓
(11) Roary
(12) Tuffy
(13) Waves

7/12/97—replacement
(1) Strut ✓

10/1/97—special holiday release
(1) 1997 Holiday Teddy
(2) Batty
(3) Gobbles ✓
(4) Snowball
(5) Spinner

10/15/97—replacement
(1) Inch (w/ yarn antennae)

10/23/97—replacement
(1) Mystic (w/ iridescent horn)

10/29/97—special commemorative release
(1) Princess ✓

12/15/97—replacement
(1) Derby (w/ diamond)

12/31/97
(1) Britannia
(2) Bruno
(3) Hissy
(4) Iggy

(5) Pounce ✓
(6) Prance
(7) Puffer
(8) Rainbow
(9) Smoochy ✓
(10) Spunky
(11) Stretch ✓

1/31/98—special St. Patrick's Day release
(1) Erin ✓

5/30/98
(1) Ants
(2) Early
(3) Fetch
(4) Fortune ✓
(5) Gigi ✓
(6) Glory ✓
(7) Jabber ✓
(8) Jake ✓
(9) Kuku
(10) Rocket ✓
(11) Stinger
(12) Tracker ✓
(13) Whisper ✓
(14) Wise—special graduation release

9/30/98
(1) 1998 Holiday Teddy
(2) Beak ✓
(3) Canyon
(4) Halo
(5) Loosy
(6) Pumkin
(7) Roam
(8) Santa ✓
(9) Scorch

1/1/99
(1) 1999 Signature Bear ✓
(2) Butch
(3) Eggbert ✓
(4) Ewey

(5) Fuzz ✓
(6) Germania
(7) Goatee
(8) Goochy
(9) Hippie
(10) Hope ✓
(11) Kicks ✓
(12) Luke
(13) Mac ✓
(14) Millennium ✓
(15) Mooch
(16) Nibbler ✓
(17) Nibbly
(18) Prickles
(19) Sammy ✓
(20) Scat
(21) Slippery
(22) Stilts
(23) Tiny ✓
(24) Valentina ·

Beanie Baby™ multiples

Following is a list of Beanie Baby™ multiples to date, including same kinds of animals and same Beanie Babies® w/ changes, listed alphabetically by category and then in order of release, for your information and shopping/collecting convenience.

Bats

1-Radar the black bat 9/1/95
2-Batty the brown bat 10/1/97
3-replaced by Batty the tie-dyed bat, fall '98

Bears

(sit-up, unless otherwise indicated)
1-Brownie the brown bear 1/8/94 (1st lay-down bear)
2-Brownie renamed Cubbie, mid '94 (1st revised bear)
3-Blackie the black bear 6/25/94 (2nd lay-down bear)
4-Teddy Brown (old face) 6/25/94
5-Teddy Cranberry (old face) 6/25/94
6-Teddy Jade (old face) 6/25/94
7-Teddy Magenta (old face) 6/25/94
8-Teddy Teal (old face) 6/25/94
9-Teddy Violet (old face) 6/25/94
10-Chilly the white polar bear 6/25/94 (3rd lay-down bear)
11-Peking the black & white panda 6/25/94 (1st panda) (4th lay-down bear)
12-Teddy Brown (new face) 1/7/95
13-Teddy Cranberry (new face) 1/7/95
14-Teddy Jade (new face) 1/7/95
15-Teddy Magenta (new face) 1/7/95
16-Teddy Teal (new face) 1/7/95
17-Teddy Violet (new face) 1/7/95
18-Valentino the white bear w/ red heart 1/7/95 (1st holiday bear) (companion to Valentina)
19-Garcia the tie-dyed bear 1/7/96 (1st tie-dyed bear)
20-Curly the brown, napped bear 6/15/96 (1st napped bear)
21-Libearty the white bear w/ U.S. flag 6/15/96 (1st American bear)
22-Maple the white bear w/ Canadian flag 1/1/97 (1st foreign release)
23-Mel the gray koala 1/1/97 (5th lay-down bear)
24-Peace the bright tie-dyed bear 5/11/97 (2nd tie-dyed bear) ✓
25-1997 Holiday Teddy (brown w/ red cap & scarf) 10/1/97 (2nd holiday bear)
26-Princess the royal purple bear 10/29/97 (1st bear to commemorate a person)
27-Britannia the brown bear w/ British flag 12/31/97 (2nd foreign release)
28-Erin the green bear w/ white shamrock 1/31/98 (3rd holiday bear) ✓
29-Fortune the black & white panda 5/30/98 (2nd panda) ✓
30-Glory the white bear w/ red & blue stars 5/30/98 (2nd American bear) ✓
31-Clubby the royal blue BBOC bear, summer '98 (for club members only)

32-Peace the pastel tie-dyed bear, summer '98 (2nd revised bear) (3rd tie-dyed bear)

33-1998 Holiday Teddy (white w/ holly & berries) 9/30/98 (4th holiday bear)

34-Halo the white bear w/ halo & wings 9/30/98 (1st religious bear)

35-1999 Signature Bear (heather w/ "1999 Ty" insignia) 1/1/99

36-Fuzz (?) 1/1/99

37-Germania (?) 1/1/99 (3rd foreign release)

38-Hope the butterscotch praying bear 1/1/99 (2nd religious bear)

39-Kicks the lime green soccer bear 1/1/99 (1st sports bear)

40-Millennium the magenta bear w/ globe insignia 1/1/99

41-Sammy the tie-dyed bear 1/1/99 (2nd bear to commemorate a person) (2nd sports bear) (4th tie-dyed bear) (6th lay-down bear)

42-Valentina the hot pink bear w/ white heart 1/1/99 (5th holiday bear) (companion to Valentino)

Birds

1-Caw the crow 6/3/95

2-Kiwi the toucan 6/3/95

3-Hoot the owl 1/7/96

4-Scoop the pelican 6/15/96

5-Gracie the swan 1/1/97

6-Baldy the eagle 5/11/97

7-Strut the rooster 7/12/97

8-Stretch the ostrich 12/31/97

9-Early the robin 5/30/98

10-Jabber the parrot 5/30/98

11-Jake the mallard 5/30/98

12-Kuku the cockatoo 5/30/98

13-Rocket the bluejay 5/30/98

14-Wise the owl 5/30/98

15-Beak the kiwi 9/30/98

16-Loosy the Canadian goose 9/30/98

17-Eggbert the chick 1/1/99

18-Mac the cardinal 1/1/99

19-Stilts the stork 1/1/99

Bulls

1-Tabasco the red bull (w/o hooves) 6/3/95

2-renamed Snort (w/ hooves) 1/1/97

Bunnies

1-Ears the brown lay-down bunny 1/7/96

2-Floppity the lavender sit-up bunny 1/1/97

3-Hippity the mint green sit-up bunny 1/1/97

4-Hoppity the pink sit-up bunny 1/1/97

5-Hippie the tie-dyed sit-up bunny 1/1/99

6-Nibbler the cream bunny 1/1/99

7-Nibbly the heather bunny 1/1/99

Cats

1-Nip the gold cat 3/10/96

2-Zip the black cat 3/10/96

3-Flip the white cat 1/7/96

4-Chip the calico cat 5/11/97

5-Snip the Siamese cat 1/1/97

6-Pounce the brown cat 12/31/97

7-Prance the tiger cat 12/31/97

8-Scat the heather cat 1/1/99

Chameleons

1-Rainbow the chameleon w/ blue tie-dyed fabric 12/31/97

2-replaced by Rainbow the chameleon w/ rainbow tie-dyed fabric 5/30/98

Crabs

1-Digger the orange crab 6/25/94
2-replaced by Digger the red crab
   6/3/95
3-Claude the tie-dyed crab
   5/11/97

Dalmations

1-Sparky 6/15/96
2-renamed Dotty 5/11/97

Derby the brown horse

1-w/ fine yarn mane & tail, '95
2-w/ coarse yarn mane & tail, '95-
   '97
3-w/ coarse yarn mane & tail +
   white diamond on forehead,
   '98
4-w/ hairy mane & tail + white
   diamond on forehead, '99

Dinosaurs

1-Bronty the brontosaurus 6/3/95
2-Rex the tyrannosaurus 6/3/95
3-Steg the stegosaurus 6/3/95

Dogs

1-Spot the dog w/o spot 1/8/94
2-replaced by Spot the dog w/ spot
   4/13/94
3-Bones the brown hound 6/25/94
4-Weenie the dachshund 1/7/96
5-Sparky the dalmatian 6/15/96
6-replaced by Dottie the dalmatian
   5/11/97
7-Rover the red hound 6/15/96
8-Wrinkles the bulldog 6/15/96

9-Scottie the napped terrier
   6/15/96
10-Bernie the St. Bernard 1/1/97
11-Doby the doberman 1/1/97
12-Nanook the husky 5/11/97
13-Pugsly the pug 5/11/97
14-Tuffy the napped terrier 5/11/97

15-Bruno the bull terrier 12/31/97
16-Spunky the cockerspaniel
   12/31/97
17-Fetch the golden lab 5/30/98
18-Gigi the poodle 5/30/98
19-Tracker the basset hound
   5/30/98
20-Butch the bull terrier 1/1/99
21-Luke the black lab 1/1/99
22-Tiny the chihuahua 1/1/99

Dolphins

1-Flash the gray dolphin 1/8/94
2-Echo the marine blue dolphin
   5/11/97

Dragons

1-Magic the white dragon 6/3/95
2-Scorch the brown dragon
   9/30/98

Elephants

1-Peanut the royal blue elephant
   6/3/95
2-replaced by Peanut the light blue
   elephant 10/2/95
3-Righty the gray Republican elephant w/ U.S. flag 6/15/96

Fish

1-Goldie the goldfish 6/25/94
2-Coral the tie-dyed fish 6/3/95
3-Bubbles the yellow fish w/ black
   stripes 6/3/95
4-Goochy the tie-dyed jellyfish
   1/1/99

Frogs

1-Legs the green frog 1/8/94
2-Smoochy the green & gold frog
   12/31/97

Happy the Hippo
1-Gray 6/25/94
2-replaced by purple Happy
6/3/95

Iguanas
1-Iggy the iguana w/ rainbow tie-
dyed fabric 12/31/97
2-Iggy the iguana w/ tongue,
spring '98
3-replaced by Iggy the iguana w/
blue tie-dyed fabric 5/30/98

Inch the multi-colored inchworm
1-w/ felt antennae 6/3/95
2-replaced by Inch w/ yarn
antennae 10/15/97

Inky the octopus
1-Tan w/o mouth 6/25/94
2-replaced by tan Inky w/ mouth
9/12/94
3-replaced by pink Inky w/ mouth
6/3/95

Lambs
1-Chops the cream-colored lamb
1/7/96
2-Fleece the white lamb 1/1/97
3-Ewey the cream-colored lamb
1/1/99

Lizzy the lizard
1-Tie-dyed 6/3/95
2-replaced by blue Lizzy 1/7/96

Lobsters
1-Punchers 1/8/94
2-renamed Pinchers, '94

Lucky the red ladybug
1-w/ felt spots 6/25/94
2-replaced by Lucky w/ printed
spots 2/27/96

Magic the white dragon
1-w/ hot pink thread, '96-'97
2-w/ pale pink thread, '95-'97

**Maple the white bear w/ Canadian
flag**
1-w/ "Pride" tush tag, '97
2-w/ "Maple" tush tag, '97

Monkeys
1-Nana the brown monkey w/ tan
tail
2-renamed Bongo the brown monkey w/ tan tail 6/3/95
3-Bongo the brown monkey w/
brown tail 2/6/96
4-Mooch the black spider monkey
1/1/99

Mystic the white unicorn
1-w/ fine yarn mane & tail + gold
horn, '94-'95
2-w/ coarse yarn mane & tail +
gold horn, '95-'97
3-w/ coarse yarn mane & tail + iridescent horn, '97-'98
4-w/ rainbow-colored hairy mane
& tail + iridescent horn, '99

Nip the gold cat
1-w/ white face 1/7/95
2-replaced by all gold Nip 1/7/96
3-replaced by Nip w/ white socks
3/10/96

Owls
1-Hoot the brown & tan owl
1/7/96
2-Wise the brown & tan owl w/
mortarboard & tassel 5/30/98

Patti the platypus
1-Maroon 1/8/94
2-replaced by magenta Patti
2/28/95

Peanut the elephant
1-Royal blue 6/3/95
2-replaced by light blue Peanut
    10/2/95

Penguins
1-Waddles 6/3/95
2-Zero w/ red cap 9/30/98

Princess the royal purple bear
1-w/ PVC filling, '97
2-w/ PE filling, '98

Quackers the yellow duck
1-w/o wings 6/25/94
2-replaced by Quackers w/ wings
    1/7/95

Roosters
1-Doodles the tie-dyed rooster
2-renamed Strut 7/12/97

Sly the fox
1-w/ brown belly 6/15/96
2-replaced by Sly w/ white belly
    8/6/96

Snakes
1-Slither the green long snake
    6/25/94
2-Hissy the blue coiled snake
    12/31/97

Spiders
1-Web the black spider 6/25/94
2-Spinner the black & brown spi-
    der 10/1/97

Spooky the white ghost
1-w/ "Spook" tag, '95
2-w/ "Spooky" tag, '95-'97

Spot the white dog
1-w/o a spot 1/8/94
2-replaced by Spot w/ a spot
    4/13/94

Stripes the gold tiger
1-w/ thin stripes 1/7/96
2-replaced by Stripes w/ wide
    stripes 6/3/96

Tank the armadillo
1-w/o shell 1/7/95
2-replaced by Tank w/ shell
    1/7/96

Tigers
1-Stripes the gold tiger w/ thin
    stripes 1/7/96
2-replaced by Stripes the gold tiger
    w/ wide stripes 6/3/96
3-Blizzard the white tiger 5/11/97

Walruses
1-Tusk the brown walrus 1/7/95
2-Jolly the brown bearded walrus
    5/11/97

Whales
1-Splash the black & white whale
    1/8/94
2-Waves the black & white whale
    5/11/97

Zip the black cat
1-w/ white face 1/7/95
2-replaced by all black Zip 1/7/96
3-replaced by Zip w/ white socks
    3/10/96

Beanie Baby™ birthdays

Some collectors like to know which Beanie Babies® were born on their birthday (or on the birthdays of other family members and friends), hence, following is a list of all Beanie Babies® with birthdays to date, for your information and shopping/collecting convenience.

January
1 Millennium, Spot
2 Zero
5 Kuku
6 Patti
13 Crunch
14 Spunky
15 Mel
17 Slippery
18 Bones
21 Nuts
25 Peanut
26 Chip

February
1 Peace
3 Beak
4 Fetch
13 Pinky, Stinky
14 Valentina, Valentino
17 Baldy
19 Prickles
20 Roary
22 Tank
25 Happy
27 Sparky
28 Flip

March
1 Ewey
2 Coral
6 Nip
8 Strut
12 Rocket
14 Ally
17 Erin

19 Seaweed
20 Early
21 Fleece
23 Hope
28 Zip
29 Loosy

April
3 Hoppity
4 Hissy
5 Whisper
6 Nibbler
7 Gigi
10 Eggbert
12 Curly
16 Jake
18 Ears
19 Quackers
23 Squealer
25 Legs
27 Chocolate

May
1 Lucky, Wrinkles
2 Pugsly
3 Chops
4 Hippie
7 Nibbly
10 Daisy
11 Lizzy
13 Flash
15 Tabasco, Snort
19 Twigs
21 Mystic
27 Scat
28 Floppity

29 Canyon
30 Rover
31 Wise

June
1 Hippity
3 Freckles
5 Tracker
8 Manny, Bucky
10 Mac
11 Stripes
15 Luke, Scottie
16 Stilts
17 Gracie
19 Pinchers
23 Sammy
27 Bessie

July
1 Maple, Scoop
2 Bubbles
4 Lefty, Righty, Glory
8 Splash
14 Ringo
15 Blackie
19 Grunt
20 Weenie
31 Scorch

August
1 Garcia, Mooch
9 Hoot
12 Iggy
13 Spike
14 Speedy
16 Kicks

17 Bongo
23 Digger
27 Sting
28 Pounce
31 Halo

September
3 Inch, Claude
5 Magic
8 Tiny
9 Bruno
12 Sly
16 Kiwi, Derby
18 Tusk
21 Stretch
27 Roam
29 Stinger

October
1 Smoochy
2 Butch
3 Bernie
9 Doby
10 Jabber
12 Tuffy
14 Rainbow
17 Dotty
22 Snip
28 Spinner
29 Batty
30 Radar
31 Pumkin, Spooky

November
3 Puffer
4 Goatee
6 Pouch
7 Ants
9 Congo
14 Cubbie, Goldie
18 Goochy
20 Prance
21 Nanook
27 Gobbles
28 Teddy Brown (new)

29 Inky

December
2 Jolly
6 Fortune
6 Santa
8 Waves
12 Blizzard
14 Seamore
15 Britannia
16 Velvet
19 Waddle
21 Echo
22 Snowball
24 Ziggy
25 1997 Holiday Teddy, 1998
        Holiday Teddy

BBB Notes

BBB Notes

BBB Notes

BBB Notes

BBB Notes

BBB Notes

BBB Notes

BBB Notes

BBB Notes

BBB Notes

BBB Notes

BBB Notes

BBB Notes

BBB Notes

BBB Notes

BBB Notes

BBB Notes

BBB Notes

New Releases

Place behind this tab
the newest Beanie Baby™ releases

Currents

Place behind this tab
all the Beanie Babies® currently
in circulation

My Beanie Baby™ Binder Summer '99 Update Pak

Table of Contents & Instructions

New tab
(1) Summer '99 Retireds
Place this tab (& the pages listed on the tab) after the Current tab & pages

3 New Release Beanie Babies® pages
(1) B.B. Bear™
(2) Flitter™
(3) Lips™
Place these 3 pages behind the New Release tab

2 New Release Beanie Buddies® pages
(1) Inch™
(2) Schweetheart™
Place these 2 pages behind Teenies™ & Buddies™ tab

Revised Shopping/Collecting Lists
Place these pages behind the Lists & Forms tab & discard previous lists pages; please note these lists are current through 12/31/99.

Current Beanie Babies®
(1) 1999 Holiday Teddy™
(2) 1999 Signature Bear™
(3) Almond™
(4) Amber™
(5) B.B. Bear™
(6) Beak™
(7) Butch™
(8) Cheeks™
(9) Chipper™
(10) Clubby II™
(11) Early™
(12) Eucalyptus™
(13) Flitter™
(14) Fuzz™
(15) Germania™
(16) Gigi™
(17) Goatee™
(18) Goochy™
(19) Groovy™
(20) Halo™
(21) Honks™
(22) Hope™
(23) Jabber™
(24) Jake™
(25) Kicks™
(26) Knuckles™
(27) Kuku™
(28) Lips™
(29) Luke™
(30) Mac™
(31) Millennium™
(32) Mooch™
(33) Neon™
(34) Osito™
(35) Paul™
(36) Pecan™
(37) Prickles™
(38) Roam™

(39) Rocket™	(49) Spangle™
(40) Sammy™	(50) Swirly™
(41) Scaly™	(51) The End™
(42) Scat™	(52) Tiny™
(43) Schweetheart™	(53) Tiptoe™
(44) Scorch™	(54) Tracker™
(45) Sheets™	(55) Ty2K™
(46) Silver™	(56) Valentina™
(47) Slippery™	(57) Wallace™
(48) Slowpoke™	(58) Whisper™

You already have these pages; this is the new line-up behind your Current tab. (All 58 of these Beanie Babies® will retire 12/31/99.)

Thank you for your business!
Peg et. al.
"My Beanie Baby™ Binder"
Vine Street Publishing, Inc.
Box 97
Orem, UT 84059
(801) 222-9670; 9680 fax
pegfugal@aol.com
www.mybeaniebabybinder.com

"My Beanie Baby™ Binder" Summer '99 Update Pak Order Form

_____ "My Beanie Baby™ Binder/Final Millennial Edition"   ~~$29.95 + s/h~~
Special price for Auto-Ship customers only   **$24.95 + s/h**
You already own and use "Beanie Baby™ Binder". If you are an Auto-Ship customer, then you will automatically receive all the Update Paks you need to complete your binder. You may also want to own a clean, unused copy of the "Final Millennial Edition" of "My Beanie Baby™ Binder", which contains every Beanie Baby™ ever released and retired from 6/25/94 thru 12/31/99, and which will surely escalate in value along with your Beanie Baby™ collection. Please indicate in the space provided how many copies you want.

_____ ***Empty "Beanie Baby™" binder***   **$10.00 + s/h**
If your original "Beanie Baby™ Binder" is getting full, you might want to buy an extra empty binder, and divide your tabs and pages between the two. Please indicate in the space provided how many empty binders you want.

Name: _____

Address: _____

City/State/Zip: _____

Phone/fax/email: _____

❏ Bill me (I agree to mail a check immediately upon receipt of my order.)

❏ Charge my charge card (My charge card is current and has credit.)

     ❏ American Express   ❏ Mastercard   ❏ Visa

Name on charge card _____

Charge card number _____ Exp. date ____

Authorized signature _____

Mail this order form to: **Or fax to:**   **Or order via our website:**
Vine Street   (801) 222-9680   www.mybeaniebabybinder.com
Box 97
Orem, UT 84059

B.B. Bear™

Type:	Bear	*Categories:*	Bear, ty-dye	*Style no.:* 4253

Birthday: None   *Released:* Summer '99   *Retired:* 12/31/99

Position: Sitting up   *Tags:* 5th/7th

Description: Ty-dyed plush body, "Birthday Bear w/ candle" full color plastic button over heart, black plastic eyes & nose, hang tag left ear, tush tag left bottom

Replaces: None

Variations: Ty-dye varies in colors

Oddities: One of few Beanie Babies® w/ neither gender nor birthday (blank line to fill in birth date of choice); one of two Beanie Babies® w/ button (see Clubby™)

Commentary: In circulation less than five months before retiring; one of many ty-dyed bears (incl. Garcia, Peace, Sammy & Groovy); first specific "birthday" Beanie Baby™, which will make it extremely popular; one of three Beanie Babies® available only to retailers who visited Ty® booth at summer '99 gift shows, hence, hard to find & pricey

Poem: The birthday Beanie was made for you
Hope your wishes and dreams come true
Be happy today and tomorrow too
Let's all celebrate the whole year through!™

My record

(Beanies are the #1 collectible in American collecting history. A complete, detailed record will vastly increase the value of this Beanie, if & when you ever appraise, trade, re-sell, gift, or bequeath it.)

Description *(which version do you have?):*

Gift from:

Date received/purchased:

Purchased from:

NAME OF PERSON OR RETAILER

ADDRESS

CITY/STATE/ZIP

PHONE

Qty. purchased: **Cost ea.**
(check one)   ❏ *Cash*   ❏ *Check*   ❏ *Charge*

Reason(s) for purchase(s):

Traded to:

NAME

ADDRESS

CITY/STATE/ZIP

PHONE

TRADED FOR

Re-sold to:

NAME

ADDRESS

CITY/STATE/ZIP

PHONE

PRICE RE-SOLD FOR

Your feelings about &/or experiences w/ this Beanie:

Flitter™

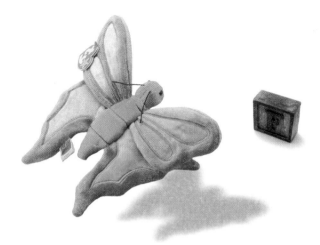

Type: Butterfly **Categories:** Insect, ty-dye **Style no.:** 4255

Birthday: June 2, 1999 **Released:** Summer '99 **Retired:** 12/31/99

Position: Flying **Tags:** 5th/7th

Description: Pink plush body w/ purple thread detailing, blue thread eyes & purple thread antennae, four purple heather plush wings w/ ty-dyed plush insets embroidered w/ pink thread

Replaces: Flitter™

Variations: Ty-dye varies in colors

Oddities: One of few Beanie Babies® with no gender; one of few poems in first person

Commentary: Released two months after birth; in circulation less than five months before retiring; one of the most detailed Beanie Babies® ever; one of three Beanie Babies® available only to retailers who visited Ty® booth at summer '99 gift shows, hence, hard to find & pricey

Poem: I did not know what I was to be
Covered in fuzz, it was hard to see
Now a butterfly, what a beautiful sight
On silken wings I take to flight!™

My record

(Beanies are the #1 collectible in American collecting history. A complete, detailed record will vastly increase the value of this Beanie, if & when you ever appraise, trade, re-sell, gift, or bequeath it.)

Description *(which version do you have?):*

Gift from:

Date received/purchased:

Purchased from:

NAME OF PERSON OR RETAILER

ADDRESS

CITY/STATE/ZIP

PHONE

Qty. purchased: **Cost ea.**
(check one)   ❏ *Cash*   ❏ *Check*   ❏ *Charge*

Reason(s) for purchase(s):

Traded to:

NAME

ADDRESS

CITY/STATE/ZIP

PHONE

TRADED FOR

Re-sold to:

NAME

ADDRESS

CITY/STATE/ZIP

PHONE

PRICE RE-SOLD FOR

Your feelings about &/or experiences w/ this Beanie:

Lips™

Type: Fish   **Categories:** Fish, ty-dye   **Style no.:** 4254

Birthday: March 15, 1999   **Released:** Summer '99   **Retired:** 12/31/99

Position: Swimming   **Tags:** 5th/7th

Description: Ty-dyed plush head w/ big black plastic eyes ringed w/ blue; big protuding bright red felt lips; blue front fins, ty-dyed tail fin, purple & pink top fins, pink bottom fin—all plush; orange plush body w/ purple silkscreened spots

Replaces: Coral™, Bubbles™ & Goldie™

Variations: Ty-dye varies in color

Oddities: One of few Beanie Babies® w/ no gender; one of few poems in first person

Commentary: Released five months after birth; in circulation less than five months before retiring; much more colorful & fanciful than most Beanie Babies®; destined to become most popular Beanie Baby™ fish; one of three Beanie Babies® available only to retailers who visited Ty® booth at summer '99 gift shows, hence, hard to find & pricey

Poem: Did you ever see a fish like me?
I'm the most colorful in the sea
Traveling with friends in a school
Swimming all day is really cool!™

My record

(Beanies are the #1 collectible in American collecting history. A complete, detailed record will vastly increase the value of this Beanie, ifand when you ever appraise, trade, re-sell, gift, or bequeath it.)

Description *(which version do you have?):*

Gift from:

Date received/purchased:

Purchased from:

NAME OF PERSON OR RETAILER

ADDRESS

CITY/STATE/ZIP

PHONE

Qty. purchased: **Cost ea.**
(check one)   ❏ *Cash*   ❏ *Check*   ❏ *Charge*

Reason(s) for purchase(s):

Traded to:

NAME

ADDRESS

CITY/STATE/ZIP

PHONE

TRADED FOR

Re-sold to:

NAME

ADDRESS

CITY/STATE/ZIP

PHONE

PRICE RE-SOLD FOR

Your feelings about &/or experiences w/ this Beanie:

Buddies®

The fourth set of Beanie Buddies® were released summer '99. In fact, they were available only to retailers who visited the Ty® booth at the various summer gift shows—making them hard to find and pricey from the very beginning.

With only two included in this release, this constitutes the smallest release of Beanie Buddies® to date. Previous releases included nine (9/98), fourteen (1/99), and five (spring '99), for a total of 30 Beanie Buddies® to date.

Like most of the Beanie Buddies® before them, both of these Beanie Buddies® are made of Ty®'s new super soft plush fabric, called Tylon®, developed by Ty Warner himself. Like previous Beanie Buddies®, stuffing includes both beans and batting.

This fourth set of Beanie Buddies® have the same 2nd generation hang and tush tags as the second and third sets of Beanie Buddies®.

Inch™

Inch™, the Beanie Baby™ inchworm, was originally released 10/15/97 and retired only seven months later. It also made an appearance as a Teenie™ in May of '98. Originally released with felt antennae, Inch™ the Beanie Baby™ was later released with yarn antennae. Inch™ the Beanie Baby™ was a popular gift item at productions of "Joseph and the Amazing Technicolor Dream Coat" for obvious reasons. It is no wonder Ty® selected the ever-popular Inch™ to reappear as a Beanie Buddy™. Major difference between Beanie Baby™ Inch™ and Beanie Buddy™ Inch™: antennae on Beanie Buddy™ are braided yarn. Inch™ is the first Beanie Buddy™ insect.

Date & place purchased＿＿＿＿＿＿＿＿＿＿＿＿＿＿Amt. pd.＿＿＿＿＿

Schweetheart™

Schweetheart™, the Beanie Baby™ orang-utan, was originally released 4/11/99 and retired only eight and a half months later on 12/31/99, along with 58 other Beanie Babies®. One of five Beanie Baby™ monkeys (including Bongo™ the brown monkey, Congo™ the black gorilla, Mooch™ the black spider monkey, and Cheeks™ the colorful baboon), Schweetheart™ is the cutest and sweetest monkey with its reddish-brown color, tuft of hair, and long huggy arms and legs—which no doubt prompted its choice as a Beanie Buddy™. Schweetheart™ is the second Beanie Buddy™ monkey.

Date & place purchased＿＿＿＿＿＿＿＿＿＿＿＿＿＿Amt. pd.＿＿＿＿＿

List #1:

Beanie Babies® by date of release
As of 12/31/99

Following is a list of all Beanie Babies® to date, listed first by date of release and then alphabetically, for your information and shopping/collecting convenience. You can tell by the length of each list which were regular releases and which were special releases.

1/8/94—original 9 Beanie Babies®
(1) Chocolate
(2) Brownie, renamed Cubbie
(3) Flash
(4) Legs
(5) Patti (maroon)
(6) Puncher, renamed Pinchers
(7) Splash
(8) Spot (w/o spot)
(9) Squealer

4/13/94—replacement
(1) Spot (w/ spot)

6/25/94
(1) Ally
(2) Blackie
(3) Bones
(4) Chilly
(5) Daisy
(6) Digger (orange)
(7) Goldie
(8) Happy (gray)
(9) Humphrey
(10) Inky (tan w/o mouth)
(11) Lucky (w/ felt spots)
(12) Mystic (w/ gold horn)
(13) Peking
(14) Quackers (w/o wings)
(15) Seamore
(16) Slither
(17) Speedy
(18) Teddy Brown (old)
(19) Teddy Cranberry (old)
(20) Teddy Jade (old)
(21) Teddy Magenta (old)

(22) Teddy Teal (old)
(23) Teddy Violet (old)
(24) Trap
(25) Web

9/12/94—replacement
(1) Inky (tan w/ mouth)

1/7/95
(1) Nip (w/ white face)
(2) Quackers (w/ wings)
(3) Tank (w/o shell)
(4) Teddy Brown (new)
(5) Teddy Cranberry (new)
(6) Teddy Jade (new)
(7) Teddy Magenta (new)
(8) Teddy Teal (new)
(9) Teddy Violet (new)
(10) Tusk
(11) Valentino
(12) Zip (w/ white face)

2/28/95—replacement
(1) Patti (magenta)

6/3/95
(1) Bessie
(2) Bongo (w/ tan tail)
(3) Bronty
(4) Bubbles
(5) Bumble
(6) Caw
(7) Coral
(8) Derby (w/o diamond)
(9) Digger (red)
(10) Flutter

(11) Happy (purple)
(12) Inch (w/ felt antennae)
(13) Inky (pink)
(14) Kiwi
(15) Lizzy (tie-dyed)
(16) Magic
(17) Peanut (royal blue)
(18) Pinky
(19) Rex
(20) Steg
(21) Sting
(22) Stinky
(23) Tabasco
(24) Velvet
(25) Waddle
(26) Ziggy

9/1/95—special Halloween release
(1) Radar
(2) Spooky

10/2/95—replacement
(1)Peanut (light blue)

1/7/96
(1) Bucky
(2) Chops
(3) Ears
(4) Flip
(5) Garcia
(6) Grunt
(7) Hoot
(8) Lizzy (blue)
(9) Manny
(10) Nip (all gold)
(11) Ringo
(12) Seaweed
(13) Stripes (w/ thin stripes)
(14) Tank (w/ shell)
(15) Twigs
(16) Weenie
(17) Zip (all black)

2/6/96—replacement
(1) Bongo (w/ brown tail)

2/27/96—replacement
(1) Lucky (w/ printed spots)

3/10/96—replacements
(1) Nip (w/ white socks)
(2) Zip (w/ white socks)

6/3/96—replacement
(1) Stripes (w/ wide stripes)

6/15/96
(1) Congo
(2) Curly
(3) Freckles
(4) Lefty
(5) Libearty
(6) Righty
(7) Rover
(8) Scoop
(9) Scottie
(10) Sly (w/ brown belly)
(11) Sparky
(12) Spike
(13) Wrinkles

8/6/96—replacement
(1) Sly (w/ white belly)

1/1/97
(1) Bernie
(2) Crunch
(3) Doby
(4) Fleece
(5) Floppity
(6) Gracie
(7) Hippity
(8) Hoppity
(9) Maple
(10) Mel
(11) Nuts
(12) Pouch
(13) Snip
(14) Snort

5/11/97
(1) Baldy
(2) Blizzard
(3) Chip
(4) Claude
(5) Dotty
(6) Echo
(7) Jolly
(8) Nanook
(9) Pugsly
(10) Peace
(11) Roary
(12) Tuffy
(13) Waves

7/12/97—replacement
(1) Strut

10/1/97—special holiday release
(1) 1997 Holiday Teddy
(2) Batty
(3) Gobbles
(4) Snowball
(5) Spinner

10/15/97—replacement
(1) Inch (w/ yarn antennae)

10/23/97—replacement
(1) Mystic (w/ iridescent horn)

10/29/97—special commemorative release
(1) Princess

12/15/97—replacement
(1) Derby (w/ diamond)

12/31/97
(1) Britannia
(2) Bruno
(3) Hissy
(4) Iggy
(5) Pounce
(6) Prance

(7) Puffer
(8) Rainbow
(9) Smoochy
(10) Spunky
(11) Stretch

1/31/98—special St. Patrick's Day release
(1) Erin

5/30/98
(1) Ants
(2) Early
(3) Fetch
(4) Fortune
(5) Gigi
(6) Glory
(7) Jabber
(8) Jake
(9) Kuku
(10) Rocket
(11) Stinger
(12) Tracker
(13) Whisper
(14) Wise—special graduation release

Summer '98—special BBOC release
(1) Clubby

9/30/98
(1) 1998 Holiday Teddy
(2) Beak
(3) Canyon
(4) Halo
(5) Loosy
(6) Pumkin
(7) Roam
(8) Santa
(9) Scorch

1/1/99
(1) 1999 Signature Bear
(2) Butch
(3) Eggbert

(4) Ewey
(5) Fuzz
(6) Germania
(7) Goatee
(8) Goochy
(9) Hippie
(10) Hope
(11) Kicks
(12) Luke
(13) Mac
(14) Millennium
(15) Mooch
(16) Nibbler
(17) Nibbly
(18) Prickles
(19) Sammy
(20) Scat
(21) Slippery
(22) Stilts
(23) Tiny
(24) Valentina

1/1/99—replacements
(1) Batty (tie-dyed)
(2) Derby (w/ hairy mane)
(3) Iggy (corrected fabric)
(4) Mystic (w/ hairy rainbow mane)
(5) Rainbow (corrected fabric)

Spring '99—special BBOC release
(1) Clubby II

4/8/99
(1) Eucalyptus
(2) Neon
(3) Pecan

4/11/99
(1) Schweetheart

4/12/99
(1) Paul

4/14/99
(1) Knuckles

(2) Swirly

4/16/99
(1) Tiptoe

4/17/99
(1) Cheeks
(2) Osito

4/19/99
(1) Almond

4/20/99
(1) Amber

4/21/99
(1) Silver

4/22/99
(1) Wiser

4/24/99
(1) Spangle

Summer '99—special release
(1) B.B. Bear
(2) Flitter
(3) Lips
(These Beanie Babies® were available only to authorized Ty® dealers who visited the Ty® booth at the summer '99 gift shows)

8/31/99—final release
(1) 1999 Holiday Teddy
(2) Chipper
(3) Groovy
(4) Honks
(5) Scaly
(6) Sheets
(7) Slowpoke
(8) The End
(9) Ty2k
(10) Wallace

Retired Beanie Babies® & values
As of 12/31/99

Following is a list of all Retired Beanie Babies® to date, followed by their current value, per J.C. at Collector's Mall in Orem, Utah.

12/31/99

(1) 1999 Holiday Teddy (baby blue bear w/ snowflakes, scarf) **$50**

(2) 1999 Signature Bear (heather w/ Ty signature) **$50**

(3) Almond (almond-colored bear) **$18**

(4) Amber (gold-striped cat) **$18**

(5) Beak (brown napped kiwi) **$18**

(6) B.B. Bear (ty-dyed birthday bear) **$45**

(7) Butch (bull terrier) **$18**

(8) Cheeks (baboon) **$18**

(9) Chipper (chipmunk) **$20**

(10) Clubby II (orchid heather bear, BBOC mascot) **$45**

(11) Early (robin) **$18**

(12) Eucalyptus (blue-green heather koala) **$18**

(13) Flitter (pastel butterfly) **$25**

(14) Fuzz (silky napped brown bear) **$30**

(15) Germania (napped brown bear w/ German flag) **$275**

(16) Gigi (black poodle) **$18**

(17) Goatee (mountain goat) **$18**

(18) Goochy (ty-dyed jellyfish)
(icy) **$20**
(pastel) **$18**

(19) Groovy (napped, ty-dyed bear) **$40**

(20) Halo (white angel bear) **$25**

(21) Honks (gray goose) **$20**

(22) Hope (butterscotch praying bear) **$25**

(23) Jabber (parrot) **$18**

(24) Jake (mallard) **$18**

(25) Kicks (lime green bear w/ soccer insignia) **$25**

(26) Knuckles (flesh-colored pig) **$20**

(27) Kuku (white cockatoo) **$18**

(28) Lips (multi-colored fish) **$30**

(29) Luke (black lab) **$18**

(30) Mac (red cardinal, Mark McGwire) **$18**

(31) Millennium (magenta bear w/ globe insignia)
(w/ 1 "n") **$30**
(w/ 2 "n"s) **$20**

(32) Mooch (black spider monkey) **$18**

(33) Neon (ty-dyed seahorse) **$18**

(34) Osito (red bear w/ Mexican flag) **$40**

(35) Paul (bearded, tusked walrus) **$20**

(36) Pecan (pecan-colored bear) **$20**

(37) Prickles (hedgehog) **$18**

(38) Roam (buffalo) **$18**

(39) Rocket (blue jay) **$18**

(40) Sammy (ty-dyed bear, Sammy Sosa) **$30**

(41) Scaly (brown-green lizard) **$20**

(42) Scat (heather cat) **$18**

(43) Schweetheart (orang-utan) **$20**

(44) Scorch (dragon) **$20**

(45) Sheets (ghost w/ sheet) **$20**

(46) Silver (tiger-striped cat) **$18**

(47) Slippery (gray heather seal) **$18**

(48) Slowpoke (sloth) **$20**

(49) Spangle (patriotic bear)
(pink face) **$45**
(blue face) **$60**
(white face) **$50**

(50) Swirly (snail) *$18*
(51) The End (black bear w/ "The End" insignia) *$50*
(52) Tiny (chihuahua) *$20*
(53) Tiptoe (brown mouse) *$20*
(54) Tracker (basset hound) *$18*
(55) Ty2K (white confetti bear) *$50*
(56) Valentina (hot pink bear w/ white heart) *$30*
(57) Wallace (Scottish bear w/ scarf) *$45*
(58) Whisper (deer) *$20*

9/1
(1) Loosy (gray & white goose) *$18*

8/27
(1) Wiser (Class of '99 owl) *$20*

8/24
(1) Fortune (panda) *$25*

8/17
(1) Canyon (cougar) *$18*

7/30
(1) Maple (white bear w/ Canadian flag) *$200*

7/28
(1) Eggbert (chick in shell) *$20*

7/26
(1) Britannia (brown bear w/ UK flag) *$200*

7/20
(1) Nibbly (brown bunny) *$18*

7/19
(1) Ewey (napped cream lamb) *$20*

7/16
(1) Peace (ty-dyed bear w/ peace symbol)
(bright) *$35*
(pastel) *$25*

7/12
(1) Hippie (ty-dyed bunny) *$35*

7/9
(1) Nibbler (cream bunny) *$18*

5/31/99
(1) Stilts (white stork) *$18*

5/26/99
(1) Derby (brown horse)
(w/o diamond, coarse mane) *$30*
(w/o diamond, fine mane) *$1,600*
(w/ diamond, fine mane) *$18*
(w/ diamond, hairy mane) *$18*

5/21/99
(1) Erin (green bear w/ white shamrock) *$25*

5/18/99
(1) Mystic (white unicorn)
(gold horn, coarse mane) *$40*
(gold horn, fine mane) *$200*
(iridescent horn, fine mane) *$18*
(iridescent horn, hairy rainbow mane) *$18*

4/13/99
(1) Princess (royal purple bear w/ white rose) *$35*

3/31/99
(1) Batty
(brown) *$18*
(tie-dyed) *$25*
(2) Chip (calico cat) *$18*

(3) Gobbles (multi-colored turkey) $15

(4) Hissy (blue coiled snake) $15

(5) Iggy (tie-dyed iguana)
(wrong fabric) $18
(correct fabric) $15

(6) Mel (gray koala) $18

(7) Nanook (gray huskie) $18

(8) Pouch (brown kangaroo) $15

(9) Pounce (brown cat) $15

(10) Prance (gray striped cat) $15

(11) Pugsly (tan pug) $18

(12) Rainbow (tie-dyed chameleon)
(wrong fabric) $18
(correct fabric) $15

(13) Smoochy (green frog)
(thread mouth) $25
(felt mouth) $18

(14) Spunky (tan cocker spaniel) $18

(15) Stretch (brown ostrich) $15

(16) Strut (tie-dyed rooster)
(Doodles) $40
(Strut) $18

3/15/99

(1) Clubby (royal blue bear, BBOC mascot) $60

12/10/98

(1) Chocolate (brown moose) $18

(2) Roary (brown lion) $18

(3) Glory (white bear w/ red & blue stars) $48

12/9/98

(1) Bongo (brown monkey) $18

(2) Freckles (spotted leopard) $22

12/8/98

(1) Congo (black gorilla) $18

(2) Pinky (pink flamingo) $18

(3) Spike (gray rhino) $18

12/7/98

(1) Fleece (white, napped lamb) $20

(2) Snip (Siamese cat) $18

12/6/98

(1) Curly (brown, napped bear) $25

12/5/98

(1) Ants (gray anteater) $18

(2) Doby (doberman) $18

(3) Dotty (dalmatian) $18

(4) Nuts (brown squirrel) $18

(5) Tuffy (brown, napped terrier) $18

12/4/98

(1) Claude (tie-dyed crab)
(tie-dyed crab w/ name in all caps) $35

(2) Pumkin (w/ green arms & legs) $35

(3) Wise ("Class of '98"owl) $25

12/3/98

(1) Valentino (white bear w/ red heart) $28

12/2/98

(1) Fetch (yellow lab) $18

(2) Scoop (blue pelican) $20

(3) Stinger (gray scorpion) $18

12/1/98

(1) 1998 Holiday Teddy (white bear w/ holly & berries) $80

(2) Santa (w/ green mittens) $50

(3) Zero (penguin w/ red cap) $40

9/28/98

(1) Stinky (black & white skunk) $20

9/24/98
(1) Crunch (blue shark) **$20**

9/22/98
(1) Bernie (St. Bernard) **$20**
(2) Sly (brown fox) **$20**
(3) Wrinkles (tan bulldog) **$18**

9/19/98
(1) Seaweed (brown otter) **$28**
(2) Spinner (black & brown spider) **$18**

9/18/98
(1) Bruno (brown & white bull terrier) **$18**
(2) Puffer (puffin) **$18**

9/16/98
(1) Ringo (raccoon) **$20**

9/15/98
(1) Blackie (black bear) **$25**
(2) Daisy (black & white cow) **$20**
(3) Snort (red bull) **$18**

5/1/98
(1) Baldy (eagle) **$30**
(2) Blizzard (white tiger) **$25**
(3) Bones (brown hound dog) **$20**
(4) Ears (brown bunny) **$22**
(5) Echo (blue dolphin) **$30**
(6) Floppity (lavender bunny) **$30**
(7) Gracie (white swan) **$22**
(8) Happy (purple hippo) **$30**
(9) Hippity (mint green bunny) **$35**
(10) Hoppity (pink bunny) **$30**
(11) Inch (multi-colored inch worm) **$30**
(12) Inky (pink octopus) **$35**
(13) Jolly (brown walrus) **$25**
(14) Lucky (ladybug) **$35**
(15) Patti (magenta platypus) **$35**
(16) Peanut (blue elephant) **$30**
(17) Pinchers (red lobster) **$30**

(18) Quackers (yellow duck) **$25**
(19) Rover (red hound dog) **$35**
(20) Scottie (black, napped terrier) **$40**
(21) Squealer (pink pig) **$35**
(22) Stripes (gold tiger) **$25**
(23) Twigs (giraffe) **$25**
(24) Waddle (penguin) **$35**
(25) Waves (black & white whale) **$30**
(26) Weenie (brown dachshund) **$38**
(27) Ziggy (zebra) **$28**
(28) Zip (black cat) **$45**

12/31/97
(1) 1997 Holiday Teddy (brown bear w/ red hat & scarf) **$58**
(2) Bucky (brown beaver) **$50**
(3) Cubbie (brown bear) **$35**
(4) Goldie (goldfish) **$55**
(5) Lizzy (multi-colored lizard) **$35**
(6) Magic (white dragon) **$55**
(7) Nip (gold cat) **$32**
(8) Snowball (snowman) **$50**
(9) Spooky (ghost) **$50**

12/15/97
(1) Derby (brown horse w/o diamond) **$35**

10/23/97
(1) Mystic (w/ brown horn) **$40**

10/15/97
(1) Inch (w/ felt antennae) **$200**

10/1/97
(1) Ally (alligator) **$65**
(2) Bessie (brown & white cow) **$85**
(3) Flip (white cat) **$45**
(4) Hoot (owl) **$45**
(5) Legs (green frog) **$35**
(6) Seamore (white seal) **$200**

(7) Speedy (turtle) **$40**
(8) Spot (white dog, black spot) **$75**
(9) Tank (gray armadillo) **$85**
(10) Teddy Brown (new face) **$125**
(11) Velvet (black panther) **$45**

5/11/97
(1) Bubbles (yellow & black fish)
   $165
(2) Digger (red crab) **$130**
(3) Flash (gray & white dolphin)
   $130
(4) Garcia (tie-dyed bear) **$200**
(5) Grunt (red razorback hog) **$200**
(6) Manny (gray manatee) **$180**
(7) Radar (black bat) **$145**
(8) Sparky (dalmatian) **$165**
(9) Splash (black & white whale)
   $165

1/1/97
(1) Chops (cream lamb) **$180**
(2) Coral (tie-dyed fish) **$225**
(3) Kiwi (toucan) **$225**
(4) Lefty (blue Democratic donkey
   w/ U.S. flag) **$300**
(5) Libearty (white bear w/ U.S. flag)
   $350
(6) Righty (gray Republican elephant
   w/ U.S. flag) **$325**
(7) Sting (tie-dyed manta ray) **$235**
(8) Tabasco (red bull) **$200**
(9) Tusk (brown walrus) **$175**

8/6/96
(1) Sly (brown-bellied fox) **$165**

6/29/96
(1) Bongo (brown monkey w/ brown
   tail) **$95**

6/15/96
(1) Bronty (tie-dyed brontosaurus)
   $1,000
(2) Bumble (bumblebee) **$700**

(3) Caw (crow) **$800**
(4) Flutter (tie-dyed butterfly)
   $1,000
(5) Rex (tie-dyed tyrannosaurus rex)
   $1,000
(6) Steg (tie-dyed stegosaurus)
   $1,150
(7) Web (black spider) **$1,500**

6/3/96
(1) Stripes (tiger w/ thin stripes)
   $475

3/10/96
(1) Nip (all gold cat) **$925**
(2) Zip (all black cat) **$975**

2/27/96
(1) Lucky (lady bug w/ felt spots)
   $275

1/7/96
(1) Chilly (polar bear) **$2,000**
(2) Lizzy (tie-dyed lizard) **$1,000**
(3) Nip (gold cat w/ white face)
   $450
(4) Peking (panda) **$1,500**
(5) Tank (w/o shell) **$225**
(6) Teddy Cranberry (new face)
   $1,900
(7) Teddy Jade (new face) **$1,900**
(8) Teddy Magenta (new face)
   $1,900
(9) Teddy Teal (new face) **$1,900**
(10) Teddy Violet (new face) **$1,900**
(11) Zip (black cat w/ white face)
   $450

10/2/95
(1) Peanut (royal blue elephant)
   $4,700

6/15/95
(1) Humphrey (camel) **$2,500**

(2) Slither (multi-colored snake) *$1,500*
(3) Trap (gray mouse) *$1,500*

6/3/95
(1) Digger (orange crab) *$700*
(2) Happy (gray hippo) *$1,600*
(3) Inky (tan octopus w/ mouth) *$800*

2/28/95
(1) Patti (maroon platypus) *$650*

1/7/95
(1) Quackers (wingless duck) *$1,900*
(2) Teddy Brown (old face) *$2,200*
(3) Teddy Cranberry (old face) *$1,800*
(4) Teddy Jade (old face) *$1,800*
(5) Teddy Magenta (old face) *$1,800*
(6) Teddy Teal (old face) *$1,800*
(7) Teddy Violet (old face) *$1,800*

9/12/94
(1) Inky (octopus w/o mouth) *$800*

4/13/94
(1) Spot (dog w/o spot) *$1,800*

(220 total Retireds to date)
(241 including oddball retirements)

Beanie Baby™ multiples
As of 12/31/99

Following is a list of Beanie Baby™ multiples to date, including same kinds of animals and same Beanie Babies® w/ changes, listed alphabetically by category and then in order of release, for your information and shopping/collecting convenience.

Bats
1-Radar the black bat 9/1/95
2-Batty the brown bat   10/1/97
3-replaced by Batty the tie-dyed bat, fall '98

Bears
(sit-up, unless otherwise indicated)
1-Brownie the brown bear 1/8/94 (1st lay-down bear)
2-Brownie renamed Cubbie, mid '94 (1st revised bear)
3-Blackie the black bear 6/25/94 (2nd lay-down bear)
4-Teddy Brown (old face) 6/25/94
5-Teddy Cranberry (old face) 6/25/94
6-Teddy Jade (old face) 6/25/94
7-Teddy Magenta (old face) 6/25/94
8-Teddy Teal (old face) 6/25/94
9-Teddy Violet (old face) 6/25/94
10-Chilly the white polar bear 6/25/94 (3rd lay-down bear)
11-Peking the black & white panda 6/25/94 (1st panda) (4th lay-down bear)
12-Teddy Brown (new face) 1/7/95
13-Teddy Cranberry (new face) 1/7/95
14-Teddy Jade (new face) 1/7/95
15-Teddy Magenta (new face) 1/7/95
16-Teddy Teal (new face) 1/7/95
17-Teddy Violet (new face) 1/7/95
18-Valentino the white bear w/ red heart 1/7/95 (1st holiday bear) (companion to Valentina)
19-Garcia the tie-dyed bear 1/7/96 (1st tie-dyed bear)
20-Curly the brown, napped bear 6/15/96 (1st napped bear)
21-Libearty the white bear w/ U.S. flag 6/15/96 (1st American bear)
22-Maple the white bear w/ Canadian flag 1/1/97 (1st foreign release) (1st International bear)
23-Mel the gray koala 1/1/97 (5th lay-down bear)
24-Peace the bright tie-dyed bear 5/11/97 (2nd tie-dyed bear)
25-1997 Holiday Teddy (brown w/ red cap & scarf) 10/1/97 (2nd holiday bear)
26-Princess the royal purple bear 10/29/97 (1st bear to commemorate a person)
27-Britannia the brown bear w/ British flag 12/31/97 (2nd foreign release) (2nd International bear)
28-Erin the green bear w/ white shamrock 1/31/98 (3rd holiday bear)(3rd International bear)
29-Fortune the black & white panda 5/30/98 (2nd panda)
30-Glory the white bear w/ red & blue stars 5/30/98 (2nd American bear)
31-Clubby the royal blue bear, summer '98 (1st BBOC mascot)
32-Peace the pastel tie-dyed bear, summer '98 (2nd revised bear) (3rd tie-dyed bear)

33-1998 Holiday Teddy (white w/ holly & berries) 9/30/98 (4th holiday bear)

34-Halo the white bear w/ halo & wings 9/30/98 (1st religious bear)

35-1999 Signature Bear (heather w/ "1999 Ty" insignia) 1/1/99

36-Fuzz the brown, silky napped bear 1/1/99 (2nd napped bear)

37-Germania the brown, thick napped bear w/ German flag 1/1/99 (4th international bear) (3rd napped bear)

38-Hope the butterscotch praying bear 1/1/99 (2nd religious bear)

39-Kicks the lime green soccer bear 1/1/99 (1st sports bear)

40-Millennium the magenta bear w/ globe insignia 1/1/99

41-Sammy the tie-dyed bear 1/1/99 (2nd bear to commemorate a person) (2nd sports bear) (4th tie-dyed bear) (6th lay-down bear)

42-Valentina the hot pink bear w/ white heart 1/1/99 (5th holiday bear) (companion to Valentino)

43-Eucalyptus the blue-green heather koala 4/8/99 (2nd koala) (1st stand-up bear)

44-Pecan the pecan heather bear 4/8/99 (2nd stand-up bear)

45-Osito the red bear w/ Mexican flag 4/17/99 (5th international bear)

46-Almond the almond heather bear 4/19/99 (3rd stand-up bear)

47-Spangle the Flag Day bear 4/24/99 (3rd American bear)

48-Clubby II the orchid heather bear, spring '99 (2nd BBOC mascot)

49-B.B. Bear the ty-dyed birthday bear, summer '99 (only birthday Beanie)

50-1999 Holiday Teddy (baby blue w/ snowflakes, scarf) 8/31/99 (6th holiday bear)

51-Groovy the napped ty-dyed bear 8/31/99 (5th ty-dyed bear) (4th napped bear)

52-The End, the black bear w/ "The End/fireworks" insignia 8/31/99 (2nd black bear)

53-Ty2K the white bear w/ confetti 8/31/99

54-Wallace the napped green Scottish bear w/ scarf 8/31/99 (5th napped bear) (6th international bear)

Birds

1-Caw the crow 6/3/95

2-Kiwi the toucan 6/3/95

3-Hoot the owl 1/7/96

4-Scoop the pelican 6/15/96

5-Gracie the swan 1/1/97

6-Baldy the eagle 5/11/97

7-Strut the rooster 7/12/97

8-Stretch the ostrich 12/31/97

9-Early the robin 5/30/98

10-Jabber the parrot 5/30/98

11-Jake the mallard 5/30/98

12-Kuku the cockatoo 5/30/98

13-Rocket the blue jay 5/30/98

14-Wise the owl 5/30/98

15-Beak the kiwi 9/30/98

16-Loosy the Canadian goose 9/30/98

17-Eggbert the chick 1/1/99

18-Mac the cardinal 1/1/99

19-Stilts the stork 1/1/99

20-Wiser the owl 4/22/99 (Class of '99)

21-Honks the gray goose 8/31/99

Bulls
1-Tabasco the red bull (w/o hooves) 6/3/95
2-renamed Snort (w/ hooves) 1/1/97

Bunnies
1-Ears the brown lay-down bunny 1/7/96
2-Floppity the lavender sit-up bunny 1/1/97
3-Hippity the mint green sit-up bunny 1/1/97
4-Hoppity the pink sit-up bunny 1/1/97
5-Hippie the tie-dyed sit-up bunny 1/1/99
6-Nibbler the cream bunny 1/1/99
7-Nibbly the heather bunny 1/1/99

Butterflies
1-Flutter the cool pastel butterfly 6/3/95
2-Flitter the warm pastel butterfly 8/31/99

Cats
1-Nip the gold cat 3/10/96
2-Zip the black cat 3/10/96
3-Flip the white cat 1/7/96
4-Chip the calico cat 5/11/97
5-Snip the Siamese cat 1/1/97
6-Pounce the brown cat 12/31/97
7-Prance the tiger cat 12/31/97
8-Scat the heather cat 1/1/99
9-Amber the gold striped cat 4/19/99
10-Silver the gray striped cat 4/21/99

Chameleons
1-Rainbow the chameleon w/ blue tie-dyed fabric 12/31/97
2-replaced by Rainbow the chameleon w/ rainbow tie-dyed fabric 5/30/98

Clubby
1-Clubby the royal blue BBOC mascot, summer '98 (1st BBOC mascot)
2-Clubby II the orchid heather BBOC mascot, spring '99 (2nd BBOC mascot)

Crabs
1-Digger the orange crab 6/25/94
2-replaced by Digger the red crab 6/3/95
3-Claude the tie-dyed crab 5/11/97

Dalmatians
1-Sparky 6/15/96
2-renamed Dotty 5/11/97

Derby the brown horse
1-w/ fine yarn mane & tail, '95
2-w/ coarse yarn mane & tail, '95-'97
3-w/ coarse yarn mane & tail + white diamond on forehead, '98
4-w/ hairy mane & tail + white diamond on forehead, '99

Dinosaurs
1-Bronty the brontosaurus 6/3/95
2-Rex the tyrannosaurus 6/3/95
3-Steg the stegosaurus 6/3/95

Dogs
1-Spot the dog w/o spot 1/8/94
2-replaced by Spot the dog w/ spot 4/13/94
3-Bones the brown hound 6/25/94
4-Weenie the dachshund 1/7/96
5-Sparky the dalmatian 6/15/96
6-replaced by Dottie the dalmatian 5/11/97
7-Rover the red hound 6/15/96
8-Wrinkles the bulldog 6/15/96
9-Scottie the napped terrier 6/15/96
10-Bernie the St. Bernard 1/1/97

11-Doby the doberman 1/1/97
12-Nanook the husky 5/11/97
13-Pugsly the pug 5/11/97
14-Tuffy the napped terrier 5/11/97
15-Bruno the bull terrier 12/31/97
16-Spunky the cockerspaniel
   12/31/97
17-Fetch the golden lab 5/30/98
18-Gigi the poodle 5/30/98
19-Tracker the basset hound
   5/30/98
20-Butch the bull terrier 1/1/99
21-Luke the black lab 1/1/99
22-Tiny the chihuahua 1/1/99

Dolphins
1-Flash the gray dolphin 1/8/94
2-Echo the marine blue dolphin
   5/11/97

Dragons
1-Magic the white dragon 6/3/95
2-Scorch the brown dragon 9/30/98

Elephants
1-Peanut the royal blue elephant
   6/3/95
2-replaced by Peanut the light blue
   elephant 10/2/95
3-Righty the gray Republican
   elephant w/ U.S. flag 6/15/96

Fish
1-Goldie the goldfish 6/25/94
2-Coral the tie-dyed fish 6/3/95
3-Bubbles the yellow fish w/ black
   stripes 6/3/95
4-Goochy the tie-dyed jellyfish
   1/1/99
5-Lips the multi-colored fish
   8/31/99

Frogs
1-Legs the green frog 1/8/94
2-Smoochy the green & gold frog
   12/31/97

Geese
1-Loosy the Canadian goose 9/30/98
2-Honks the gray goose 8/31/99

Ghosts
1-Spooky the white ghost 9/1/95
2-Sheets the white ghost in a sheet
   8/31/99

Happy the Hippo
1-Gray 6/25/94
2-replaced by purple Happy 6/3/95

Iguanas
1-Iggy the iguana w/ rainbow tie-
   dyed fabric 12/31/97
2-Iggy the iguana w/ tongue, spring
   '98
3-replaced by Iggy the iguana w/
   blue tie-dyed fabric 5/30/98

Inch the multi-colored inchworm
1-w/ felt antennae 6/3/95
2-replaced by Inch w/ yarn
   antennae 10/15/97

Inky the octopus
1-Tan w/o mouth 6/25/94
2-replaced by tan Inky w/ mouth
   9/12/94
3-replaced by pink Inky w/ mouth
   6/3/95

Lambs
1-Chops the cream-colored lamb
   1/7/96
2-Fleece the white lamb 1/1/97
3-Ewey the cream-colored lamb
   1/1/99

Lizards
1-Lizzy the ty-dyed lizard 6/3/95
2-replaced by LIzzy the blue lizard 1/7/96
3-Scaly the green-tan lizard 8/31/99

Lobsters
1-Punchers 1/8/94
2-renamed Pinchers, '94

Lucky the red ladybug
1-w/ felt spots 6/25/94
2-replaced by Lucky w/ printed spots 2/27/96

Magic the white dragon
1-w/ hot pink thread, '96-'97
2-w/ pale pink thread, '95-'97

Maple the white bear w/ Canadian flag
1-w/ "Pride" tush tag, '97
2-w/ "Maple" tush tag, '97

Mice
1-Trap the gray mouse 6/25/94
2-Tiptoe the brown mouse 4/16/99

Monkeys
1-Nana the brown monkey w/ tan tail
2-renamed Bongo the brown monkey w/ tan tail 6/3/95
3-Bongo the brown monkey w/ brown tail 2/6/96
4-Mooch the black spider monkey 1/1/99
5-Schweetheart the red orang-utan 4/11/99
6-Cheeks the brown heather baboon 4/17/99

Mystic the white unicorn
1-w/ fine yarn mane & tail + gold horn, '94-'95
2-w/ coarse yarn mane & tail + gold horn, '95-'97
3-w/ coarse yarn mane & tail + iridescent horn, '97-'98
4-w/ rainbow-colored hairy mane & tail + iridescent horn, '99

Nip the gold cat
1-w/ white face 1/7/95
2-replaced by all gold Nip 1/7/96
3-replaced by Nip w/ white socks 3/10/96

Owls
1-Hoot the brown & tan owl 1/7/96
2-Wise the brown owl/Class of '98 5/30/98 (1st graduation owl)
3-Wiser the gray striped owl/Class of '99 4/22/99 (2nd graduation owl)

Patti the platypus
1-Maroon 1/8/94
2-replaced by magenta Patti 2/28/95

Peanut the elephant
1-Royal blue 6/3/95
2-replaced by light blue Peanut 10/2/95

Penguins
1-Waddles 6/3/95
2-Zero w/ red cap 9/30/98

Pigs
1-Squealer the pink pig 1/8/94
2-Knuckles the flesh-colored pig 4/14/99

Princess the royal purple bear
1-w/ PVC filling, '97
2-w/ PE filling, '98

Quackers the yellow duck
1-w/o wings 6/25/94
2-replaced by Quackers w/ wings
 1/7/95

Roosters
1-Doodles the tie-dyed rooster
2-renamed Strut 7/12/97

Sly the fox
1-w/ brown belly 6/15/96
2-replaced by Sly w/ white belly
 8/6/96

Snakes
1-Slither the green long snake
 6/25/94
2-Hissy the blue coiled snake
 12/31/97

Spiders
1-Web the black spider 6/25/94
2-Spinner the black & brown spider
 10/1/97

Spooky the white ghost
1-w/ "Spook" tag, '95
2-w/ "Spooky" tag, '95-'97

Spot the white dog
1-w/o a spot 1/8/94
2-replaced by Spot w/ a spot 4/13/94

Stripes the gold tiger
1-w/ thin stripes 1/7/96
2-replaced by Stripes w/ wide stripes
 6/3/96

Tank the armadillo
1-w/o shell 1/7/95
2-replaced by Tank w/ shell 1/7/96

Tigers
1-Stripes the gold tiger w/ thin
 stripes 1/7/96
2-replaced by Stripes the gold tiger
 w/ wide stripes 6/3/96
3-Blizzard the white tiger 5/11/97

Walruses
1-Tusk the brown walrus 1/7/95
2-Jolly the brown bearded walrus
 5/11/97
3-Paul the brown walrus w/ tusks &
 beard 4/12/99

Whales
1-Splash the black & white whale
 1/8/94
2-Waves the black & white whale
 5/11/97

Zip the black cat
1-w/ white face 1/7/95
2-replaced by all black Zip 1/7/96
3-replaced by Zip w/ white socks
 3/10/96

Beanie Baby™ birthdays
As of 12/31/99

Some collectors like to know which Beanie Babies® were born on their birthday (or on the birthdays of family members and friends), hence, following is a list of all Beanie Babies® with birthdays to date, for your information and shopping/collecting convenience.

January
1 Millennium, Spot, Ty2k
2 Zero
5 Kuku
6 Patti
8 Tiptoe
10 Groovy
13 Crunch
14 Spunky
15 Mel
17 Slippery
18 Bones
21 Nuts
23 Schweetheart
25 Peanut, Wallace
26 Chip

February
1 Peace
3 Beak
4 Fetch
5 Osito
9 Scaly
11 Silver
13 Pinky, Stinky
14 Valentina, Valentino
17 Baldy
19 Prickles
20 Roary
21 Amber
22 Tank
23 Paul
25 Happy
27 Sparky
28 Flip

March
1 Ewey
2 Coral
6 Nip
8 Strut
10 Swirly
11 Honks
12 Rocket
14 Ally
15 Lips
17 Erin
19 Seaweed
20 Early
21 Fleece
23 Hope
25 Knuckles
28 Zip
29 Loosy

April
1 Neon
3 Hoppity
4 Hissy
5 Whisper
6 Nibbler
7 Gigi
10 Eggbert
12 Curly
14 Almond
15 Pecan
16 Jake
18 Ears
19 Quackers
21 Chipper
23 Squealer
25 Legs

27 Chocolate
28 Eucalyptus

May
1 Lucky, Wrinkles
2 Pugsly
3 Chops
4 Hippie
7 Nibbly
10 Daisy
11 Lizzy
13 Flash
15 Tabasco, Snort
18 Cheeks
19 Twigs
20 Slowpoke
21 Mystic
27 Scat
28 Floppity
29 Canyon
30 Rover
31 Wise

June
1 Hippity
2 Flitter
3 Freckles
4 Wiser
5 Tracker
8 Manny, Bucky
10 Mac
11 Stripes
14 Spangle
15 Luke, Scottie
16 Stilts
17 Gracie

19 Pinchers
23 Sammy
27 Bessie

July
1 Maple, Scoop
2 Bubbles
4 Lefty, Righty, Glory
8 Splash
14 Ringo
15 Blackie
19 Grunt
20 Weenie
23 Fuzz
31 Scorch

August
1 Garcia, Mooch
9 Hoot
12 Iggy
13 Spike
14 Speedy
16 Kicks
17 Bongo
23 Digger
27 Sting
28 Pounce
31 Halo

September
3 Inch, Claude
5 Magic
8 Tiny
9 Bruno
12 Sly
16 Kiwi, Derby
18 Tusk
21 Stretch
27 Roam
29 Stinger

October
1 Smoochy
2 Butch
3 Bernie, Germania

9 Doby
10 Jabber
12 Tuffy
14 Rainbow
17 Dotty
22 Snip
28 Spinner
29 Batty
30 Radar
31 Pumkin, Spooky, Sheets

November
3 Puffer
4 Goatee
6 Pouch
7 Ants
9 Congo
14 Cubbie, Goldie
18 Goochy
20 Prance
21 Nanook
27 Gobbles
28 Teddy Brown (new)
29 Inky

December
2 Jolly
6 Fortune, Santa
8 Waves
12 Blizzard
14 Seamore
15 Britannia
16 Velvet
19 Waddle
21 Echo
22 Snowball
24 Ziggy
25 1997 Holiday Teddy,
   1998 Holiday Teddy,
   1999 Holiday Teddy

BBB Notes

BBB Notes

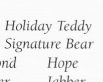
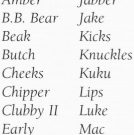

12/31/99 Retireds

Place behind this tab the
following 58 Beanie Babies®:

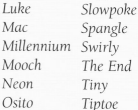

1999 Holiday Teddy
1999 Signature Bear

Almond	Hope	Scaly
Amber	Jabber	Scat
B.B. Bear	Jake	Schweetheart
Beak	Kicks	Scorch
Butch	Knuckles	Sheets
Cheeks	Kuku	Silver
Chipper	Lips	Slippery
Clubby II	Luke	Slowpoke
Early	Mac	Spangle
Eucalyptus	Millennium	Swirly
Flitter	Mooch	The End
Fuzz	Neon	Tiny
Germania	Osito	Tiptoe
Gigi	Paul	Tracker
Goatee	Pecan	Ty2K
Goochy	Prickles	Valentina
Groovy	Roam	Wallace
Halo	Rocket	Whisper
Honks	Sammy	

Beanie Baby™ Binder
Final Millennial Update Pak

Table of Contents & Instructions

New tab
(1) 12/31/99 Retireds
Place this tab (and the pages listed on the tab) in front of your "Summer '99 Retireds" tab; now that all the Beanie Babies® are officially retired, you may discard your "New Releases" and "Currents" tabs.

10 New Release Beanie Babies® pages
(listed alphabetically)
(1) 1999 Holiday Teddy™
(2) Chipper™
(3) Groovy™
(4) Honks™
(5) Scaly™
(6) Sheets™
(7) Slowpoke™
(8) The End™
(9) Ty2K™
(10) Wallace™
Because these New Release Beanie Babies® also retired 12/31/99, place them behind the "12/31/99 Retireds" tab, in the order listed on the front of that tab.

8 New Release Beanie Buddies® pages

(1) Amber™	(2) Fetch™
(3) Gobbles™	(4) Halo™
(5) Peace™	(6) Pumkin™
(7) Silver™	(8) Slither™
(9) Snowboy™	(10) Spangle™
(11) Spinner™	(12) Clubby™
(13) Clubby II™	(14) Britannia™
(15) Maple	

Place these 8 pages behind the "Teenies & Buddies" tab, after all the other "Teenies" and "Buddies" pages.

Lists

You will note that your "Summer '99 Update Pak" included all the lists, updated through 12/31/99; hence, there are no lists included in this package.

This is it!

With this Final Millennial Update Pak, you now have a full page on every Ty® Beanie Baby™ ever released and retired from 6/25/94 through 12/31/99, making this the most complete Beanie Baby™ book ever.

Along with your now fully retired Beanie Baby™ collection, which will surely escalate in value, your now complete "My Beanie Baby™ Binder" will also escalate in value. Take good care of both. And thank you for your business!

Peg et. al.
"My Beanie Baby™ Binder"
Vine Street Publishing, Inc.
Box 97
Orem, UT 84059
(801) 222-9670; 9680 fax
pegfugal@aol.com
www.mybeaniebabybinder.com

"My Beanie Baby™ Binder"
Final Millennial Update Pak
Order Form

_____ "My Beanie Baby™ Binder/Final Millennial Edition"   ~~$29.95 + s/h~~
Special price for Auto-Ship customers only   **$24.95 + s/h**
You already own and use "Beanie Baby™ Binder". If you are an Auto-Ship customer, then you will automatically receive all the Update Paks you need to complete your binder. You may also want to own a clean, unused copy of the "Final Millennial Edition" of "My Beanie Baby™ Binder", which contains every Beanie Baby™ ever released and retired from 6/25/94 thru 12/31/99, and which will surely escalate in value along with your Beanie Baby™ collection. Please indicate in the space provided how many copies you want.

_____ **Empty "Beanie Baby™" binder**   **$10.00 + s/h**
If your original "Beanie Baby™ Binder" is getting full, you might want to buy an extra empty binder, and divide your tabs and pages between the two. Please indicate in the space provided how many empty binders you want.

Name: _____

Address: _____

City/State/Zip: _____

Phone/fax/email: _____

❏ Bill me (I agree to mail a check immediately upon receipt of my order.)

❏ Charge my charge card (My charge card is current and has credit.)
        ❏ American Express   ❏ Mastercard   ❏ Visa

Name on charge card _____

Charge card number _____ Exp. date _____

Authorized signature _____

Mail this order form to: **Or fax to:**   **Or order via our website:**
Vine Street   (801) 222-9680   www.mybeaniebabybinder.com
Box 97
Orem, UT 84059

1999 Holiday Teddy™

Type: Bear   **Categories:** Bear, blue, holiday   **Style no.:** 4257

Birthday: December 25, 1999   **Released:** 8/31/99   **Retired:** 12/31/99

Position: Sitting up   **Tags:** 5th/7th

Description: Body of baby blue plush w/ white snowflakes, scarf of darker blue plush w/ white snowflakes & white tassles tied around neck, black plastic eyes & nose, hang tag left ear, tush tag left bottom

Replaces: 1997 Holiday Teddy™, 1998 Holiday Teddy™

Variations: Pattern of snowflakes

Oddities: No gender indicated, released four months prior to birth, shares birthday w/ 1997 Holiday Teddy™ & 1998 Holiday Teddy™

Commentary: In circulation only four months before retiring, making it one of the shortest-lived Beanie Babies® ever, hence, hard to find & pricey; baby blue color makes it one of the prettiest Beanie Babies® ever; the prettiest of the holiday teddies; one of five bears this release

Poem: Peace on earth as the holidays grow near
The season is all about giving good cheer
With love and joy in your hearts
Let's all be friends as the century starts!™

My record

(Beanies are the #1 collectible in American collecting history. A complete, detailed record will vastly increase the value of this Beanie, if & when you ever appraise, trade, re-sell, gift, or bequeath it.)

Description *(which version do you have?):*

Gift from:

Date received/purchased:

Purchased from:

NAME OF PERSON OR RETAILER

ADDRESS

CITY/STATE/ZIP

PHONE

Qty. purchased: **Cost ea.**
(check one)   ❏ *Cash*   ❏ *Check*   ❏ *Charge*

Reason(s) for purchase(s):

Traded to:

NAME

ADDRESS

CITY/STATE/ZIP

PHONE

TRADED FOR

Re-sold to:

NAME

ADDRESS

CITY/STATE/ZIP

PHONE

PRICE RE-SOLD FOR

Your feelings about &/or experiences w/ this Beanie:

Chipper™

Type:	Chipmunk *Categories:* Brown, woodland *Style no.:* 4259
Birthday:	April 21, 1999 *Released:* 8/31/99 *Retired:* 12/31/99
Position:	Scampering *Tags:* 5th/7th
Description:	Brown-gray heather plush body w/ black & cream plush stripes on each side; cream chin, belly & inner ears; big, brown, hairy, bushy tail; black plastic eyes surrounded by white felt; black thread whiskers, nose & mouth; hang tag left ear; tush tag left bottom
Replaces:	None
Variations:	Heather coloring varies
Oddities:	No gender indicated; poem in first person
Commentary:	Released four months after birth; in circulation only four months before retiring, making it one of the shortest-lived Beanie Babies® ever, hence, hard to find & pricey; one of the most detailed and realistic Beanie Babies® ever; one of two heather Beanie Babies® this release; companion to Nuts™ the squirrel
Poem:	I'm quick, I'm fast, I don't make a peep But I love to snuggle when I sleep Take me along when you go play And I'll make sure you have a nice day!™

My record

(Beanies are the #1 collectible in American collecting history. A complete, detailed record will vastly increase the value of this Beanie, if & when you ever appraise, trade, re-sell, gift, or bequeath it.)

Description *(which version do you have?):*

Gift from:

Date received/purchased:

Purchased from:

NAME OF PERSON OR RETAILER

ADDRESS

CITY/STATE/ZIP

PHONE

Qty. purchased: **Cost ea.**
(check one)   ❏ *Cash*   ❏ *Check*   ❏ *Charge*

Reason(s) for purchase(s):

Traded to:

NAME

ADDRESS

CITY/STATE/ZIP

PHONE

TRADED FOR

Re-sold to:

NAME

ADDRESS

CITY/STATE/ZIP

PHONE

PRICE RE-SOLD FOR

Your feelings about &/or experiences w/ this Beanie:

Groovy™

Type:	Bear **Categories:** Bear, napped, ty-dyed **Style no.:** 4256
Birthday:	January 10, 1999 **Released:** 8/31/99 **Retired:** 12/31/99
Position:	Sitting up Tags: 5th/7th
Description:	Napped, pastel ty-dyed plush body; purple plush nose; black plastic eyes; multi pastel satin ribbon tied around neck; hang tag left ear; tush tag left bottom
Replaces:	Garcia™, Peace™
Variations:	Ty-dye varies in colors
Oddities:	No gender indicated; poem in first person; only Beanie Baby™ bear w/ colored, plush nose
Commentary:	Released more than seven months after birth; in circulation only four months before retiring, making it one of the shortest-lived Beanie Babies® ever, hence, hard to find & pricey; fourth napped & sixth ty-dyed bear; first napped & ty-dyed bear; one of five bears this release
Poem:	Wearing colors of the rainbow Making good friends wherever I go Take me with you, don't let me stray I need your love all night and day!™

My record

(Beanies are the #1 collectible in American collecting history. A complete, detailed record will vastly increase the value of this Beanie, ifand when you ever appraise, trade, re-sell, gift, or bequeath it.)

Description *(which version do you have?)*:

Gift from:

Date received/purchased:

Purchased from:

NAME OF PERSON OR RETAILER

ADDRESS

CITY/STATE/ZIP

PHONE

Qty. purchased: **Cost ea.**
(check one)   ❑ *Cash*   ❑ *Check*   ❑ *Charge*

Reason(s) for purchase(s):

Traded to:

NAME

ADDRESS

CITY/STATE/ZIP

PHONE

TRADED FOR

Re-sold to:

NAME

ADDRESS

CITY/STATE/ZIP

PHONE

PRICE RE-SOLD FOR

Your feelings about &/or experiences w/ this Beanie:

Honks™

Type: Male gander **Categories:** Bird, goose, gray **Style no.:** 4258

Birthday: March 11, 1999 **Released:** 8/31/99 **Retired:** 12/31/99

Position: Squatting **Tags:** 5th/7th

Description: Gray-white patterned plush body, orange plush bill w/ thread detailing, orange felt webbed feet, three-pronged tail, black plastic eyes, black thread nostrils, hang tag left wing, tush tag left bottom

Replaces: Loosy™

Variations: None

Oddities: New patterned fabric, similar to Scaly™ the lizard

Commentary: Released five months after birth; in circulation only four months before retiring, making it one of the shortest-lived Beanie Babies® ever, hence, hard to find & pricey; one of two Beanie Babies® this release in new patterned fabric; companion to Loosy™ the female Canadian geese

Poem: Honks the goose likes to fly away
South for the Winter he will stay
When Spring comes back, North he will fly
And swim in ponds and lakes nearby!™

My record

(Beanies are the #1 collectible in American collecting history. A complete, detailed record will vastly increase the value of this Beanie, if & when you ever appraise, trade, re-sell, gift, or bequeath it.)

Description *(which version do you have?):*

Gift from:

Date received/purchased:

Purchased from:

NAME OF PERSON OR RETAILER

ADDRESS

CITY/STATE/ZIP

PHONE

Qty. purchased: **Cost ea.**
(check one)   ❏ *Cash*   ❏ *Check*   ❏ *Charge*

Reason(s) for purchase(s):

Traded to:

NAME

ADDRESS

CITY/STATE/ZIP

PHONE

TRADED FOR

Re-sold to:

NAME

ADDRESS

CITY/STATE/ZIP

PHONE

PRICE RE-SOLD FOR

Your feelings about &/or experiences w/ this Beanie:

Scaly™

Type: Lizard   **Categories:** Lizard, patterned, reptile   **Style no.:** 4263

Birthday: February 9, 1999   **Released:** 8/31/99   **Retired:** 12/31/99

Position: Crawling   **Tags:** 5th/7th

Description: Gold-teal patterned plush body, gold plastic eyes w/ black slit pupil, red velveteen forked tongue, red thread nostrils, webbed feet, long tail, hang tag left front foot, tush tag left tail

Replaces: Lizzy™ the ty-dyed lizard, Lizzy™ the blue lizard

Variations: None

Oddities: No gender indicated; poem in first person; new patterned fabric, similar to Honks™ the goose

Commentary: Released more than six months after birth; in circulation only four months before retiring, making it one of the shortest-lived Beanie Babies® ever, hence, hard to find & pricey; one of two Beanie Babies® this release in new patterned fabric; companion to Lizzy™

Poem: I love to lie, basking in the sun
Living in the desert sure is fun
Climbing up cactus, avoiding a spike
I'm the Beanie you're sure to like!™

My record

(Beanies are the #1 collectible in American collecting history. A complete, detailed record will vastly increase the value of this Beanie, if & when you ever appraise, trade, re-sell, gift, or bequeath it.)

Description *(which version do you have?)*:

Gift from:

Date received/purchased:

Purchased from:

NAME OF PERSON OR RETAILER

ADDRESS

CITY/STATE/ZIP

PHONE

Qty. purchased: **Cost ea.**
(check one)   ❏ *Cash*   ❏ *Check*   ❏ *Charge*

Reason(s) for purchase(s):

Traded to:

NAME

ADDRESS

CITY/STATE/ZIP

PHONE

TRADED FOR

Re-sold to:

NAME

ADDRESS

CITY/STATE/ZIP

PHONE

PRICE RE-SOLD FOR

Your feelings about &/or experiences w/ this Beanie:

Sheets™

Type: Ghost   **Categories:** Halloween, holiday, white   **Style no.:** 4260

Birthday: October 31, 1999   **Released:** 8/31/99   **Retired:** 12/31/99

Position: Flying   **Tags:** 5th/7th

Description: White plush body; black felt attached eyes & nose; wearing white plush sheet w/ a sheen, attached at neck; hang tag left arm; tush tag left side

Replaces: Spooky™

Variations: Attached facial features

Oddities: Released two months prior to birth; no gender indicated; one of few Beanies w/ clothing; ghosts don't wear sheets: people wear sheets to look like ghosts! Shares birthday w/ Pumpkin™ & Spooky™

Commentary: In circulation only four months before retiring, making it one of the shortest-lived Beanie Babies® ever, hence, hard to find & pricey; one of several Halloween Beanie Babies®; popular Halloween decoration/gift; companion to Spooky™ the ghost

Poem: Living alone in a haunted house
Friend to the spider, bat and mouse
Often heard, but never seen
Waiting to wish you "Happy Halloween!"™

My record

(Beanies are the #1 collectible in American collecting history. A complete, detailed record will vastly increase the value of this Beanie, if & when you ever appraise, trade, re-sell, gift, or bequeath it.)

Description *(which version do you have?):*

Gift from:

Date received/purchased:

Purchased from:

NAME OF PERSON OR RETAILER

ADDRESS

CITY/STATE/ZIP

PHONE

Qty. purchased: **Cost ea.**
(check one)   ❏ *Cash*   ❏ *Check*   ❏ *Charge*

Reason(s) for purchase(s):

Traded to:

NAME

ADDRESS

CITY/STATE/ZIP

PHONE

TRADED FOR

Re-sold to:

NAME

ADDRESS

CITY/STATE/ZIP

PHONE

PRICE RE-SOLD FOR

Your feelings about &/or experiences w/ this Beanie:

Slowpoke™

Type:	Sloth **Categories:** Aussie, brown, heather **Style no.:** 4261
Birthday:	May 20, 1999 **Released:** 8/31/99 **Retired:** 12/31/99
Position:	Hanging **Tags:** 5th/7th
Description:	Black-brown heather plush body; cream plush face; tan plush snout; black plastic eyes; tan plush "bags" under eyes; gray plush, two-toed hands & feet; black, matte, textured, detailed nose; black thread mouth; stubby tail; hang tag left hand; tush tag left bottom
Replaces:	None
Variations:	Heather coloring varies
Oddities:	No gender indicated; sloths have three toes, not two; odd choice for Beanie Baby™
Commentary:	Released three months after birth; in circulation only four months before retiring, making it one of the shortest-lived Beanie Babies® ever, hence, hard to find & pricey; one of few Australian Beanie Babies®; one of two heather Beanie Babies® this release; one of the most detailed Beanie Baby™ faces ever
Poem:	Look up in the sky to the top of the tree What in the world is that you see? A little sloth as sweet as can be Munching on leaves very slowly!™

My record

(Beanies are the #1 collectible in American collecting history. A complete, detailed record will vastly increase the value of this Beanie, if & when you ever appraise, trade, re-sell, gift, or bequeath it.)

Description *(which version do you have?):*

Gift from:

Date received/purchased:

Purchased from:

NAME OF PERSON OR RETAILER
ADDRESS
CITY/STATE/ZIP
PHONE

Qty. purchased: **Cost ea.**
(check one)   ❏ *Cash*   ❏ *Check*   ❏ *Charge*

Reason(s) for purchase(s):

Traded to:

NAME
ADDRESS
CITY/STATE/ZIP
PHONE
TRADED FOR

Re-sold to:

NAME
ADDRESS
CITY/STATE/ZIP
PHONE
PRICE RE-SOLD FOR

Your feelings about &/or experiences w/ this Beanie:

The End™

Type: Bear   **Categories:** Bear, black   **Style no.:** 4265

Birthday: None   **Released:** 8/31/99   **Retired:** 12/31/99

Position: Sitting up   **Tags:** 5th/7th

Description: Black plush body; "The End" in gold metallic thread & fireworks burst in multi thread embroidered over heart; gold metallic bow-tie attached to gold satin ribbon, tied around neck; black plastic eyes & nose; hang tag left ear; tush tag left bottom

Replaces: Blackie™

Variations: None

Oddities: Neither gender nor birthday indicated; birthday replaced by "dash dot dash dot dash"

Commentary: In circulation only four months before retiring, making it one of the shortest-lived Beanie Babies® ever, hence, hard to find & pricey; signifies "The End" of Beanie Babies®; only second black bear; companion to Blackie™ the lay-down bear; one of five bears this release

Poem: All good things come to an end
It's been fun for everyone
Peace and hope are never gone
Love you all and say, "So long!"™

My record

(Beanies are the #1 collectible in American collecting history. A complete, detailed record will vastly increase the value of this Beanie, if & when you ever appraise, trade, re-sell, gift, or bequeath it.)

Description *(which version do you have?):*

Gift from:

Date received/purchased:

Purchased from:

NAME OF PERSON OR RETAILER

ADDRESS

CITY/STATE/ZIP

PHONE

Qty. purchased: **Cost ea.**
(check one)   ❑ *Cash*   ❑ *Check*   ❑ *Charge*

Reason(s) for purchase(s):

Traded to:

NAME

ADDRESS

CITY/STATE/ZIP

PHONE

TRADED FOR

Re-sold to:

NAME

ADDRESS

CITY/STATE/ZIP

PHONE

PRICE RE-SOLD FOR

Your feelings about &/or experiences w/ this Beanie:

Ty2k™

Type: Bear   **Categories:** Bears, multi   **Style no.:** 4262

Birthday: January 1, 2000   **Released:** 8/31/99   **Retired:** 12/31/99

Position: Sitting up   **Tags:** 5th/7th

Description: Body of white plush dotted w/ mutli-colored confetti, multi-colored sheer ribbon w/ edging of gold metallic thread & multi bows attached at neck, black plastic eyes & nose, hang tag left ear, tush tag left bottom

Replaces: None

Variations: Pattern of confetti, color variations in ribbon

Oddities: No gender indicated, only Beanie Baby™ with a birthdate in the new millennium, released four months prior to birth, shares birthday w/ Millennium™ & Spot™

Commentary: In circulation only four months before retiring, making it one of the shortest-lived Beanie Babies® ever, hence, hard to find & pricey; commemorates dreaded Y2K; one of the most colorful Beanie Babies™ & Beanie Baby™ bears ever; one of five bears this release

Poem:
Red, yellow, green and blue
Let's have some fun me and you
So join the party, and let's all say
"Happy New Millennium," from Ty 2K!™

My record

(Beanies are the #1 collectible in American collecting history. A complete, detailed record will vastly increase the value of this Beanie, if & when you ever appraise, trade, re-sell, gift, or bequeath it.)

Description *(which version do you have?):*

Gift from:

Date received/purchased:

Purchased from:

NAME OF PERSON OR RETAILER

ADDRESS

CITY/STATE/ZIP

PHONE

Qty. purchased: **Cost ea.**
(check one)   ❏ *Cash*   ❏ *Check*   ❏ *Charge*

Reason(s) for purchase(s):

Traded to:

NAME

ADDRESS

CITY/STATE/ZIP

PHONE

TRADED FOR

Re-sold to:

NAME

ADDRESS

CITY/STATE/ZIP

PHONE

PRICE RE-SOLD FOR

Your feelings about &/or experiences w/ this Beanie:

Wallace™

Type: Bear **Categories:** Bear, green, ty-dyed **Style no.:** 4264

Birthday: January 25, 1999 **Released:** 8/31/99 **Retired:** 12/31/99

Position: Sitting up **Tags:** 5th/7th

Description: Body of napped, lighter green-darker green ty-dyed plush; tartan red, green & white wool scarf w/ red tassles wrapped around neck; black plastic eyes & nose; hang tag left ear; tush tag left bottom

Replaces: Erin™

Variations: Ty-dye varies in colors

Oddities: No gender indicated, ty-dye barely perceptible, shares birthday w/ Peanut™

Commentary: Released seven months after birth; in circulation only four months before retiring, making it one of the shortest-lived Beanie Babies® ever, hence, hard to find & pricey; fifth napped bear; seventh ty-dyed bear; second napped & ty-dyed bear; sixth international bear; one of five bears this release; companion to Erin™ the Irish bear

Poem: Castles rise from misty glens
Shielding bands of warrior men
Wearing tartan of their clan
Red, green and a little tan!™

My record

(Beanies are the #1 collectible in American collecting history. A complete, detailed record will vastly increase the value of this Beanie, if & when you ever appraise, trade, re-sell, gift, or bequeath it.)

Description *(which version do you have?):*

Gift from:

Date received/purchased:

Purchased from:

NAME OF PERSON OR RETAILER
ADDRESS
CITY/STATE/ZIP
PHONE

Qty. purchased: **Cost ea.**
(check one)   ❏ *Cash*   ❏ *Check*   ❏ *Charge*

Reason(s) for purchase(s):

Traded to:

NAME
ADDRESS
CITY/STATE/ZIP
PHONE
TRADED FOR

Re-sold to:

NAME
ADDRESS
CITY/STATE/ZIP
PHONE
PRICE RE-SOLD FOR

Your feelings about &/or experiences w/ this Beanie:

Buddies®

8/31/99

The fifth set of 11 Beanie Buddies® were announced 8/31/99, along with the final set of 10 Beanie Babies®. Though Ty® Inc. announced on that same date the retirement of all Beanie Babies® as of 12/31/99, there was no mention of retiring Beanie Buddies®.

There are 4 additional Beanie Buddies®, related to this release, but not pictured here: Britannia™ and Maple™, which are exclusive foreign releases, and Clubby™ and Clubby II™, which are exclusive BBOC releases. They appear on separate pages.

The aforementioned 15 Beanie Buddies® bring the total number of Beanie Buddies® released to date to 45, with only 4 retired to date (Twigs™, Beak™, Quackers™, and Patti™), leaving 41 total Beanie Buddies® in circulation as of this printing.

This release of Beanie Buddies® is unique in that it includes the first holiday Beanie Buddies®: Gobbles™, Pumkin™, Snowboy™, and Spinner™.

What makes this release even more unique is that Snowboy™ has no Beanie Baby™ predecessor—the only Beanie Buddy™ with that distinction.

It seems odd that Ty® would released both Gobbles™ and Spinner™ as Beanie Buddies® when they didn't appear to sell that well as Beanie Babies®, but Ty® knows numbers we do not.

It seems equally odd to release Pumkin™ as a Beanie Buddy™ when it had been in circulation less than three months as a Beanie Baby™ before retiring.

Three of these 11 pictured Beanie Buddies® (Amber™, Silver™, and

Spangle™) were released as Beanie Babies® just four months prior to being released as Beanie Buddies®—a record for Ty®!

Six of these 11 pictured Beanie Buddies® (Fetch™, Gobbles™, Peace™, Pumkin™, Slither™, and Spinner™) were retired as Beanie Babies® before they were released as Beanie Buddies®.

Four of these 11 pictured Beanie Buddies® (Amber™, Halo™, Silver™, and Spangle™) were in circulation as Beanie Babies® when they were released as Beanie Buddies®.

One of these 11 pictured Beanie Buddies® (Snowboy™) never existed as a Beanie Baby™.

None of these 11 pictured Beanie Buddies® ever made an appearance as a Teenie Beanie Baby™.

Like all previous Beanie Buddies®, these Beanie Buddies® are all made of Ty®'s own super-plush fabric, Tylon®.

(1) Amber™ the gold-striped cat

Amber™, the gold-striped Beanie Baby™ cat, was originally released 4/20/99, and remained in circulation until the final 12/31/99 retirement. Because Amber™ represents a new style of cats for Ty®—one that can stand up on its legs or sit up on its haunches (as opposed to the previous lay-down cats)—it is right that Amber™ be selected as a Beanie Buddy™. Identical to its Beanie™, Amber™ the Buddy™ is as sweet and cuddly as a kitty should be, especially in companionship with its twin Buddy™, Silver™.

Date & place purchased_____Amt. pd._____

(2) Fetch™ the golden lab

Fetch™, the golden lab Beanie Baby™ dog, was originally released 5/30/98 and retired 12/2/98. Fetch™ the Buddy™ is much cuter than Fetch™ the Beanie™ because it is more detailed. While the Beanie™ has simple black plastic eyes and nose, the Buddy™ has more life-like eyes and nose, as well as plush paw pads with thread detailing. While the Beanie™ is a lay-down dog, the Buddy™ can stand up on its legs or sit up on its haunches. Fetch™ is one of the cutest Beanie Buddies® this release.

Date & place purchased_____Amt. pd._____

(3) Gobbles™ the turkey

Gobbles™, the multi-colored Beanie Baby™ turkey, was originally released 10/1/97 and retired 3/31/99. One of four holiday Beanie Buddies® this release, Gobbles™ the Buddy™ is as colorful and detailed as Gobbles™ the Beanie™. The only difference between the two is their eyes: while the Beanie™ has black plastic eyes, the Buddy™ has eyes ringed in red.

Date & place purchased_____Amt. pd._____

(4) Halo™ the angel bear

Halo™, the white Beanie Baby™ angel bear, was originally released 9/30/98, and remained in circulation until the final 12/31/99 retirement. Halo™ the Buddy™ is identical to its Beanie™, with two exceptions: the Buddy™ has pink paw pads, and black plastic eyes, ringed with rust. One of the most beautiful and popular Beanies™ ever, Halo™ is the perfect candidate for Buddy™-dom.

Date & place purchased_____Amt. pd._____

(5) Peace™ the ty-dyed bear

Peace™, the multi-colored, ty-dyed Beanie Baby™ bear, was originally released 5/11/97 and retired 7/16/99. One of the most popular, and long-running Beanie Baby™ bears ever, it seems only right that Peace™ also make an appearance as a Beanie Buddy™. Peace™ the Buddy™ is identical to its Beanie™, with two exceptions: the Buddy™ has pastel plush paw pads, and black plastic eyes, ringed with rust. Though the ty-dye on Peace™ the Beanie™ "works", the ty-dye on the super-plush Buddy™ does not: Tylon® is better suited to solid colors.

Date & place purchased_____Amt. pd._____

(6) Pumkin™ the pumpkin

Pumkin™, the orange Beanie Baby™ pumpkin with green arms and legs, was originally released 9/30/98 and retired 12/4/98. One of four holiday Beanie Buddies® this release, Pumkin™ the Buddy™ is as colorful and detailed as Pumkin™ the Beanie™. Unlike the Beanie™, the Buddy™ has a super-plush body. Like its Beanie™, the Buddy™ has plush arms and legs.

Date & place purchased_____Amt. pd._____

(7) Silver™ the silver-striped cat

Silver™, the silver-striped Beanie Baby™ cat, was originally released 4/21/99, and remained in circulation until the final 12/31/99 retirement. Like Amber™, Silver™ represents a new style of cat, that can both stand up and sit up. Like Amber™, Silver™ is identical to its Beanie™. Twins, Amber™ and Silver™ create the first matched set of Beanie Buddies® to date.

Date & place purchased_____Amt. pd._____

(8) Slither™ the snake

Slither™, the multi-colored Beanie Baby™ snake, was originally released 6/25/99 and retired 6/15/95, making it not only one of the oldest Beanie Babies®, but also one of the oldest Beanie Babies® to reappear as a Beanie Buddy™. Slither™ the Buddy™ is identical to its Beanie™, with two exceptions: the Buddy™ has an elastic spine that coils, as well as gold plastic eyes with black slit pupils.

Date & place purchased_____Amt. pd._____

(9) Snowboy™ the snowboy

Snowboy™ the white Beanie Buddy™ snowboy, has no Beanie Baby™ counter-part. The closest relative would be Snowball™, the Beanie Baby™ snowman, originally released 10/1/97 and retired 12/31/97. Unlike Snowball™who has only arms, Snowboy™ has both arms and legs. Unlike Snowball™ who has a felt hat and scarf, Snowboy™ has a detailed, knitted cap and scarf. Snowboy™ also has black plastic eyes, ringed with rust; a big, red, velveteen nose; a red, braided yarn mouth; and plush white paw pads.

Date & place purchased_____Amt. pd._____

(10) Spangle™ the patriotic bear

Spangle™, the red, white, and blue patriotic Beanie Baby™ bear, was originally released 4/24/99 and remained in circulation until the final 12/31/99 retirement. One of only three patriotic Beanie Baby™ bears (including Libearty™ and Glory™), and the cutest of the three with its patriotic pj's, Spangle™ was an obvious choice as a Beanie Buddy™. The only difference between the Beanie™ and the Buddy™ is the eyes: the Buddy™ has black plastic eyes, ringed with rust.

Date & place purchased_____Amt. pd._____

(11) Spinner™ the spider

Spinner™, the black and brown-striped Beanie Baby™ spider, was originally released 10/1/97 and retired 9/19/98. While Spinner™ the Beanie™ has red thread eyes (the only Beanie™ with thread eyes), Spinner™ the Buddy™ has black plastic eyes, ringed with red. Unlike its Beanie™, the Buddy™ has a super-plush body. Like its Beanie™, the Buddy™ has plush legs.

Date & place purchased_____Amt. pd._____

Buddies®

Summer '99 — special BBOC release

Summer '98, Ty® released the first Beanie Baby™ Official Club (BBOC) kit—a paper briefcase with documents and a gold membership card inside. Using the forms inside, purchasers of the kit could register as a charter club member and order a special royal blue Clubby™ Beanie Baby™ bear— which they did in droves. Ty™ retired Clubby™ on 2/15/99, and stopped taking orders on 3/15/99.

Spring '99, Ty® released the second BBOC kit—a clear plastic briefcase with documents, a platinum membership card, a Beanie Baby™ coin, Beanie Baby™ trading cards, and an orchid heather Clubby II™ Beanie Baby™ bear inside.

Summer '99, Ty® announced a special release of two Beanie Buddies®— Clubby™ and Clubby II™—available exclusively to BBOC members via the BBOC website.

To order, BBOC members had to enter the BBOC website and, using their BBOC gold and/or platinum membership card numbers, order the two Buddies®. Charter gold card BBOC members were allowed to order both Clubby™ and Clubby II™, while later platinum card BBOC members were allowed to order only Clubby II™.

Many weeks later, during the fall of '99, the two Clubby™ Buddies® started arriving in plain brown boxes. (Had the contents been obvious, they might have been stolen!)

Both Clubby™ Buddies® are made of Ty®'s own super plush Tylon™.

Clubby™

Clubby™ the Beanie Baby™ bear was originally released the summer of '98 and retired the following winter on 2/15/99. Clubby™ the Beanie Buddy™ bear was released the summer of '99. Clubby™ the Beanie and Clubby™ the Buddy™ are identical in every way, except, Clubby™ the Buddy™ has plush paw pads. Because both the Beanie and the Buddy™ were in such limited circulation, both are hard to find and pricey.

Date & place purchased_____Amt. pd._____

Clubby II™

Clubby II™ the Beanie Baby™ bear was originally released the spring of '99 and retired, along with all the other Beanie Babies®, on 12/31/99. Clubby II™ the Beanie Buddy™ bear was released the summer of '99. Clubby II™ the Beanie and Clubby II™ the Buddy™ are identical in every way, except, Clubby II™ the Buddy™ has plush paw pads. Because both the Beanie and the Buddy™ were in such limited circulation, both are hard to find and pricey.

Date & place purchased_____Amt. pd._____

Buddies®

When on 8/31/99, Ty® announced the last 10 Beanie Babies®, as well as the retirement of all Beanie Babies® on 12/31/99, they also announced 13 new Beanie Buddies®—two of which were the first exclusively foreign release Beanie Buddies®—Britannia™, the Beanie Buddy™ bear, a United Kingdom exclusive, and Maple™, the Beanie Buddy™ bear, a Canadian exclusive.

Because they are exclusively foreign releases, the chances of either Britannia™ the Buddy™ or Maple™ the Buddy™ making their way to American collectors are slim to none.

Both foreign Buddies® are made of Ty®'s own super plush Tylon™.

Britannia™

Britannia™ the Beanie Baby™ bear was originally released 12/31/97 and retired 19 months later on 7/26/99. Also a foreign exclusive, it was many months before Britannia™ the Beanie Baby™ bear made its way to America, and many more months before it was available at a reasonable price. Britannia™ the Beanie Buddy™ bear was released 8/31/99. It has yet to make it to America. Both Britannia™ the Beanie and Britannia™ the Buddy™ are identical, except, Britannia™ the Buddy™ has plush paw pads. Because both the Beanie and the Buddy™ were/are in such limited circulation, both will be forever hard to find and pricey.

Date & place purchased_____Amt. pd._____

Maple™

Maple™ the Beanie Baby™ bear was originally released 1/1/97 and retired 31 months later, making it one of the longest-running Beanie Babies® ever. Also a foreign exclusive, Maple™ the Beanie was never readily available in America, and sold for hundreds of dollars on the secondary market. Maple™ the Beanie Buddy™ bear was released 8/31/99. It has yet to make it to America. Both Maple™ the Beanie and Maple™ the Buddy™ are identical, except, Maple™ the Buddy™ has plush paw pads. Because both the Beanie and the Buddy™ were/are in such limited circulation, both will be forever hard to find and pricey.

Date & place purchased_____Amt. pd._____

12/98 Retireds

Place behind this tab
the following Beanie Babies®:

12/1
1998 Holiday Teddy ✓
Santa ✓
Zero

12/2
Fetch
Scoop
Stinger

12/3
Valentino

12/4
Claude
Pumkin
Wise

12/5
Ants
Doby
Dotty
Nuts ✓
Tuffy

12/6
Curly

12/7
Fleece ✓
Snip

12/8
Congo
Pinky ✓
Spike

12/9
Bongo
Freckles

12/10
Chocolate
Glory
Roary

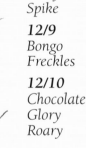

1998 Holiday Teddy™

✓ Retired

Type:	Male bear	**Categories:** Bear, holiday		**Style no.:** 4204

Birthday: December 25, 1998   **Released:** 9/30/98   **Retired:** 12/1/98

Position: Sitting up   **Tags:** 5th generation   **Teenie:**

Description: White plush body w/ green holly leaves & red berries silk-screened on fabric, cap over right ear in same fabric w/ red trim and ball, bell in cap, double red & green satin ribbon tied around neck, black plastic eyes & nose, hang tag left ear, tush tag left bottom.

Replaces: 1997 Holiday Teddy, style no. 4200, birthday 12/25/96, released 10/1/97, retired 12/31/97, hard to find & expensive

Variations: None

Oddities: Released three months before birth; one of only two Beanies with silk-screened pattern on fabric; only Beanie with sound (ringing bell in end of cap); first Beanie with double ribbon

Commentary: In circulation only three months before retiring; because it is both a bear & a holiday Beanie with such a short lifespan, it will sky-rocket in popularity & value

Poem: Dressed in his PJ's and ready for bed
Hugs given, good nights said
This little Beanie will stay close at night
Ready for a hug at first morning light!™

My record

(Beanies are the #1 collectible in American collecting history. A complete, detailed record will vastly increase the value of this Beanie, if and when you ever appraise, trade, re-sell, gift, or bequeath it.)

Description *(which version do you have?):*

Gift from:

Date received/purchased:

Purchased from: A R Inc   Gift Shop

NAME OF PERSON OR RETAILER

ADDRESS

CITY/STATE/ZIP

PHONE

Qty. purchased: **Cost ea.**
(check one) ❑ *Cash* ❑ *Check* ❑ *Charge*

Reason(s) for purchase(s):

Traded to:

NAME

ADDRESS

CITY/STATE/ZIP

PHONE

TRADED FOR

Re-sold to:

NAME

ADDRESS

CITY/STATE/ZIP

PHONE

PRICE RE-SOLD FOR

Your feelings about and/or experiences with this Beanie:

Santa™

Type: Male Santa   **Categories:** Holiday, red   **Style no.:** 4203

Birthday: December 6, 1998   **Released:** 9/30/98   **Retired:** 12/1/98

Position: Standing   **Tags:** 5th generation   **Teenie:**

Description: Traditional Santa in red plush suit w/ white trim, green mittens & black boots; black felt belt w/ white felt buckle; cream plush face w/ black plastic eyes, red plush nose, white felt mustache & white hairy beard; hang tag left hand; tush tag left bottom

Replaces: None

Variations: None

Oddities: Released three months before birth

Commentary: In circulation only three months before retiring, making it one of the shortest-lived Beanies ever; first human Beanie; popular Christmas decoration/gift; like all holiday Beanies, will escalate in popularity & value

Poem: Known by all in his suit of red
Piles of presents on his sled
Generous and giving, he brings us joy
Peace and love, plus this special toy!™

2

My record

(Beanies are the #1 collectible in American collecting history. A complete, detailed record will vastly increase the value of this Beanie, if and when you ever appraise, trade, re-sell, gift, or bequeath it.)

Description (which version do you have?):

Gift from:

Date received/purchased:

Purchased from: *A R m a Gift Shop*

NAME OF PERSON OR RETAILER

ADDRESS

CITY/STATE/ZIP

PHONE

Qty. purchased: **Cost ea.**
(check one)   ❏ *Cash*   ❏ *Check*   ❏ *Charge*

Reason(s) for purchase(s):

Traded to:

NAME

ADDRESS

CITY/STATE/ZIP

PHONE

TRADED FOR

Re-sold to:

NAME

ADDRESS

CITY/STATE/ZIP

PHONE

PRICE RE-SOLD FOR

Your feelings about and/or experiences with this Beanie:

Zero™

Type:	Penguin	*Categories:*	Arctic, holiday	*Style no.:*	4207
Birthday:	January 2, 1998	*Released:*	9/30/98	*Retired:*	12/1/98
Position:	Standing	*Tags:*	5th generation	*Teenie:*	

Description: White plush front, bottom & under wings; black plush head, back & wings; yellow throat; orange beak & feet; red plush cap w/ white trim & ball; black plastic eyes; hang tag left wing; tush tag left bottom

Replaces: Waddle, style no. 4075, birthday 12/19/95, released 6/3/95, retired 5/1/98, hard to find & pricey

Variations: None

Oddities: No gender; almost identical to Waddle; poem in first person

Commentary: Released eight months after birth; in circulation only three months before retiring; because it is a holiday Beanie with such a short lifespan, it will sky-rocket in popularity & value

Poem: Penguins love the ice and snow
Playing in weather twenty below
Antarctica is where I love to be
Splashing in the cold, cold sea!™

3

My record

(Beanies are the #1 collectible in American collecting history. A complete, detailed record will vastly increase the value of this Beanie, if and when you ever appraise, trade, re-sell, gift, or bequeath it.)

Description *(which version do you have?):*

Gift from:

Date received/purchased:

Purchased from:

NAME OF PERSON OR RETAILER

ADDRESS

CITY/STATE/ZIP

PHONE

Qty. purchased: **Cost ea.**
(check one)   ❏ *Cash*   ❏ *Check*   ❏ *Charge*

Reason(s) for purchase(s):

Traded to:

NAME

ADDRESS

CITY/STATE/ZIP

PHONE

TRADED FOR

Re-sold to:

NAME

ADDRESS

CITY/STATE/ZIP

PHONE

PRICE RE-SOLD FOR

Your feelings about and/or experiences with this Beanie:

Fetch™

Type:	Golden lab	**Categories:** Brown, dog	**Style no.:** 4189
Birthday:	February 4, 1997	**Released:** 5/30/98	**Retired** 12/2/98
Position:	Laying down	**Tags:** 5th generation	**Teenie:**

Description: Light brown plush body, black plastic eyes & nose, black thread mouth, hang tag left ear, tush tag back left leg

Replaces: None

Variations: None

Oddities: One of few Beanies w/ no gender indicated

Commentary: Released 15 months after birth; in circulation only seven months before retiring, making it one of the shortest-lived Beanies ever; one of the cutest Beanie dogs; will continue to escalate in popularity & value

Poem: Fetch is alert at the crack of dawn
Walking through dewdrops on the lawn
Always golden, loyal and true
This little puppy is the one for you!™

4

My record

(Beanies are the #1 collectible in American collecting history. A complete, detailed record will vastly increase the value of this Beanie, if and when you ever appraise, trade, re-sell, gift, or bequeath it.)

Description *(which version do you have?):*

Gift from:

Date received/purchased:

Purchased from: ARMa gift Shy

NAME OF PERSON OR RETAILER

ADDRESS

CITY/STATE/ZIP

PHONE

Qty. purchased: **Cost ea.**
(check one)   ❏ *Cash*   ❏ *Check*   ❏ *Charge*

Reason(s) for purchase(s):

Traded to:

NAME

ADDRESS

CITY/STATE/ZIP

PHONE

TRADED FOR

Re-sold to:

NAME

ADDRESS

CITY/STATE/ZIP

PHONE

PRICE RE-SOLD FOR

Your feelings about and/or experiences with this Beanie:

Scoop™

Type:	Male pelican	***Categories:*** Bird, blue, sea	***Style no.:*** 4107
Birthday:	July 1, 1996	***Released:*** 6/15/96	***Retired:*** 12/2/98
Position:	Perching	***Tags:*** 4th & 5th generation	***Teenie:*** 5/98

Description: Marine blue plush body; orange beak & feet; black plastic eyes; black thread nostrils; large, scoop beak; hang tag left wing; tush tag left side

Replaces: None

Variations: None

Oddities: Odd animal to turn into a Beanie; released two weeks before birth; pelicans are white, not blue; Scoop shares same birthday w/ Maple

Commentary: In circulation two and a half years before retiring, making it one of the longest-running Beanies; readily available; will be slow to escalate in value

Poem: All day long he scoops up fish
To fill his bill, is his wish
Diving fast and diving low
Hoping those fish are very slow!™

My record

(Beanies are the #1 collectible in American collecting history. A complete, detailed record will vastly increase the value of this Beanie, if and when you ever appraise, trade, re-sell, gift, or bequeath it.)

Description *(which version do you have?):*

Gift from:

Date received/purchased:

Purchased from:

NAME OF PERSON OR RETAILER

ADDRESS

CITY/STATE/ZIP

PHONE

Qty. purchased: **Cost ea.**
(check one)   ❏ *Cash*   ❏ *Check*   ❏ *Charge*

Reason(s) for purchase(s):

Traded to:

NAME

ADDRESS

CITY/STATE/ZIP

PHONE

TRADED FOR

Re-sold to:

NAME

ADDRESS

CITY/STATE/ZIP

PHONE

PRICE RE-SOLD FOR

Your feelings about and/or experiences with this Beanie:

Stinger™

Type:	Male scorpion	*Categories:* Creepie crawlie	*Style no.:* 4193

Birthday:	September 29, 1997	*Released:* 5/30/98 *Retired:* 12/2/98

Position:	Crawling	*Tags:* 5th generation	*Teenie:*

Description: Gray-brown plush body; black plastic eyes; black thread mouth; two pinchers; eight legs; long, curved tail; hang tag left pincher; tush tag left back side

Replaces: None

Variations: None

Oddities: Odd animal to turn into a Beanie

Commentary: Released eight months after birth; in circulation only seven months before retiring, making it one of the shortest-lived Beanies ever; not particularly popular, hence, lots of inventory; will be slow to escalate in value

Poem: Stinger the scorpion will run and dart
But this little fellow is really all heart
So if you see him don't run away
Say hello and ask him to play!™

My record

(Beanies are the #1 collectible in American collecting history. A complete, detailed record will vastly increase the value of this Beanie, if and when you ever appraise, trade, re-sell, gift, or bequeath it.)

Description *(which version do you have?):*

Gift from:

Date received/purchased:

Purchased from:

NAME OF PERSON OR RETAILER

ADDRESS

CITY/STATE/ZIP

PHONE

Qty. purchased: **Cost ea.**
(check one) ❏ *Cash* ❏ *Check* ❏ *Charge*

Reason(s) for purchase(s):

Traded to:

NAME

ADDRESS

CITY/STATE/ZIP

PHONE

TRADED FOR

Re-sold to:

NAME

ADDRESS

CITY/STATE/ZIP

PHONE

PRICE RE-SOLD FOR

Your feelings about and/or experiences with this Beanie:

Valentino™

Type:	Male bear	*Categories:*	Bear, holiday, white		*Style no.:*	4058
Birthday:	February 14, 1994		*Released:*	1/7/95	*Retired:*	12/3/98
Position:	Sitting up	*Tags:*	2nd-5th generation		*Teenie:*	

Description: White plush body, red heart embroidered over heart, black plastic eyes, brown plastic nose, red satin ribbon tied around neck, hang tag left ear, tush tag left bottom

Replaces: None

Variations: None

Oddities: One of few holiday Beanies; some missing heart

Commentary: Released eleven months after birth; in circulation four years before retiring, making it one of the longest-running Beanies ever; special Valentine's Day release; more available than most bears; like all bears & holiday Beanies, will sky-rocket in popularity & value

Poem: His heart is red and full of love
He cares for you so give him a hug
Keep him close when feeling blue
Feel the love he has for you!™

My record

(Beanies are the #1 collectible in American collecting history. A complete, detailed record will vastly increase the value of this Beanie, if and when you ever appraise, trade, re-sell, gift, or bequeath it.)

Description *(which version do you have?):*

Gift from:

Date received/purchased:

Purchased from:

NAME OF PERSON OR RETAILER

ADDRESS

CITY/STATE/ZIP

PHONE

Qty. purchased: **Cost ea.**
(check one)   ❏ *Cash*   ❏ *Check*   ❏ *Charge*

Reason(s) for purchase(s):

Traded to:

NAME

ADDRESS

CITY/STATE/ZIP

PHONE

TRADED FOR

Re-sold to:

NAME

ADDRESS

CITY/STATE/ZIP

PHONE

PRICE RE-SOLD FOR

Your feelings about and/or experiences with this Beanie:

Claude™

Type: Male crab   **Categories:** Sea, tie-dyed   **Style no.:** 4083

Birthday: September 3, 1996   **Released:** 5/11/97   **Retired:** 12/4/98

Position: Crawling   **Tags:** 4th-5th generation   **Teenie:**

Description: Tie-dyed plush body, cream under side, black plastic eyes, black thread antennae, two pinchers, eight legs, hang tag left pincher, tush tag back

Replaces: Digger the orange crab, style no. 4027, birthday 8/23/95, released 6/25/94, retired 6/3/95, extremely rare & expensive; Digger the red crab, style no. 4027, birthday 8/23/95, released 6/3/95, retired 5/11/97; very hard to find & expensive

Variations: Tie-dye varies in colors from cool to warm

Oddities: Claude released same day Digger retired; Claude shares same birthday w/ Inch; name in all caps on some hang tags

Commentary: Released eight months after birth; in circulation only 19 months before retiring; not particularly popular, hence, lots of inventory; will be slow to escalate in value

Poem: Claude the crab paints by the sea
A famous artist he hopes to be
But the tide came in and his paints fell
Now his art is on his shell!™

8

My record

(Beanies are the #1 collectible in American collecting history. A complete, detailed record will vastly increase the value of this Beanie, if and when you ever appraise, trade, re-sell, gift, or bequeath it.)

Description *(which version do you have?):*

Gift from:

Date received/purchased:

Purchased from:

NAME OF PERSON OR RETAILER

ADDRESS

CITY/STATE/ZIP

PHONE

Qty. purchased: **Cost ea.**
(check one)   ❏ *Cash*   ❏ *Check*   ❏ *Charge*

Reason(s) for purchase(s):

Traded to:

NAME

ADDRESS

CITY/STATE/ZIP

PHONE

TRADED FOR

Re-sold to:

NAME

ADDRESS

CITY/STATE/ZIP

PHONE

PRICE RE-SOLD FOR

Your feelings about and/or experiences with this Beanie:

Pumkin™

Type:	Male pumpkin	*Categories:*	Holiday, orange	*Style no.:*	4205

Birthday: October 31,1998   *Released:* 9/30/98   *Retired:* 12/4/98

Position: Sitting   *Tags:* 5th generation   *Teenie:*

Description: Orange plush body; green plush arms, legs & stem; black felt eyes, nose & mouth; hang tag left arm; tush tag left back

Replaces: None

Variations: None

Oddities: Released one month before birth

Commentary: In circulation only three months before retiring, making it one of the shortest-lived Beanies ever; first "garden" Beanie; popular Halloween decoration/gift; like all holiday Beanies, will continue to to escalate in both popularity & value

Poem: Ghost and goblins are out tonight
Witches try hard to cause fright
This little pumpkin is very sweet
He only wants to trick or treat!™

My record

(Beanies are the #1 collectible in American collecting history. A complete, detailed record will vastly increase the value of this Beanie, if and when you ever appraise, trade, re-sell, gift, or bequeath it.)

Description *(which version do you have?):*

Gift from:

Date received/purchased:

Purchased from:

NAME OF PERSON OR RETAILER

ADDRESS

CITY/STATE/ZIP

PHONE

Qty. purchased:　　　**Cost ea.**
(check one)　　　❏ *Cash*　　　❏ *Check*　　　❏ *Charge*

Reason(s) for purchase(s):

Traded to:

NAME

ADDRESS

CITY/STATE/ZIP

PHONE

TRADED FOR

Re-sold to:

NAME

ADDRESS

CITY/STATE/ZIP

PHONE

PRICE RE-SOLD FOR

Your feelings about and/or experiences with this Beanie:

Wise™

Type: Male owl   **Categories:** Brown, fanciful   **Style no.:** 4187

Birthday: May 31, 1997   **Released:** 5/30/98   **Retired:** 12/4/98

Position: Perching   **Tags:** 5th generation   **Teenie:**

Description: Dark brown plush backside; tan face, frontside & under tail; lighter brown feet; black plastic eyes ringed w/ gold; orange felt beak; three-pronged tail; black felt mortarboard w/ orange braided yarn tassel; imprinted: Class of '98

Replaces: Hoot the owl, style no. 4073, birthday 8/9/95, released 1/7/96, retired 10/1/97, hard to find & pricey

Variations: None

Oddities: The only dated Beanie

Commentary: Released one year after birth; in circulation only seven months before retiring, making it one of the shortest-lived Beanies; popular graduation decoration/gift; pricey & hard to find even before retirement; will continue to escalate in popularity & value

Poem: Wise is at the head of the class
With A's and B's he'll always pass
He's got his diploma and feels really great
Meet the newest graduate: Class of '98!™

My record

(Beanies are the #1 collectible in American collecting history. A complete, detailed record will vastly increase the value of this Beanie, if and when you ever appraise, trade, re-sell, gift, or bequeath it.)

Description *(which version do you have?):*

Gift from:

Date received/purchased:

Purchased from:

NAME OF PERSON OR RETAILER

ADDRESS

CITY/STATE/ZIP

PHONE

Qty. purchased: **Cost ea.**
(check one) ❏ Cash ❏ Check ❏ Charge

Reason(s) for purchase(s):

Traded to:

NAME

ADDRESS

CITY/STATE/ZIP

PHONE

TRADED FOR

Re-sold to:

NAME

ADDRESS

CITY/STATE/ZIP

PHONE

PRICE RE-SOLD FOR

Your feelings about and/or experiences with this Beanie:

Ants™

Type:	Male anteater	**Categories:** Gray, striped	**Style no.:** 4195

Birthday: November 7, 1997   **Released:** 5/30/98   **Retired:** 12/5/98

Position: Standing   **Tags:** 5th generation   **Teenie:**

Description: Gray plush body, black & white stripes, darker gray felt ears, black plastic eyes, long snout & tail, hang tag left front leg, tush tag left bottom

Replaces: None

Variations: None

Oddities: Odd animal to turn into a Beanie

Commentary: Released six months after birth; in circulation only seven months before retiring, making it one of the shortest-lived Beanies; not particularly popular, hence, lots of inventory; will be slow to escalate in value

Poem: Most anteaters love to eat bugs
But this little fellow gives big hugs
He'd rather dine on apple pie
Than eat an ant or harm a fly!™

My record

(Beanies are the #1 collectible in American collecting history. A complete, detailed record will vastly increase the value of this Beanie, if and when you ever appraise, trade, re-sell, gift, or bequeath it.)

Description *(which version do you have?)*:

Gift from:

Date received/purchased:

Purchased from:

NAME OF PERSON OR RETAILER

ADDRESS

CITY/STATE/ZIP

PHONE

Qty. purchased: **Cost ea.**
(check one)   ❏ *Cash*   ❏ *Check*   ❏ *Charge*

Reason(s) for purchase(s):

Traded to:

NAME

ADDRESS

CITY/STATE/ZIP

PHONE

TRADED FOR

Re-sold to:

NAME

ADDRESS

CITY/STATE/ZIP

PHONE

PRICE RE-SOLD FOR

Your feelings about and/or experiences with this Beanie:

Doby™

Type:	Male doberman	*Categories:* Black & brown, dog	*Style no.:* 4110
Birthday:	October 9, 1996	*Released:* 1/1/97	*Retired:* 12/5/98
Position:	Laying down	*Tags:* 4th & 5th generation	*Teenie:* 5/98

Description: Black plush body; brown chin, belly, under side of ears & legs, markings above eyes & paws; black plastic eyes & nose; black thread mouth; stubby tail; hang tag left ear; tush tag left back leg

Replaces: None

Variations: None

Oddities: None

Commentary: Released three months after birth; in circulation for two years before retiring; not particularly popular, hence, lots of inventory; will be slow to escalate in value

Poem: This dog is little but he has might
Keep him close when you sleep at night
He lays around with nothing to do
Until he sees it's time to protect you!™

My record

(Beanies are the #1 collectible in American collecting history. A complete, detailed record will vastly increase the value of this Beanie, if and when you ever appraise, trade, re-sell, gift, or bequeath it.)

Description *(which version do you have?):*

Gift from:

Date received/purchased:

Purchased from:

NAME OF PERSON OR RETAILER

ADDRESS

CITY/STATE/ZIP

PHONE

Qty. purchased: **Cost ea.**
(check one)   ❏ *Cash*   ❏ *Check*   ❏ *Charge*

Reason(s) for purchase(s):

Traded to:

NAME

ADDRESS

CITY/STATE/ZIP

PHONE

TRADED FOR

Re-sold to:

NAME

ADDRESS

CITY/STATE/ZIP

PHONE

PRICE RE-SOLD FOR

Your feelings about and/or experiences with this Beanie:

Dotty™

Type: Female dalmatian **Categories:** Black & white, dog **Style no.:** 4100

Birthday: October 17, 1996 **Released:** 5/11/97 **Retired:** 12/5/98

Position: Laying down **Tags:** 4th & 5th generation **Teenie:**

Description: White plush body w/ black spots, black ears & tail, black plastic eyes & nose, black thread mouth, stubby tail, hang tag left ear, tush tag left back leg

Replaces: Sparky, style no. 4100, birthday 2/27/96, released 6/15/96, retired 5/11/97, very hard to find & very expensive

Variations: None

Oddities: Both have same style no., Dotty released same day Sparky retired

Commentary: Released seven months after birth; in circulation only 19 months before retiring, making it one of the shortest-lived Beanies; because it replaced Sparky, always popular; will continue to escalate in popularity & value

Poem: The Beanies all thought it was a big joke
While writing her tag, their ink pen broke
She got in the way, and got all spotty
So now the Beanies call her Dotty!™

My record

(Beanies are the #1 collectible in American collecting history. A complete, detailed record will vastly increase the value of this Beanie, if and when you ever appraise, trade, re-sell, gift, or bequeath it.)

Description *(which version do you have?):*

Gift from:

Date received/purchased:

Purchased from:

NAME OF PERSON OR RETAILER

ADDRESS

CITY/STATE/ZIP

PHONE

Qty. purchased: **Cost ea.**
(check one)   ❏ *Cash*   ❏ *Check*   ❏ *Charge*

Reason(s) for purchase(s):

Traded to:

NAME

ADDRESS

CITY/STATE/ZIP

PHONE

TRADED FOR

Re-sold to:

NAME

ADDRESS

CITY/STATE/ZIP

PHONE

PRICE RE-SOLD FOR

Your feelings about and/or experiences with this Beanie:

Nuts™

Type: Male squirrel	***Categories:*** Brown, woodland	***Style no.:*** 4114
Birthday: January 21, 1996	***Released:*** 1/1/97	***Retired*** 12/5/98
Position: Standing up	***Tags:*** 4th & 5th generation	***Teenie:***

Description: Brown plush body; cream belly, chin & inner ears; long, hairy, bushy tail; black plastic eyes & nose; brown thread whiskers; hang tag left ear; tush tag left bottom

Replaces: None

Variations: None

Oddities: None

Commentary: Released one year after birth; in circulation two years before retiring; always popular; one of last woodland animals; will continue to escalate in popularity & value

Poem: With his bushy tail, he'll scamper up a tree
The most cheerful critter you'll ever see.
He's nuts about nuts, and he loves to chat
Have you ever seen a squirrel like that?™

My record

(Beanies are the #1 collectible in American collecting history. A complete, detailed record will vastly increase the value of this Beanie, if and when you ever appraise, trade, re-sell, gift, or bequeath it.)

Description *(which version do you have?):*

Gift from:

Date received/purchased:

Purchased from:

NAME OF PERSON OR RETAILER
ADDRESS
CITY/STATE/ZIP
PHONE

Qty. purchased: **Cost ea.**
(check one)   ❏ *Cash*   ❏ *Check*   ❏ *Charge*

Reason(s) for purchase(s):

Traded to:

NAME
ADDRESS
CITY/STATE/ZIP
PHONE
TRADED FOR

Re-sold to:

NAME
ADDRESS
CITY/STATE/ZIP
PHONE
PRICE RE-SOLD FOR

Your feelings about and/or experiences with this Beanie:

Tuffy™

Type: Male terrier   **Categories:** Brown, dog, napped   **Style no.:** 4108

Birthday: October 12, 1996   **Released:** 5/11/97   **Retired:** 12/5/98

Position: Standing   **Tags:** 4th & 5th generation   **Teenie:**

Description: Brown napped body; darker brown neck, back & tail; medium brown under ears; black plastic eyes & nose; black thread mouth; stubby tail; tips of ears curl under; hang tag left ear; tush tag left back leg

Replaces: None

Variations: None

Oddities: One of few napped Beanies

Commentary: Released seven months after birth; in circulation only 19 months before retiring, making it one of the shortest-lived Beanies; one of few napped, standing Beanies, hence, very popular; will continue to escalate in popularity & value

Poem: Taking off with a thunderous blast
Tuffy rides his motorcycle fast
The Beanies roll with laughs & squeals
He never took off his training wheels!™

15

My record

(Beanies are the #1 collectible in American collecting history. A complete, detailed record will vastly increase the value of this Beanie, if and when you ever appraise, trade, re-sell, gift, or bequeath it.)

Description *(which version do you have?):*

Gift from:

Date received/purchased:

Purchased from:

NAME OF PERSON OR RETAILER

ADDRESS

CITY/STATE/ZIP

PHONE

Qty. purchased: **Cost ea.**
(check one)   ❏ *Cash*   ❏ *Check*   ❏ *Charge*

Reason(s) for purchase(s):

Traded to:

NAME

ADDRESS

CITY/STATE/ZIP

PHONE

TRADED FOR

Re-sold to:

NAME

ADDRESS

CITY/STATE/ZIP

PHONE

PRICE RE-SOLD FOR

Your feelings about and/or experiences with this Beanie:

Curly™

Type:	Male bear	***Categories:*** Bear, brown, napped	***Style no.:*** 4052

Birthday: April 12, 1996   ***Released:*** 6/15/96   ***Retired:*** 12/6/98

Position: Sitting up   ***Tags:*** 4th & 5th generation   ***Teenie:***

Description: Brown napped body, black plastic eyes, brown plastic nose, wine-colored satin ribbon tied around neck, hang tag left ear, tush tag left bottom

Replaces: None

Variations: None

Oddities: The only napped bear; one of few napped Beanies; shares same style no. w/ old- and new-faced Teddy Cranberry

Commentary: Released two months after birth; in circulation two & a half years before retiring, making it one of the longest-running Beanies; first & only napped Bear until Fuzz, hence, very popular; more available than most bears; like all bears, will sky-rocket in popularity & value

Poem: A bear so cute with hair that's curly
You will love and want him surely
To this bear always be true
He will be a friend to you!™

16

My record

(Beanies are the #1 collectible in American collecting history. A complete, detailed record will vastly increase the value of this Beanie, if and when you ever appraise, trade, re-sell, gift, or bequeath it.)

Description *(which version do you have?)*:

Gift from:

Date received/purchased:

Purchased from:

NAME OF PERSON OR RETAILER

ADDRESS

CITY/STATE/ZIP

PHONE

Qty. purchased: **Cost ea.**
(check one)   ❏ *Cash*   ❏ *Check*   ❏ *Charge*

Reason(s) for purchase(s):

Traded to:

NAME

ADDRESS

CITY/STATE/ZIP

PHONE

TRADED FOR

Re-sold to:

NAME

ADDRESS

CITY/STATE/ZIP

PHONE

PRICE RE-SOLD FOR

Your feelings about and/or experiences with this Beanie:

Fleece™

Type: Female lamb   *Categories:* Farm, napped, white   *Style no.:* 4125

Birthday: March 21, 1996   *Released:* 1/1/97   *Retired:* 12/7/98

Position: Laying down   *Tags:* 4th & 5th generation   *Teenie:*

Description: White napped body, cream plush face & inner ears, black plastic eyes, pink plastic nose, pink thread mouth, stubby tail, hang tag left ear, tush tag left back leg

Replaces: Chops, style no. 4019, birthday 5/3/96, released: 1/7/96, retired 1/1/97, very hard to find & very expensive

Variations: None

Oddities: One of few napped Beanies; born the first day of spring; Fleece released same day Chops retired

Commentary: Released ten months after birth; in circulation two years before retiring; one of the cutest, sweetest, most popular Beanies ever; popular baby & Easter decoration/gift; one of few napped Beanies; like Chops, will skyrocket in popularity & value

Poem: Fleece would like to sing a lullaby
Please be patient, she's really shy
When you sleep, keep her by your ear
Her song will leave you nothing to fear.™

17

My record

(Beanies are the #1 collectible in American collecting history. A complete, detailed record will vastly increase the value of this Beanie, if and when you ever appraise, trade, re-sell, gift, or bequeath it.)

Description *(which version do you have?):*

Gift from:

Date received/purchased:

Purchased from:

NAME OF PERSON OR RETAILER

ADDRESS

CITY/STATE/ZIP

PHONE

Qty. purchased: **Cost ea.**
(check one)   ❏ *Cash*   ❏ *Check*   ❏ *Charge*

Reason(s) for purchase(s):

Traded to:

NAME

ADDRESS

CITY/STATE/ZIP

PHONE

TRADED FOR

Re-sold to:

NAME

ADDRESS

CITY/STATE/ZIP

PHONE

PRICE RE-SOLD FOR

Your feelings about and/or experiences with this Beanie:

Snip™

Type:	Female Siamese cat	**Categories:** Brown, cat	**Style no.:** 4120
Birthday:	October 22, 1996	**Released:** 1/1/97	**Retired:** 12/7/98
Position:	Laying down	**Tags:** 4th & 5th generation	**Teenie:**

Description: Cream plush body; light brown snout, ears, socks & tip of tail; black plastic eyes ringed w/ blue; black plastic nose; brown thread whiskers & mouth; hang tag left ear; tush tag left back leg

Replaces: None

Variations: None

Oddities: One of few Beanies with blue eyes

Commentary: Released three months after birth; in circulation two years before retiring; one of the most beautiful Beanies ever; popular w/ cat lovers; like all cats, will continue to escalate in popularity & value

Poem: Snip the cat is Siamese
She'll be your friend if you please
So toss her a toy or piece of string
Playing with you is her favorite thing!™

My record

(Beanies are the #1 collectible in American collecting history. A complete, detailed record will vastly increase the value of this Beanie, if and when you ever appraise, trade, re-sell, gift, or bequeath it.)

Description *(which version do you have?):*

Gift from:

Date received/purchased:

Purchased from:

NAME OF PERSON OR RETAILER

ADDRESS

CITY/STATE/ZIP

PHONE

Qty. purchased: **Cost ea.**
(check one) ❏ *Cash* ❏ *Check* ❏ *Charge*

Reason(s) for purchase(s):

Traded to:

NAME

ADDRESS

CITY/STATE/ZIP

PHONE

TRADED FOR

Re-sold to:

NAME

ADDRESS

CITY/STATE/ZIP

PHONE

PRICE RE-SOLD FOR

Your feelings about and/or experiences with this Beanie:

Congo™

Type:	Male gorilla	*Categories:*	Black, jungle	*Style no.:*	4160
Birthday:	November 9, 1996	*Released:*	6/15/96	*Retired:*	12/8/98
Position:	Sitting up	*Tags:*	4th & 5th generation	*Teenie:*	

Description: Black plush body; dark brown face, ears, hands & feet; black plastic eyes & nose; hang tag left ear; tush tag bottom

Replaces: None

Variations: None

Oddities: Released four months before birth

Commentary: In circulation two & a half years before retiring; companion to Bongo the monkey; not as popular as Bongo; one of last jungle Beanies; not particularly popular, hence, lots of inventory; will be slow to escalate in value

Poem: Black as night and fierce is he
On the ground or in a tree
Strong and mighty as the Congo
He's related to our Bongo!™

19

My record

(Beanies are the #1 collectible in American collecting history. A complete, detailed record will vastly increase the value of this Beanie, if and when you ever appraise, trade, re-sell, gift, or bequeath it.)

Description *(which version do you have?)*:

Gift from:

Date received/purchased:

Purchased from:

NAME OF PERSON OR RETAILER

ADDRESS

CITY/STATE/ZIP

PHONE

Qty. purchased: **Cost ea.**
(check one)   ❏ *Cash*   ❏ *Check*   ❏ *Charge*

Reason(s) for purchase(s):

Traded to:

NAME

ADDRESS

CITY/STATE/ZIP

PHONE

TRADED FOR

Re-sold to:

NAME

ADDRESS

CITY/STATE/ZIP

PHONE

PRICE RE-SOLD FOR

Your feelings about and/or experiences with this Beanie:

Pinky™

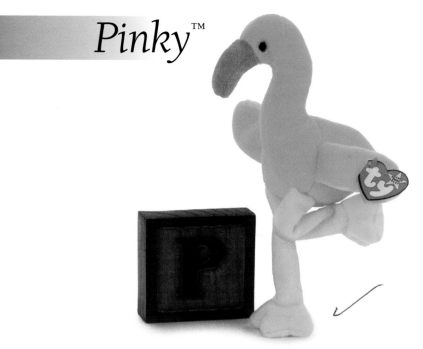

Type: Female flamingo   **Categories:** Bird, jungle, pink   **Style no.:** 4072

Birthday: February 13, 1995   **Released:** 6/3/95   **Retired:** 12/8/98

Position: Standing up   **Tags:** 3rd-5th generation   **Teenie:** 4/97

Description: Hot pink plush body, pale pink legs & under wings, orange beak, black plastic eyes, long legs, big feet, long beak, hang tag left wing, tush tag bottom

Replaces: None

Variations: None

Oddities: Pinky shares same birthday w/ Stinky

Commentary: Released four months after birth; in circulation three & a half years before retiring, making it one of the longest-running Beanies ever; one of the most unique & colorful Beanies ever; will continue to escalate in popularity & value

Poem: Pinky loves the Everglades
From the hottest pink she's made
With floppy legs and big orange beak
She's the Beanie that you seek!™

My record

(Beanies are the #1 collectible in American collecting history. A complete, detailed record will vastly increase the value of this Beanie, if and when you ever appraise, trade, re-sell, gift, or bequeath it.)

Description *(which version do you have?):*

Gift from:

Date received/purchased:

Purchased from:

NAME OF PERSON OR RETAILER

ADDRESS

CITY/STATE/ZIP

PHONE

Qty. purchased: **Cost ea.**
(check one)   ❏ *Cash*   ❏ *Check*   ❏ *Charge*

Reason(s) for purchase(s):

Traded to:

NAME

ADDRESS

CITY/STATE/ZIP

PHONE

TRADED FOR

Re-sold to:

NAME

ADDRESS

CITY/STATE/ZIP

PHONE

PRICE RE-SOLD FOR

Your feelings about and/or experiences with this Beanie:

Spike™

Type:	Male rhino	**Categories:** Gray, jungle	**Style no.:** 4060
Birthday:	August 13, 1996	**Released:** 6/15/96	**Retired:** 12/8/98
Position:	Standing	**Tags:** 4th & 5th generation	**Teenie:**

Description: Gray plush body, brown horn & inner ears, black plastic eyes, stubby tail, hang tag left ear, tush tag left back side

Replaces: None

Variations: None

Oddities: Released two months before birth, shares same style no. w/ Humphrey

Commentary: In circulation two & a half years before retiring, making it one of the longest-running Beanies; one of last jungle Beanies; will continue to escalate in popularity & value

Poem: Spike the rhino likes to stampede
He's the bruiser that you need
Gentle to birds on his back and spike
You can be his friend if you like!™

My record

(Beanies are the #1 collectible in American collecting history. A complete, detailed record will vastly increase the value of this Beanie, if and when you ever appraise, trade, re-sell, gift, or bequeath it.)

Description *(which version do you have?):*

Gift from:

Date received/purchased:

Purchased from:

NAME OF PERSON OR RETAILER

ADDRESS

CITY/STATE/ZIP

PHONE

Qty. purchased: **Cost ea.**
(check one)   ❏ *Cash*   ❏ *Check*   ❏ *Charge*

Reason(s) for purchase(s):

Traded to:

NAME

ADDRESS

CITY/STATE/ZIP

PHONE

TRADED FOR

Re-sold to:

NAME

ADDRESS

CITY/STATE/ZIP

PHONE

PRICE RE-SOLD FOR

Your feelings about and/or experiences with this Beanie:

Bongo™

Type: Male monkey	*Categories:* Brown, jungle	*Style no.:* 4067
Birthday: August 17, 1995	*Released:* 6/3/95	*Retired* 12/9/98:
Position: Sitting up	*Tags:* 3rd-5th generation	*Teenie:* 5/98

Description: Reddish brown plush body; lighter brown face, ears, hands, feet & tail; black plastic eyes; black thread nostrils; knotted tail; hang tag left ear; tush tag left bottom

Replaces: Bongo w/ brown tail, style no. 4067, birthday 8/17/95, released 2/6/96, retired 6/29/96, hard to find & expensive

Variations: Formerly named Nana, extremely rare & expensive

Oddities: One of few renamed Beanies; all three versions share same style no. & birthday; tan tail released before brown tail; brown tail retired before tan tail; released two months before birth

Commentary: In circulation three & a half years before retiring, making it one of the longest-running Beanies ever; one of few Beanies with all five generations of tags; one of the most popular Beanies ever; companion to Congo the gorilla; one of the last jungle Beanies; will continue to escalate in popularity & value

Poem: Bongo the monkey lives in a tree
The happiest monkey you'll ever see
In his spare time he plays the guitar
One of these days he'll be a big star!™

22

My record

(Beanies are the #1 collectible in American collecting history. A complete, detailed record will vastly increase the value of this Beanie, if and when you ever appraise, trade, re-sell, gift, or bequeath it.)

Description *(which version do you have?)*:

Gift from:

Date received/purchased:

Purchased from:

NAME OF PERSON OR RETAILER

ADDRESS

CITY/STATE/ZIP

PHONE

Qty. purchased: **Cost ea.**
(check one)   ❏ *Cash*   ❏ *Check*   ❏ *Charge*

Reason(s) for purchase(s):

Traded to:

NAME

ADDRESS

CITY/STATE/ZIP

PHONE

TRADED FOR

Re-sold to:

NAME

ADDRESS

CITY/STATE/ZIP

PHONE

PRICE RE-SOLD FOR

Your feelings about and/or experiences with this Beanie:

Freckles™

Type:	Male leopard	**Categories:**	Big cat, jungle, spotted	**Style no.:**	4066

Birthday: June 3, 1996   **Released:** 6/15/96   **Retired:** 12/9/98

Position: Laying down   **Tags:** 4th & 5th generation   **Teenie:**

Description: Beige plush body w/ gold spots surrounded by brown circles, black plastic eyes ringed w/ gold, flesh velvet nose, black thread whiskers, long tail, hang tag left ear, tush tag left back leg

Replaces: None

Variations: None

Oddities: A second birthday (7/28/96) erroneously appears on some tags; one of few Beanies born and released the same month; some w/o tails; some w/ more muted fabric

Commentary: In circulation 30 months before retiring; due to detailing, one of the most popular Beanies ever; one of the last jungle Beanies; will continue to escalate in popularity & value

Poem: From trees he hunts his prey
In the night and in the day
He's the king of camouflage
Look real close, he's no mirage!™

My record

(Beanies are the #1 collectible in American collecting history. A complete, detailed record will vastly increase the value of this Beanie, if and when you ever appraise, trade, re-sell, gift, or bequeath it.)

Description *(which version do you have?):*

Gift from:

Date received/purchased:

Purchased from:

NAME OF PERSON OR RETAILER

ADDRESS

CITY/STATE/ZIP

PHONE

Qty. purchased: **Cost ea.**
(check one)   ❏ *Cash*   ❏ *Check*   ❏ *Charge*

Reason(s) for purchase(s):

Traded to:

NAME

ADDRESS

CITY/STATE/ZIP

PHONE

TRADED FOR

Re-sold to:

NAME

ADDRESS

CITY/STATE/ZIP

PHONE

PRICE RE-SOLD FOR

Your feelings about and/or experiences with this Beanie:

Chocolate®

Type:	Male moose	*Categories:* Brown, woodland	*Style no.:* 4015
Birthday:	April 27, 1993	*Released:* 1/8/94	*Retired:* 12/10/98
Position:	Laying down	*Tags:* 1st-5th generation	*Teenie:* 4/97

Description: Brown plush body, orange antlers, black plastic eyes, stubby tail, hang tag left ear, tush tag left back leg

Replaces: None

Variations: None

Oddities: Moose don't have orange antlers

Commentary: Released nine months after birth; in circulation five years before retiring, making it the longest-running Beanie ever; because it was one of the original nine Beanies, it will continue to escalate in both popularity & value

Poem: Licorice, gum and peppermint candy
This moose always has these handy
But there is one more thing he likes to eat
Can you guess his favorite sweet?™

24

My record

(Beanies are the #1 collectible in American collecting history. A complete, detailed record will vastly increase the value of this Beanie, if and when you ever appraise, trade, re-sell, gift, or bequeath it.)

Description *(which version do you have?):*

Gift from:

Date received/purchased:

Purchased from:

NAME OF PERSON OR RETAILER

ADDRESS

CITY/STATE/ZIP

PHONE

Qty. purchased: **Cost ea.**
(check one)   ❏ *Cash*   ❏ *Check*   ❏ *Charge*

Reason(s) for purchase(s):

Traded to:

NAME

ADDRESS

CITY/STATE/ZIP

PHONE

TRADED FOR

Re-sold to:

NAME

ADDRESS

CITY/STATE/ZIP

PHONE

PRICE RE-SOLD FOR

Your feelings about and/or experiences with this Beanie:

Glory™

Type:	Bear	*Categories:*	Bear, white	*Style no.:*	4188
Birthday:	July 4, 1997	*Released:*	5/30/98	*Retired:*	12/10/98
Position:	Sitting up	*Tags:*	5th generation	*Teenie:*	

Description: White plush body silk-screened w/ red & blue stars; black plastic eyes & nose; red, white & blue U.S. flag stitched w/ white thread over heart; hang tag left ear; tush tag left bottom

Replaces: Libearty, style no. 4057, birthday summer '96, released 6/15/96, retired 1/1/97, very hard to find & expensive

Variations: Placement of stars

Oddities: One of few Beanies w/ no gender indicated; like Lefty & Righty, born on the 4th of July; one of four patriotic Beanies; silk-screening inconsistent; due to seams, stars sometimes fall in odd places

Commentary: Released ten months after birth; in circulation only five months before retiring, making it one of the shortest-lived Beanies ever; like the American trio, one of the most popular, sought-after Beanies ever; due to theme, will sky-rocket in popularity & value

Poem: Wearing the flag for all to see
Symbol of freedom for you and me
Red, white and blue–Independence Day
Happy Birthday, USA!™

My record

(Beanies are the #1 collectible in American collecting history. A complete, detailed record will vastly increase the value of this Beanie, if and when you ever appraise, trade, re-sell, gift, or bequeath it.)

Description *(which version do you have?):*

Gift from:

Date received/purchased:

Purchased from:

NAME OF PERSON OR RETAILER

ADDRESS

CITY/STATE/ZIP

PHONE

Qty. purchased: **Cost ea.**
(check one)   ❏ *Cash*   ❏ *Check*   ❏ *Charge*

Reason(s) for purchase(s):

Traded to:

NAME

ADDRESS

CITY/STATE/ZIP

PHONE

TRADED FOR

Re-sold to:

NAME

ADDRESS

CITY/STATE/ZIP

PHONE

PRICE RE-SOLD FOR

Your feelings about and/or experiences with this Beanie:

Roary

Type: Male lion	***Categories:*** Brown, jungle	***Style no.:*** 4069
Birthday: February 20, 1996	***Released:*** 5/11/97	***Retired:*** 12/10/98
Position: Laying down	***Tags:*** 4th & 5th generation	***Teenie:***

Description: Brown plush body, brown & gray hairy mane & tip of tail, white inner ears & chin, black plastic eyes ringed w/ gold, flesh velvet nose, brown thread whiskers & mouth, long tail, hang tag left ear, tush tag left back leg

Replaces: None

Variations: None

Oddities: None

Commentary: Released 15 months after birth; in circulation only 19 months before retiring, making it one of the shortest-lived Beanies; legal trouble with name made it hard to find & pricey even before retirement; will continue to escalate in popularity & value

Poem: Deep in the jungle they crowned him king
But being brave is not his thing
A cowardly lion some may say
He hears his roar and runs away!™

26

My record

(Beanies are the #1 collectible in American collecting history. A complete, detailed record will vastly increase the value of this Beanie, if and when you ever appraise, trade, re-sell, gift, or bequeath it.)

Description *(which version do you have?):*

Gift from:

Date received/purchased:

Purchased from:

NAME OF PERSON OR RETAILER

ADDRESS

CITY/STATE/ZIP

PHONE

Qty. purchased: **Cost ea.**
(check one)   ❏ *Cash*   ❏ *Check*   ❏ *Charge*

Reason(s) for purchase(s):

Traded to:

NAME

ADDRESS

CITY/STATE/ZIP

PHONE

TRADED FOR

Re-sold to:

NAME

ADDRESS

CITY/STATE/ZIP

PHONE

PRICE RE-SOLD FOR

Your feelings about and/or experiences with this Beanie:

9/98 Retireds

Place behind this tab
the following Beanie Babies®:

9/15
Blackie
Daisy
Snort

9/16
Ringo

9/18
Bruno
Puffer

9/19
Seaweed
Spinner

9/22
Bernie
Sly
Wrinkles

9/24
Crunch

9/28
Stinky

Blackie™

Type:	Male bear	***Categories:*** Bear, black, woodland	***Style no.:*** 4011

Birthday: July 15, 1994   ***Released:*** 6/25/94   ***Retired:*** 9/15/98

Position: Laying down   ***Tags:*** 1st-5th generation   ***Teenie:***

Description: Black plush body, brown snout, black plastic eyes & nose, stubby tail, hang tag left ear, tush tag left back leg

Replaces: None

Variations: None

Oddities: Released almost one month before birth

Commentary: In circulation 51 months, making it one of the longest running Beanies ever; like all Beanie bears, very popular, hence, very hard to find & expensive; one of few Beanies w/ all five generations of tags;

Poem: Living in a national park
He only played after dark
Then he met his friend Cubbie
Now they play when it's sunny!™

My record

(Beanies are the #1 collectible in American collecting history. A complete, detailed record will vastly increase the value of this Beanie, if and when you ever appraise, trade, re-sell, gift, or bequeath it.)

Description *(which version do you have?):*

Gift from:

Date received/purchased:

Purchased from:

NAME OF PERSON OR RETAILER

ADDRESS

CITY/STATE/ZIP

PHONE

Qty. purchased: **Cost ea.**
(check one)   ❏ *Cash*   ❏ *Check*   ❏ *Charge*

Reason(s) for purchase(s):

Traded to:

NAME

ADDRESS

CITY/STATE/ZIP

PHONE

TRADED FOR

Re-sold to:

NAME

ADDRESS

CITY/STATE/ZIP

PHONE

PRICE RE-SOLD FOR

Your feelings about and/or experiences with this Beanie:

Daisy™

Type:	Female cow	*Categories:*	Black & white, farm	*Style no.:*	4006
Birthday:	May 10, 1994	*Released:*	6/25/94	*Retired:*	9/15/98
Position:	Laying down	*Tags:*	1st-5th generation	*Teenie:*	

Description: Black plush body; white face, inner ears, spot on back; tan horns; black plastic eyes; black thread nostrils; knotted tail; hang tag left ear; tush tag left back leg

Replaces: Bessie the brown & white cow, style no. 4009, birthday 6/27/95, released 6/3/95, retired 10/1/97, hard to find & expensive

Variations: None

Oddities: All cows are females; cows have utters; cows don't drink milk

Commentary: Released one month after birth; in circulation 51 months, making it one of the longest running Beanies ever; like Bessie the brown & white cow, very popular, hence, hard to find & pricey; one of few Beanies w/ all five generations of tags; one of few poems w/ message

Poem: Daisy drinks milk each night
So her coat is shiny and bright
Milk is good for your hair & skin
What a way for your day to begin!™

My record

(Beanies are the #1 collectible in American collecting history. A complete, detailed record will vastly increase the value of this Beanie, if and when you ever appraise, trade, re-sell, gift, or bequeath it.)

Description *(which version do you have?):*

Gift from:

Date received/purchased:

Purchased from:

NAME OF PERSON OR RETAILER

ADDRESS

CITY/STATE/ZIP

PHONE

Qty. purchased: **Cost ea.**
(check one)   ❏ *Cash*   ❏ *Check*   ❏ *Charge*

Reason(s) for purchase(s):

Traded to:

NAME

ADDRESS

CITY/STATE/ZIP

PHONE

TRADED FOR

Re-sold to:

NAME

ADDRESS

CITY/STATE/ZIP

PHONE

PRICE RE-SOLD FOR

Your feelings about and/or experiences with this Beanie:

Snort®

Type:	Male bull	**Categories:** Farm, red **Style no.:** 4002
Birthday:	May 15, 1995	**Released:** 1/1/97 **Retired:** 9/15/98
Position:	Laying down	**Tags:** 4th & 5th generation **Teenie:** 4/97

Description: Bright red plush body; cream horns, inner ears, end of snout & hooves; black plastic eyes; black thread nostrils; knotted tail; hang tag left ear; tush tag left back leg

Replaces: Tabasco, style no. 4002, birthday 5/15/95, released 6/3/95, retired 1/1/97, very hard to find & very expensive

Variations: Chicago Bulls special edition w/ commemorative card

Oddities: Both share same style no. & birthday; Snort released same day Tabasco retired; snout makes Snort look more like a pig; obvious tie-in to Chicago Bulls mascot, no bull is this shade of red

Commentary: Released 20 months after birth; in circulation only 20 months before retiring, making it one of the shortest-lived Beanies, hence, hard to find & pricey; unrealistic coloring; unofficial mascot of Chicago Bulls; very popular w/ boys

Poem: Although snort is not so tall
He loves to play basketball
He is a star player in his dream
Can you guess his favorite team?™

3

My record

(Beanies are the #1 collectible in American collecting history. A complete, detailed record will vastly increase the value of this Beanie, if and when you ever appraise, trade, re-sell, gift, or bequeath it.)

Description *(which version do you have?):*

Gift from:

Date received/purchased: 4 - 20 - 99

Purchased from:

NAME OF PERSON OR RETAILER *Fred Meyer*
ADDRESS
CITY/STATE/ZIP
PHONE

Qty. purchased: Cost ea. 6 ^{99} + tax
(check one) ☑ *Cash* ❑ *Check* ❑ *Charge*

Reason(s) for purchase(s): *I liked the beanie & color red.*

Traded to:

NAME
ADDRESS
CITY/STATE/ZIP
PHONE
TRADED FOR

Re-sold to:

NAME
ADDRESS
CITY/STATE/ZIP
PHONE
PRICE RE-SOLD FOR

Your feelings about and/or experiences with this Beanie:

Ringo™

Type:	Male raccoon	**Categories:** Brown, woodland		**Style no.:** 4014
Birthday:	July 14, 1995	**Released:** 1/7/96		**Retired:** 9/16/98
Position:	Laying down	**Tags:** 3rd-5th generation	**Teenie:**	

Description: Brown-gray plush body, white snout & inner ears, black circles around eyes, black outer ears, black-ringed tail, black plastic eyes & nose, black thread whiskers, hang tag left ear, tush tag left back leg

Replaces: None

Variations: None

Oddities: None

Commentary: Released six months after birth; in circulation 32 months before retiring; like all woodland animals, very popular, hence, hard to find & pricey

Poem: Ringo hides behind his mask
He will come out, if you should ask
He loves to chitter, He loves to chatter
Just about anything, it doesn't matter!™

My record

(Beanies are the #1 collectible in American collecting history. A complete, detailed record will vastly increase the value of this Beanie, if and when you ever appraise, trade, re-sell, gift, or bequeath it.)

Description *(which version do you have?):*

Gift from:

Date received/purchased:

Purchased from:

NAME OF PERSON OR RETAILER

ADDRESS

CITY/STATE/ZIP

PHONE

Qty. purchased: **Cost ea.**
(check one)   ❑ *Cash*   ❑ *Check*   ❑ *Charge*

Reason(s) for purchase(s):

Traded to:

NAME

ADDRESS

CITY/STATE/ZIP

PHONE

TRADED FOR

Re-sold to:

NAME

ADDRESS

CITY/STATE/ZIP

PHONE

PRICE RE-SOLD FOR

Your feelings about and/or experiences with this Beanie:

Bruno™

Type: Male bull terrier **Categories:** Brown, dog **Style no.:** 4183

Birthday: September 9, 1997 **Released:** 12/31/97 **Retired:** 9/18/98

Position: Laying down **Tags:** 5th generation **Teenie:**

Description: Dark brown plush body; white snout, forehead, belly, feet & tip of tail; black plastic eyes & nose; black thread mouth; hang tag left ear; tush tag left back leg

Replaces: None

Variations: None

Oddities: Several tags printed w/o style no.

Commentary: Released three months after birth; in circulation only nine months, making it one of the shortest lived Beanies ever, hence, hard to find & pricey; not as popular as other Beanie dogs

Poem: Bruno the dog thinks he's a brute
But all the other Beanies think he's cute
He growls at his tail and runs in a ring
And everyone says, "Oh, how darling!"™

My record

(Beanies are the #1 collectible in American collecting history. A complete, detailed record will vastly increase the value of this Beanie, if and when you ever appraise, trade, re-sell, gift, or bequeath it.)

Description *(which version do you have?):*

Gift from:

Date received/purchased:

Purchased from:

NAME OF PERSON OR RETAILER

ADDRESS

CITY/STATE/ZIP

PHONE

Qty. purchased: **Cost ea.**
(check one)   ❏ *Cash*   ❏ *Check*   ❏ *Charge*

Reason(s) for purchase(s):

Traded to:

NAME

ADDRESS

CITY/STATE/ZIP

PHONE

TRADED FOR

Re-sold to:

NAME

ADDRESS

CITY/STATE/ZIP

PHONE

PRICE RE-SOLD FOR

Your feelings about and/or experiences with this Beanie:

Puffer™

Type: Female puffin   **Categories:** Arctic, bird   **Style no.:** 4181

Birthday: November 3, 1997   **Released:** 12/31/97   **Retired:** 9/18/98

Position: Perching   **Tags:** 5th generation   **Teenie:**

Description: Black plush body, forehead, wings & top side of tail; white face, belly & under tail; reddish-orange beak w/ gold band; reddish-orange feet; black plastic eyes ringed w/ gold; black felt markings around eyes; three-pronged tail; hang tag left wing; tush tag bottom

Replaces: None

Variations: None

Oddities: Odd animal to turn into a Beanie

Commentary: Released one month after birth; in circulation only nine months, making it one of the shortest-lived Beanies ever, hence, hard to find & pricey; one of the most colorful Beanies; one of few arctic Beanies; often confused w/ Waddle the penguin

Poem: What in the world does a puffin do?
We're sure that you would like to know, too
We asked Puffer how she spends her days
Before she answered, she flew away!™

My record

(Beanies are the #1 collectible in American collecting history. A complete, detailed record will vastly increase the value of this Beanie, if and when you ever appraise, trade, re-sell, gift, or bequeath it.)

Description *(which version do you have?)*:

Gift from:

Date received/purchased:

Purchased from:

NAME OF PERSON OR RETAILER

ADDRESS

CITY/STATE/ZIP

PHONE

Qty. purchased: **Cost ea.**
(check one)   ❏ *Cash*   ❏ *Check*   ❏ *Charge*

Reason(s) for purchase(s):

Traded to:

NAME

ADDRESS

CITY/STATE/ZIP

PHONE

TRADED FOR

Re-sold to:

NAME

ADDRESS

CITY/STATE/ZIP

PHONE

PRICE RE-SOLD FOR

Your feelings about and/or experiences with this Beanie:

Seaweed™

Type:	Female otter	**Categories:**	Brown, woodland	**Style no.:**	4080
Birthday:	March 19, 1996	**Released:**	1/7/96	**Retired:**	9/19/98
Position:	Floating on back	**Tags:**	3rd-5th generation	**Teenie:**	

Description: Dark brown plush body, lighter brown snout, holding & eating piece of green felt seaweed, black plastic eyes & nose, long tail, hang tag left paw, tush tag bottom of tail

Replaces: None

Variations: None

Oddities: Released two months before birth

Commentary: In circulation 32 months before retiring; one of the cutest, most popular Beanies ever; only Beanie holding something; like his friend Seamore the white seal, hard to find (even when current) & pricey

Poem: Seaweed is what she likes to eat
It's supposed to be a delicious treat
Have you tried a treat from the water?
If you haven't, maybe you "otter"!™

7

My record

(Beanies are the #1 collectible in American collecting history. A complete, detailed record will vastly increase the value of this Beanie, if and when you ever appraise, trade, re-sell, gift, or bequeath it.)

Description *(which version do you have?):*

Gift from:

Date received/purchased:

Purchased from:

NAME OF PERSON OR RETAILER

ADDRESS

CITY/STATE/ZIP

PHONE

Qty. purchased: **Cost ea.**

(check one)   ❏ *Cash*   ❏ *Check*   ❏ *Charge*

Reason(s) for purchase(s):

Traded to:

NAME

ADDRESS

CITY/STATE/ZIP

PHONE

TRADED FOR

Re-sold to:

NAME

ADDRESS

CITY/STATE/ZIP

PHONE

PRICE RE-SOLD FOR

Your feelings about and/or experiences with this Beanie:

Spinner™

Type:	Spider	**Categories:** Creepie crawlie	**Style no.:** 4036

Birthday: October 28, 1996   **Released:** 10/1/97   **Retired:** 9/19/98

Position: Crawling   **Tags:** 4th & 5th generation   **Teenie:**

Description: Brown plush body w/ black stripes, black head & legs, red thread eyes, eight legs, hang tag left front, tush tag back

Replaces: Web, style no. 4042, birthday none, released 6/25/94, retired 1/7/96, extremely rare & expensive

Variations: None

Oddities: One of few Beanies w/ no gender indicated, one of few Beanies w/ thread eyes, one of few holiday Beanies; some tush tags read "Creepie"

Commentary: Released one year after birth, in circulation only 11 months before retiring, making it one of the shortest lived Beanies ever, hence hard to find & pricey; special Halloween release, popular Halloween decoration/gift, very popular w/ boys

Poem: Does this spider make you scared?
Among many people that feeling is shared
Remember spiders have feelings too
In fact, this spider really likes you!™

My record

(Beanies are the #1 collectible in American collecting history. A complete, detailed record will vastly increase the value of this Beanie, if and when you ever appraise, trade, re-sell, gift, or bequeath it.)

Description *(which version do you have?):*

Gift from:

Date received/purchased:

Purchased from:

NAME OF PERSON OR RETAILER

ADDRESS

CITY/STATE/ZIP

PHONE

Qty. purchased: **Cost ea.**
(check one)   ❏ *Cash*   ❏ *Check*   ❏ *Charge*

Reason(s) for purchase(s):

Traded to:

NAME

ADDRESS

CITY/STATE/ZIP

PHONE

TRADED FOR

Re-sold to:

NAME

ADDRESS

CITY/STATE/ZIP

PHONE

PRICE RE-SOLD FOR

Your feelings about and/or experiences with this Beanie:

Bernie™

Type:	Male St. Bernard	*Categories:*	Brown, dog	*Style no.:*	4109
Birthday:	October 3, 1996	*Released:*	1/1/97	*Retired:*	9/22/98
Position:	Laying down	*Tags:*	4th & 5th generation	*Teenie:*	

Description: Tan plush face, shoulders, belly, feet & tip of tail; lighter brown sides of head, back & upper tail; dark brown ears; black markings around eyes; black plastic eyes ringed w/ brown; black plastic nose; black thread mouth; hang tag left ear; tush tag left back leg

Replaces: None

Variations: None

Oddities: None

Commentary: Released three months after birth; in circulation only 20 months, making it one of the shortest lived Beanies, hence hard to find & pricey; like all Beanie dogs, very popular; one of the most detailed Beanie dogs

Poem: This little dog can't wait to grow
To rescue people lost in snow
Don't let him out—keep him on your shelf
He doesn't know how to rescue himself!™

9

My record

(Beanies are the #1 collectible in American collecting history. A complete, detailed record will vastly increase the value of this Beanie, if and when you ever appraise, trade, re-sell, gift, or bequeath it.)

Description *(which version do you have?):*

Gift from:

Date received/purchased:

Purchased from:

NAME OF PERSON OR RETAILER

ADDRESS

CITY/STATE/ZIP

PHONE

Qty. purchased: **Cost ea.**
(check one)   ❏ *Cash*   ❏ *Check*   ❏ *Charge*

Reason(s) for purchase(s):

Traded to:

NAME

ADDRESS

CITY/STATE/ZIP

PHONE

TRADED FOR

Re-sold to:

NAME

ADDRESS

CITY/STATE/ZIP

PHONE

PRICE RE-SOLD FOR

Your feelings about and/or experiences with this Beanie:

Sly™

Type:	Male fox	**Categories:** Brown, woodland	**Style no.:** 4115
Birthday:	September 12, 1996	**Released:** 8/6/96	**Retired:** 9/22/98
Position:	Laying down	**Tags:** 4th & 5th generation	**Teenie:**

Description: Reddish-brown plush body; white belly, chin & inner ears; darker brown outer ears; black plastic eyes & nose; black thread whiskers; long, fat tail; hang tag left ear; tush tag left back leg

Replaces: Sly w/ brown belly, style no. 4115, birthday 9/12/96, released 6/15/96, retired 8/6/96, extremely rare & expensive

Variations: None

Oddities: Both share same style no. & birthday, white belly released same day brown belly retired, released one month before birth

Commentary: In circulation 25 months before retiring; like all woodland animals, very popular, hence, hard to find & pricey

Poem: Sly is a fox and tricky is he
Please don't chase him, let him be
If you want him, just say when
He'll peek out from his den!™

10

My record

(Beanies are the #1 collectible in American collecting history. A complete, detailed record will vastly increase the value of this Beanie, if and when you ever appraise, trade, re-sell, gift, or bequeath it.)

Description *(which version do you have?):*

Gift from:

Date received/purchased:

Purchased from:

NAME OF PERSON OR RETAILER

ADDRESS

CITY/STATE/ZIP

PHONE

Qty. purchased: **Cost ea.**
(check one)   ❏ *Cash*   ❏ *Check*   ❏ *Charge*

Reason(s) for purchase(s):

Traded to:

NAME

ADDRESS

CITY/STATE/ZIP

PHONE

TRADED FOR

Re-sold to:

NAME

ADDRESS

CITY/STATE/ZIP

PHONE

PRICE RE-SOLD FOR

Your feelings about and/or experiences with this Beanie:

Wrinkles™

Type:	Male bulldog	*Categories:* Brown, dog	*Style no.:* 4103

Birthday: May 1, 1996   *Released:* 6/15/96   *Retired:* 9/22/98

Position: Laying down   *Tags:* 4th & 5th generation   *Teenie:*

Description: Light brown plush body; white belly, chin, snout, forehead & inner ears; black plastic eyes & nose; wrinkled face & back w/ detail stitching; stubby tail; hang tag left ear; tush tag left back leg

Replaces: None

Variations: None

Oddities: One of few wrinkled Beanies; big, square face; Wrinkles shares same birthday w/ Lucky

Commentary: Released one month after birth; in circulation 27 months before retiring; one of the cutest, most detailed Beanie dogs; like all Beanie dogs, very popular, hence, hard to find & pricey; sometimes confused w/ Pugsly the pug

Poem: This little dog is named Wrinkles
His nose is soft and often crinkles
Likes to climb up on your lap
He's a cheery sort of chap!™

11

My record

(Beanies are the #1 collectible in American collecting history. A complete, detailed record will vastly increase the value of this Beanie, if and when you ever appraise, trade, re-sell, gift, or bequeath it.)

Description *(which version do you have?):*

Gift from:

Date received/purchased: 4 — 20 — 99

Purchased from:

NAME OF PERSON OR RETAILER Fred Meyer
ADDRESS
CITY/STATE/ZIP
PHONE

Qty. purchased: **Cost ea.** 6 99 plus tax
(check one) ☑ *Cash* ☐ *Check* ☐ *Charge*

Reason(s) for purchase(s):

Traded to:

NAME
ADDRESS
CITY/STATE/ZIP
PHONE
TRADED FOR

Re-sold to:

NAME
ADDRESS
CITY/STATE/ZIP
PHONE
PRICE RE-SOLD FOR

Your feelings about and/or experiences with this Beanie:

Crunch™

Type:	Male shark	**Categories:** Blue, sea		**Style no.:** 4130	
Birthday:	January 13, 1996	**Released:** 1/1/97		**Retired:** 9/24/98	
Position:	Swimming	**Tags:** 4th & 5th generation		**Teenie:**	

Description: Marine blue plush body, white belly, white felt teeth, red felt mouth, black plastic eyes, three sets of fins, thread detailing on back fin, hang tag left fin, tush tag left side

Replaces: None

Variations: None

Oddities: None

Commentary: Released one year after birth; in circulation only 20 months, making it one of the shortest-lived Beanies, hence, hard to find & pricey; one of the fiercest-looking Beanies; very popular w/ boys.

Poem: What's for breakfast? What's for lunch?
Yum! Delicious! Munch, munch, munch!
He's eating everything by the bunch
That's the reason we named him Crunch!™

My record

(Beanies are the #1 collectible in American collecting history. A complete, detailed record will vastly increase the value of this Beanie, if and when you ever appraise, trade, re-sell, gift, or bequeath it.)

Description *(which version do you have?):*

Gift from:

Date received/purchased:

Purchased from:

NAME OF PERSON OR RETAILER

ADDRESS

CITY/STATE/ZIP

PHONE

Qty. purchased: **Cost ea.**

(check one)   ❏ *Cash*   ❏ *Check*   ❏ *Charge*

Reason(s) for purchase(s):

Traded to:

NAME

ADDRESS

CITY/STATE/ZIP

PHONE

TRADED FOR

Re-sold to:

NAME

ADDRESS

CITY/STATE/ZIP

PHONE

PRICE RE-SOLD FOR

Your feelings about and/or experiences with this Beanie:

Stinky™

Type: Male skunk   **Categories:** Woodland   **Style no.:** 4017

Birthday: February 13, 1995   **Released:** 6/3/95   **Retired:** 9/28/98

Position: Laying down   **Tags:** 3rd-5th generation   **Teenie:**

Description: Black plush body w/ white stripe running from nose to tip of tail, white inner ears, black plastic eyes & nose, long tail, hang tag left ear, tush tag left back leg

Replaces: None

Variations: None

Oddities: Stinky shares same birthday w/ Pinky

Commentary: Released four months after birth; in circulation for 39 months, making it one of the longest-running Beanies; upon retirement, immediately hard to find & pricey; like all woodland animals, very popular; very popular w/ boys

Poem: Deep in the woods he lived in a cave
Perfume and mints were the gifts he gave
He showered every night in the kitchen sink
Hoping one day he wouldn't stink!™

My record

(Beanies are the #1 collectible in American collecting history. A complete, detailed record will vastly increase the value of this Beanie, if and when you ever appraise, trade, re-sell, gift, or bequeath it.)

Description *(which version do you have?):*

Gift from:

Date received/purchased:

Purchased from:

NAME OF PERSON OR RETAILER

ADDRESS

CITY/STATE/ZIP

PHONE

Qty. purchased: **Cost ea.**
(check one)   ❏ *Cash*   ❏ *Check*   ❏ *Charge*

Reason(s) for purchase(s):

Traded to:

NAME

ADDRESS

CITY/STATE/ZIP

PHONE

TRADED FOR

Re-sold to:

NAME

ADDRESS

CITY/STATE/ZIP

PHONE

PRICE RE-SOLD FOR

Your feelings about and/or experiences with this Beanie:

5/1/98 Retireds

Place behind this tab
the following Beanie Babies®:

Baldy	Patti
Blizzard	Peanut
Bones	Pinchers
Ears	Quackers
Echo	Rover
Floppity	Scottie
Gracie	Squealer
Happy	Stripes
Hippity	Twigs
Hoppity	Waddle
Inch	Waves
Inky	Weenie
Jolly	Ziggy
Lucky	Zip

Baldy™

Type:	Male eagle *Categories:* Birds, black & white *Style no.:* 4074
Birthday:	February 17, 1996 *Released:* 5/11/97 *Retired:* 5/1/98
Position:	Perching *Tags:* 4th & 5th generation *Teenie:*
Description:	Black plush body, white head, gold beak & feet, black plastic eyes ringed w/ gold, black thread nostrils, three-pronged tail, hang tag left wing, tush tag left bottom
Replaces:	None
Variations:	None
Oddities:	None
Commentary:	Released 15 months after birth; in circulation only 12 months, making it one of the shortest-lived Beanies, hence, hard to find & pricey
Poem:	Hair on his head is quite scant We suggest Baldy get a transplant Watching over the land of the free Hair in his eyes would make it hard to see!™

My record

(Beanies are the #1 collectible in American collecting history. A complete, detailed record will vastly increase the value of this Beanie, if and when you ever appraise, trade, re-sell, gift, or bequeath it.)

Description *(which version do you have?)*:

Gift from:

Date received/purchased:

Purchased from:

NAME OF PERSON OR RETAILER

ADDRESS

CITY/STATE/ZIP

PHONE

Qty. purchased: **Cost ea.**
(check one)   ❏ *Cash*   ❏ *Check*   ❏ *Charge*

Reason(s) for purchase(s):

Traded to:

NAME

ADDRESS

CITY/STATE/ZIP

PHONE

TRADED FOR

Re-sold to:

NAME

ADDRESS

CITY/STATE/ZIP

PHONE

PRICE RE-SOLD FOR

Your feelings about and/or experiences with this Beanie:

Blizzard™

Type:	Female tiger	***Categories:***	Big cat, striped	***Style no.:***	4163

Birthday: December 12, 1996   ***Released:*** 5/11/97   ***Retired:*** 5/1/98

Position: Laying down   ***Tags:*** 4th & 5th generation   ***Teenie:***

Description: White plush body w/ black stripes, black plastic eyes ringed w/ blue, flesh-colored velvet nose, black thread whiskers, hang tag left ear, tush tag left back leg

Replaces: None

Variations: Width of stripes

Oddities: None

Commentary: Released five months after birth; in circulation only 12 months, making it one of the shortest-lived Beanies, hence, hard to find & pricey; one of the most beautiful Beanies, hence, very popular

Poem: In the mountains, where it's snowy and cold
Lives a beautiful tiger, I've been told
Black and white, she's hard to compare
Of all the tigers, she is most rare!™

My record

(Beanies are the #1 collectible in American collecting history. A complete, detailed record will vastly increase the value of this Beanie, if and when you ever appraise, trade, re-sell, gift, or bequeath it.)

Description *(which version do you have?):*

_____

_____

_____

Gift from: _____

Date received/purchased: _____

Purchased from:

NAME OF PERSON OR RETAILER

ADDRESS

CITY/STATE/ZIP

PHONE

Qty. purchased: **Cost ea.**
(check one)   ❏ *Cash*   ❏ *Check*   ❏ *Charge*

Reason(s) for purchase(s):

_____

_____

_____

Traded to:

NAME

ADDRESS

CITY/STATE/ZIP

PHONE

TRADED FOR

Re-sold to:

NAME

ADDRESS

CITY/STATE/ZIP

PHONE

PRICE RE-SOLD FOR

Your feelings about and/or experiences with this Beanie:

_____

_____

_____

_____

Bones™

Type: Male hound **Categories:** Brown, dog **Style no.:** 4001

Birthday: January 18, 1994 **Released:** 6/25/94 **Retired:** 5/1/98

Position: Laying down **Tags:** 1st-5th generation **Teenie:** 5/98

Description: Light brown plush body, darker brown long ears & stubby tail, black plastic eyes & nose, black thread eyebrows, hang tag left ear, tush tag left back leg

Replaces: None

Variations: Three versions of last line of poem

Oddities: None

Commentary: Released five months after birth; in circulation 47 months before retiring, making it one of the longest-running Beanies, hence, more readily available; one of few Beanies w/ all five generations of tags

Poem: Bones is a dog that loves to chew
Chairs and tables and a smelly old shoe
"You're so destructive," all would shout
That stopped when his teeth fell out!™

My record

(Beanies are the #1 collectible in American collecting history. A complete, detailed record will vastly increase the value of this Beanie, if and when you ever appraise, trade, re-sell, gift, or bequeath it.)

Description *(which version do you have?):*

Gift from:

Date received/purchased:

Purchased from:

NAME OF PERSON OR RETAILER

ADDRESS

CITY/STATE/ZIP

PHONE

Qty. purchased: **Cost ea.**
(check one)   ❏ *Cash*   ❏ *Check*   ❏ *Charge*

Reason(s) for purchase(s):

Traded to:

NAME

ADDRESS

CITY/STATE/ZIP

PHONE

TRADED FOR

Re-sold to:

NAME

ADDRESS

CITY/STATE/ZIP

PHONE

PRICE RE-SOLD FOR

Your feelings about and/or experiences with this Beanie:

Ears™

Type:	Male bunny	***Categories:***	Brown, bunny	***Style no.:***	4018
Birthday:	April 18, 1995	***Released:***	1/7/96	***Retired:***	5/1/98
Position:	Laying down	***Tags:***	3rd-5th generation	***Teenie:***	

Description: Brown plush body; white under snout, under ears & tail; black plastic eyes; pink plastic nose; pink thread whiskers; long ears & stubby tail; hang tag left ear; tush tag left back leg

Replaces: None

Variations: None

Oddities: All four bunnies retired same date

Commentary: Released nine months after birth; in circulation 28 months before retiring; popular Easter decoration/gift; popular quartet w/ 3 pastel bunnies

Poem: He's been eating carrots so long
Didn't understand what was wrong
Couldn't see the board during classes
Until the doctor gave him glasses!™

My record

(Beanies are the #1 collectible in American collecting history. A complete, detailed record will vastly increase the value of this Beanie, if and when you ever appraise, trade, re-sell, gift, or bequeath it.)

Description *(which version do you have?):*

Gift from:

Date received/purchased:

Purchased from:

NAME OF PERSON OR RETAILER

ADDRESS

CITY/STATE/ZIP

PHONE

Qty. purchased: **Cost ea.**
(check one)   ❑ *Cash*   ❑ *Check*   ❑ *Charge*

Reason(s) for purchase(s):

Traded to:

NAME

ADDRESS

CITY/STATE/ZIP

PHONE

TRADED FOR

Re-sold to:

NAME

ADDRESS

CITY/STATE/ZIP

PHONE

PRICE RE-SOLD FOR

Your feelings about and/or experiences with this Beanie:

Echo™

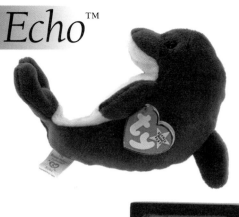

Type:	Female dolphin	*Categories:*	Blue, sea	*Style no.:*	4180
Birthday:	December 21, 1996	*Released:*	5/11/97	*Retired:*	5/1/98
Position:	Leaping	*Tags:*	4th & 5th generation	*Teenie:*	

Description: Marine blue plush body, white belly & under chin, black plastic eyes, three sets of fins, split tail fin, hang tag left fin, tush tag back

Replaces: Flash the gray dolphin, style no. 4021, birthday 5/13/93, released 1/8/94, retired 5/11/97, rare & expensive

Variations: None

Oddities: Originally released w/ Waves tag

Commentary: Released five months after birth; in circulation only one year, making it one of the shortest-lived Beanies, hence, hard to find & pricey

Poem: Echo the dolphin lives in the sea
Playing with her friends, like you and me
Through the waves she echoes the sound
"I'm so glad to have you around!"™

My record

(Beanies are the #1 collectible in American collecting history. A complete, detailed record will vastly increase the value of this Beanie, if and when you ever appraise, trade, re-sell, gift, or bequeath it.)

Description *(which version do you have?):*

Gift from:

Date received/purchased:

Purchased from:

NAME OF PERSON OR RETAILER

ADDRESS

CITY/STATE/ZIP

PHONE

Qty. purchased: **Cost ea.**
(check one)   ❏ *Cash*   ❏ *Check*   ❏ *Charge*

Reason(s) for purchase(s):

Traded to:

NAME

ADDRESS

CITY/STATE/ZIP

PHONE

TRADED FOR

Re-sold to:

NAME

ADDRESS

CITY/STATE/ZIP

PHONE

PRICE RE-SOLD FOR

Your feelings about and/or experiences with this Beanie:

Floppity™

Type:	Bunny	***Categories:***	Bunny, lavender	***Style no.:***	4118
Birthday:	May 28, 1996	***Released:***	1/1/97	***Retired:***	5/1/98
Position:	Sitting up	***Tags:***	4th & 5th generation	***Teenie:***	

Description: Lavender plush body, pink flannel under ears, white stubby tail, black plastic eyes, pink plastic nose, pink thread whiskers, lavender satin ribbon tied around neck, long ears, hang tag left ear, tush tag left bottom

Replaces: None

Variations: None

Oddities: Only bunny w/ no gender indicated; bunnies are not lavender; all three pastel bunnies released & retired same dates.

Commentary: Released eight months after birth; in circulation only 16 months before retiring, making it one of the shortest-lived Beanies, hence, hard to find & pricey; one of few Beanies w/ unrealistic coloring; popular Easter decoration/gift; popular trio w/ other 2 pastel bunnies

Poem: Floppity hops from here to there
Searching for eggs without a care
Lavender coat from head to toe
All dressed up and nowhere to go!™

My record

(Beanies are the #1 collectible in American collecting history. A complete, detailed record will vastly increase the value of this Beanie, if and when you ever appraise, trade, re-sell, gift, or bequeath it.)

Description *(which version do you have?):*

Gift from:

Date received/purchased:

Purchased from:

NAME OF PERSON OR RETAILER

ADDRESS

CITY/STATE/ZIP

PHONE

Qty. purchased: **Cost ea.**
(check one)   ❑ *Cash*   ❑ *Check*   ❑ *Charge*

Reason(s) for purchase(s):

Traded to:

NAME

ADDRESS

CITY/STATE/ZIP

PHONE

TRADED FOR

Re-sold to:

NAME

ADDRESS

CITY/STATE/ZIP

PHONE

PRICE RE-SOLD FOR

Your feelings about and/or experiences with this Beanie:

Gracie™

Type:	Female swan	***Categories:*** Bird, farm	***Style no.:*** 4126

Birthday: June 17, 1996   ***Released:*** 1/1/97   ***Retired:*** 5/1/98

Position: Swimming   ***Tags:*** 4th & 5th generation   ***Teenie:***

Description: White plush body, bright orange beak & webbed feet, black plastic eyes, long neck, hang tag left wing, tush tag left bottom

Replaces: None

Variations: None

Oddities: None

Commentary: Released six months after birthday; in circulation only 16 months before retiring, making it one of the shortest-lived Beanies, hence, hard to find & pricey; one of the most beautiful Beanies, hence, very popular

Poem: As a duckling, she was confused
Birds on the lake were quite amused.
Poking fun until she would cry,
Now the most beautiful swan at Ty!™

7

My record

(Beanies are the #1 collectible in American collecting history. A complete, detailed record will vastly increase the value of this Beanie, if and when you ever appraise, trade, re-sell, gift, or bequeath it.)

Description *(which version do you have?):*

Gift from:

Date received/purchased:

Purchased from:

NAME OF PERSON OR RETAILER

ADDRESS

CITY/STATE/ZIP

PHONE

Qty. purchased: **Cost ea.**

(check one)   ❏ *Cash*   ❏ *Check*   ❏ *Charge*

Reason(s) for purchase(s):

Traded to:

NAME

ADDRESS

CITY/STATE/ZIP

PHONE

TRADED FOR

Re-sold to:

NAME

ADDRESS

CITY/STATE/ZIP

PHONE

PRICE RE-SOLD FOR

Your feelings about and/or experiences with this Beanie:

Happy™

Type:	Male hippo	*Categories:*	Jungle, purple	*Style no.:*	4061
Birthday:	February 25, 1994	*Released:*	6/3/95	*Retired:*	5/1/98
Position:	Laying down	*Tags:*	3rd-5th generation	*Teenie:*	5/98

Description: Purple plush body, black plastic eyes, hang tag left ear, tush tag left back leg

Replaces: Happy the gray hippo, style no. 4061, birthday 2/25/94, released 6/25/94, retired 6/3/95, extremely rare & expensive

Variations: None

Oddities: Both have same style no. & birthday; purple released same day gray retired; hippos are gray, not purple

Commentary: Released 16 months after birth; in circulation 35 months; one of few Beanies w/ unrealistic coloring

Poem: Happy the hippo loves to wade
In the river and in the shade
When Happy shoots water out of his snout
You know he's happy without a doubt!™

My record

(Beanies are the #1 collectible in American collecting history. A complete, detailed record will vastly increase the value of this Beanie, if and when you ever appraise, trade, re-sell, gift, or bequeath it.)

Description *(which version do you have?):*

Gift from:

Date received/purchased:

Purchased from:

NAME OF PERSON OR RETAILER

ADDRESS

CITY/STATE/ZIP

PHONE

Qty. purchased: **Cost ea.**
(check one)   ❏ *Cash*   ❏ *Check*   ❏ *Charge*

Reason(s) for purchase(s):

Traded to:

NAME

ADDRESS

CITY/STATE/ZIP

PHONE

TRADED FOR

Re-sold to:

NAME

ADDRESS

CITY/STATE/ZIP

PHONE

PRICE RE-SOLD FOR

Your feelings about and/or experiences with this Beanie:

Hippity™

Type:	Male bunny	*Categories:*	Bunny, green	*Style no.:*	4119	

Birthday: June 1, 1996   *Released:* 1/1/97   *Retired:* 5/1/98

Position: Sitting up   *Tags:* 4th & 5th generation   *Teenie:*

Description: Mint green plush body, pink flannel under ears & white stubby tail, black plastic eyes, pink plastic nose, pink thread whiskers, kelly green ribbon tied around neck, long ears, hang tag left ear, tush tag left bottom

Replaces: None

Variations: None

Oddities: Bunnies are not mint green; all three pastel bunnies released & retired same dates

Commentary: Released seven months after birth, in circulation only 16 months before retiring, making it one of the shortest-lived Beanies, hence, hard to find & pricey; one of few Beanies w/ unrealistic coloring; popular Easter decoration/gift; popular trio w/ other 2 pastel bunnies

Poem: Hippity is a cute little bunny
Dressed in green, he looks quite funny
Twitching his nose in the air
Sniffing a flower here and there!™

9

My record

(Beanies are the #1 collectible in American collecting history. A complete, detailed record will vastly increase the value of this Beanie, if and when you ever appraise, trade, re-sell, gift, or bequeath it.)

Description *(which version do you have?):*

Gift from:

Date received/purchased:

Purchased from:

NAME OF PERSON OR RETAILER

ADDRESS

CITY/STATE/ZIP

PHONE

Qty. purchased: **Cost ea.**
(check one)   ❏ *Cash*   ❏ *Check*   ❏ *Charge*

Reason(s) for purchase(s):

Traded to:

NAME

ADDRESS

CITY/STATE/ZIP

PHONE

TRADED FOR

Re-sold to:

NAME

ADDRESS

CITY/STATE/ZIP

PHONE

PRICE RE-SOLD FOR

Your feelings about and/or experiences with this Beanie:

Hoppity™

Type:	Female bunny	*Categories:* Bunny, pink	*Style no.:* 4117
Birthday:	April 3, 1996	*Released:* 1/1/97	*Retired:* 5/1/98
Position:	Sitting up	*Tags:* 4th & 5th generation	*Teenie:*

Description: Pink plush body, pink flannel under ears, white stubby tail, black plastic eyes, pink plastic nose, pink thread whiskers, pink satin ribbon tied around neck, long ears, hang tag left ear, tush tag left bottom

Replaces: None

Variations: None

Oddities: Bunnies are not pink; all three pastel bunnies released & retired same dates

Commentary: Released nine months after birth; in circulation only 16 months before retiring, making it one of the shortest-lived Beanies, hence, hard to find & pricey; one of few Beanies w/ unrealistic coloring; popular Easter decoration/gift; popular trio w/ other 2 pastel bunnies

Poem: Hopscotch is what she likes to play
If you don't join in, she'll hop away
So play a game if you have the time
She likes to play, rain or shine!™

My record

(Beanies are the #1 collectible in American collecting history. A complete, detailed record will vastly increase the value of this Beanie, if and when you ever appraise, trade, re-sell, gift, or bequeath it.)

Description *(which version do you have?):*

Gift from:

Date received/purchased:

Purchased from:

NAME OF PERSON OR RETAILER

ADDRESS

CITY/STATE/ZIP

PHONE

Qty. purchased: **Cost ea.**
(check one)   ❑ *Cash*   ❑ *Check*   ❑ *Charge*

Reason(s) for purchase(s):

Traded to:

NAME

ADDRESS

CITY/STATE/ZIP

PHONE

TRADED FOR

Re-sold to:

NAME

ADDRESS

CITY/STATE/ZIP

PHONE

PRICE RE-SOLD FOR

Your feelings about and/or experiences with this Beanie:

Inch™

Type: Male inchworm **_Categories:_** Insect, multi-colored **_Style no.:_** 4044

Birthday: September 3, 1995 **_Released:_** 10/15/97 **_Retired:_** 5/1/98

Position: Crawling **_Tags:_** 4th & 5th generation **_Teenie:_** 5/98

Description: Yellow, orange, green, blue, purple plush sectioned body, black plastic eyes, black yarn antennae, hang tag left side, tush tag bottom

Replaces: Inch the inchworm w/ felt antennae, style no. 4044, birthday 9/3/95, retired 10/15/97, extremely rare & expensive

Variations: None

Oddities: Both have same style no. & birthday; yarn released same day felt retired; inchworms are brown, not rainbow-colored; Inch shares same birthday w/ Claude, too

Commentary: Released 25 months after birth, in circulation only 7 months before retiring, making it one of the shortest-lived Beanies, hence, hard to find and expensive; one of few Beanies w/ unrealistic coloring; sold at stage performances of "Joseph and the Amazing Technicolor Dream Coat"

Poem: Inch the worm is a friend of mine
He goes so slow all the time
Inching around from here to there
Traveling the world without a care!™

11

My record

(Beanies are the #1 collectible in American collecting history. A complete, detailed record will vastly increase the value of this Beanie, if and when you ever appraise, trade, re-sell, gift, or bequeath it.)

Description *(which version do you have?):*

Gift from:

Date received/purchased:

Purchased from:

NAME OF PERSON OR RETAILER

ADDRESS

CITY/STATE/ZIP

PHONE

Qty. purchased: **Cost ea.**
(check one) ❏ *Cash* ❏ *Check* ❏ *Charge*

Reason(s) for purchase(s):

Traded to:

NAME

ADDRESS

CITY/STATE/ZIP

PHONE

TRADED FOR

Re-sold to:

NAME

ADDRESS

CITY/STATE/ZIP

PHONE

PRICE RE-SOLD FOR

Your feelings about and/or experiences with this Beanie:

Inky™

Type: Male octopus   **Categories:** Pink, sea   **Style no.:** 4028

Birthday: November 29, 1994   **Released:** 6/3/95   **Retired:** 5/1/98

Position: Swimming   **Tags:** 3rd-5th generation   **Teenie:**

Description: Pink plush body w/ eight legs, black & white plastic eyes, black thread v-shaped mouth, hang tag left leg, tush tag left face

Replaces: Inky the tan octopus w/o mouth, style no. 4028, birthday 11/29/94, released 6/25/94, retired 9/12/94; Inky the tan octopus w/ mouth, style no. 4028, birthday 11/29/94, released 9/12/94, retired 6/3/95; both extremely rare & expensive

Variations: None

Oddities: All have same style no. & birthday; some w/ 7 or 9 legs; tan w/ mouth released same day tan w/o mouth retired; pink released same day tan w/ mouth retired; octopuses come in many colors, but not pink

Commentary: Released seven months after birth; in circulation 35 months before retiring; one of few Beanies w/ unrealistic coloring; immediately scarce & pricey upon retirement

Poem: Inky's head is big and round
As he swims he makes no sound
If you need a hand, don't hesitate
Inky can help because he has eight!™

12

My record

(Beanies are the #1 collectible in American collecting history. A complete, detailed record will vastly increase the value of this Beanie, if and when you ever appraise, trade, re-sell, gift, or bequeath it.)

Description *(which version do you have?):*

Gift from:

Date received/purchased:

Purchased from:

NAME OF PERSON OR RETAILER

ADDRESS

CITY/STATE/ZIP

PHONE

Qty. purchased: **Cost ea.**
(check one)   ❏ *Cash*   ❏ *Check*   ❏ *Charge*

Reason(s) for purchase(s):

Traded to:

NAME

ADDRESS

CITY/STATE/ZIP

PHONE

TRADED FOR

Re-sold to:

NAME

ADDRESS

CITY/STATE/ZIP

PHONE

PRICE RE-SOLD FOR

Your feelings about and/or experiences with this Beanie:

Jolly™

Type:	Male walrus	***Categories:***	Arctic, sea	***Style no.:***	4082
Birthday:	December 2, 1996	***Released:***	5/11/97	***Retired:***	5/1/98
Position:	Leaping	***Tags:***	4th & 5th generation	***Teenie:***	

Description: Brown-gray plush body, brown hairy beard, cream felt tusks, black plastic eyes & nose, split-fin tail, hang tag left fin, tush tag back

Replaces: Tusk the walrus, style 4076, birthday 9/18/95, released 1/7/95, retired 1/1/97, rare & expensive

Variations: None

Oddities: None

Commentary: Released five months after birth; in circulation only 12 months, making it one of the shortest-lived Beanies, hence, hard to find & pricey

Poem: Jolly the walrus is not very serious
He laughs and laughs until he's delirious
He often reminds me of my dad
Always happy, never sad!™

My record

(Beanies are the #1 collectible in American collecting history. A complete, detailed record will vastly increase the value of this Beanie, if and when you ever appraise, trade, re-sell, gift, or bequeath it.)

Description *(which version do you have?):*

Gift from:

Date received/purchased:

Purchased from:

NAME OF PERSON OR RETAILER

ADDRESS

CITY/STATE/ZIP

PHONE

Qty. purchased: **Cost ea.**
(check one)   ❏ *Cash*   ❏ *Check*   ❏ *Charge*

Reason(s) for purchase(s):

Traded to:

NAME

ADDRESS

CITY/STATE/ZIP

PHONE

TRADED FOR

Re-sold to:

NAME

ADDRESS

CITY/STATE/ZIP

PHONE

PRICE RE-SOLD FOR

Your feelings about and/or experiences with this Beanie:

Lucky™

Type:	Female ladybug	***Categories:***	Insect, red	***Style no.:***	4040
Birthday:	May 1, 1995	***Released:***	2/27/96	***Retired:***	5/1/98
Position:	Crawling	***Tags:***	4th & 5th generation	***Teenie:***	

Description: Red plush body w/ black printed spots, black head & feet, black plastic eyes, black thread antennae, hang tag left side, tush tag back

Replaces: Lucky w/ felt spots, style no. 4040, birthday 5/1/95, released 6/25/94, retired 2/27/96, extremely rare & expensive

Variations: 1st version, 7 glued spots; 2nd, 11 printed; 3rd, 21 printed

Oddities: Both have same style no. & birthday; printed spots released same day felt spots retired; Lucky shares same birthday w/ Wrinkles, too

Commentary: Released nine months after birth; in circulation only 21 months, making it one of the shortest-lived Beanies, hence, hard to find & pricey; very popular with girls

Poem: Lucky the ladybug loves the lotto
"Someone must win" that's her motto
But save your dimes and even a penny
Don't spend on the lotto and you'll have many!™

My record

(Beanies are the #1 collectible in American collecting history. A complete, detailed record will vastly increase the value of this Beanie, if and when you ever appraise, trade, re-sell, gift, or bequeath it.)

Description *(which version do you have?):*

Gift from:

Date received/purchased:

Purchased from:

NAME OF PERSON OR RETAILER

ADDRESS

CITY/STATE/ZIP

PHONE

Qty. purchased: **Cost ea.**
(check one)   ❏ *Cash*   ❏ *Check*   ❏ *Charge*

Reason(s) for purchase(s):

Traded to:

NAME

ADDRESS

CITY/STATE/ZIP

PHONE

TRADED FOR

Re-sold to:

NAME

ADDRESS

CITY/STATE/ZIP

PHONE

PRICE RE-SOLD FOR

Your feelings about and/or experiences with this Beanie:

Patti®

1 of the original 9 Beanies

Type:	Female platypus	**Categories:**	Aussie, sea	**Style no.:**	4025
Birthday:	January 6, 1993	**Released:**	2/28/95	**Retired:**	5/1/98
Position:	Swimming	**Tags:**	3rd-5th generation	**Teenie:**	5/97

Description: Magenta plush body, gold bill & webbed feet, black plastic eyes, hang tag left front foot, tush tag bottom

Replaces: Patti the maroon platypus, style no. 4025, birthday 1/6/93, released 1/8/94, retired 2/28/95, one of the rarest and most expensive Beanies ever

Variations: None

Oddities: Both have same style no. & birthday; magenta released same day maroon retired; platypuses are brown, not maroon or magenta

Commentary: Released two years after birth; in circulation 39 months before retiring; one of few Beanies w/ unrealistic coloring; 1 of the original 9 Beanies, hence, very popular

Poem: Ran into Patti one day while walking
Believe me she wouldn't stop talking
Listened and listened to her speak
That would explain her extra large beak!™

My record

(Beanies are the #1 collectible in American collecting history. A complete, detailed record will vastly increase the value of this Beanie, if and when you ever appraise, trade, re-sell, gift, or bequeath it.)

Description *(which version do you have?):*

Gift from:

Date received/purchased:

Purchased from:

NAME OF PERSON OR RETAILER

ADDRESS

CITY/STATE/ZIP

PHONE

Qty. purchased:　　**Cost ea.**
(check one)　　❑ *Cash*　　　❑ *Check*　　　❑ *Charge*

Reason(s) for purchase(s):

Traded to:

NAME

ADDRESS

CITY/STATE/ZIP

PHONE

TRADED FOR

Re-sold to:

NAME

ADDRESS

CITY/STATE/ZIP

PHONE

PRICE RE-SOLD FOR

Your feelings about and/or experiences with this Beanie:

Peanut™

Type:	Female elephant	*Categories:* Blue, jungle	*Style no.:* 4062	
Birthday:	January 25, 1995	*Released:* 10/2/95	*Retired:* 5/1/98	
Position:	Laying down	*Tags:* 3rd-5th generation	*Teenie:* 5/98	

Description: Light blue plush, pink inner ears, black plastic eyes, trunk, knotted tail, hang tag left ear, tush tag left back leg

Replaces: Peanut the royal blue elephant, style no. 4062, birthday 1/25/95, released 6/3/95, retired 10/2/95, one of the rarest and most expensive Beanies ever

Variations: None

Oddities: Both have same style no. & birthday; elephants are gray, not blue

Commentary: Released nine months after birth; in circulation 31 months before retiring; one of few Beanies w/ unrealistic coloring

Poem: Peanut the elephant walks on tip-toes
Quietly sneaking wherever she goes
She'll sneak up on you and a hug you'll get
Peanut is a friend you won't soon forget!™

My record

(Beanies are the #1 collectible in American collecting history. A complete, detailed record will vastly increase the value of this Beanie, if and when you ever appraise, trade, re-sell, gift, or bequeath it.)

Description *(which version do you have?):*

Gift from:

Date received/purchased:

Purchased from:

NAME OF PERSON OR RETAILER

ADDRESS

CITY/STATE/ZIP

PHONE

Qty. purchased: **Cost ea.**
(check one)   ❏ *Cash*   ❏ *Check*   ❏ *Charge*

Reason(s) for purchase(s):

Traded to:

NAME

ADDRESS

CITY/STATE/ZIP

PHONE

TRADED FOR

Re-sold to:

NAME

ADDRESS

CITY/STATE/ZIP

PHONE

PRICE RE-SOLD FOR

Your feelings about and/or experiences with this Beanie:

Pinchers™

1 of the original 9 Beanies

Type:	Male lobster	*Categories:* Red, sea	*Style no.:* 4026
Birthday:	June 19, 1993	*Released:* 1/8/94	*Retired:* 5/1/98
Position:	Swimming	*Tags:* 1st-5th generation	*Teenie:* 5/98

Description: Bright red plush body, black plastic eyes, black thread antennae, two claws, fan tail, hang tag left claw, tush tag left back

Replaces: None

Variations: Formerly named Punchers, extremely rare & expensive

Oddities: Lobsters are blue/green when alive, red when boiled

Commentary: Released six months after birth; in circulation 52 months, making it one of the longest-running Beanies ever; 1 of the original 9 Beanies, hence, very popular; immediately scarce & pricey upon retirement; one of few Beanies w/ all five generations of tags

Poem: This lobster wants to pinch
Eating his food inch by inch
Balancing carefully with his tail
Moving forward slow as a snail!™

17

My record

(Beanies are the #1 collectible in American collecting history. A complete, detailed record will vastly increase the value of this Beanie, if and when you ever appraise, trade, re-sell, gift, or bequeath it.)

Description *(which version do you have?):*

Gift from:

Date received/purchased:

Purchased from:

NAME OF PERSON OR RETAILER

ADDRESS

CITY/STATE/ZIP

PHONE

Qty. purchased: **Cost ea.**
(check one)   ❏ *Cash*   ❏ *Check*   ❏ *Charge*

Reason(s) for purchase(s):

Traded to:

NAME

ADDRESS

CITY/STATE/ZIP

PHONE

TRADED FOR

Re-sold to:

NAME

ADDRESS

CITY/STATE/ZIP

PHONE

PRICE RE-SOLD FOR

Your feelings about and/or experiences with this Beanie:

Quackers™

Type: Male duck   **Categories:** Bird, farm   **Style no.:** 4024

Birthday: April 19, 1994   **Released:** 1/7/95   **Retired:** 5/1/98

Position: Squatting   **Tags:** 2nd-5th generation   **Teenie:** 4/97

Description: Bright yellow plush body, bright orange beak & webbed feet, black plastic eyes, black thread eyebrows, two wings, hang tag left wing, tush tag bottom

Replaces: Quackers w/o wings, style no. 4024, birthday 4/19/94, released 6/25/94, retired 1/7/95, one of the rarest and most expensive Beanies ever

Variations: Some w/ iridescent orange feet

Oddities: None

Commentary: Released eight months after birth; in circulation 40 months, making it one of the longest-running Beanies; popular Easter decoration/gift

Poem: There is a duck by the name of Quackers
Every night he eats animal crackers
He swims in a lake that's clear and blue
But he'll come to the shore to be with you!™

18

My record

(Beanies are the #1 collectible in American collecting history. A complete, detailed record will vastly increase the value of this Beanie, if and when you ever appraise, trade, re-sell, gift, or bequeath it.)

Description *(which version do you have?):*

Gift from:

Date received/purchased:

Purchased from:

NAME OF PERSON OR RETAILER

ADDRESS

CITY/STATE/ZIP

PHONE

Qty. purchased: **Cost ea.**
(check one)   ❏ *Cash*   ❏ *Check*   ❏ *Charge*

Reason(s) for purchase(s):

Traded to:

NAME

ADDRESS

CITY/STATE/ZIP

PHONE

TRADED FOR

Re-sold to:

NAME

ADDRESS

CITY/STATE/ZIP

PHONE

PRICE RE-SOLD FOR

Your feelings about and/or experiences with this Beanie:

Rover™

Type: Male hound dog   **Categories:** Dog, red   **Style no.:** 4101

Birthday: May 30, 1996   **Released:** 6/15/96   **Retired:** 5/1/98

Position: Standing   **Tags:** 4th & 5th generation   **Teenie:**

Description: Bright red plush body, black plastic eyes & big nose, exaggerated snout & ears, stubby tail, hang tag left ear, tush tag left back leg

Replaces: None

Variations: None

Oddities: No dog has ever been this shade of red

Commentary: Released one month after birth; in circulation 23 months before retiring, making it one of the shortest-lived Beanies, hence, hard to find & pricey; similar to the story-book dog Clifford

Poem: This dog is red and his name is Rover
If you call him he is sure to come over
He barks and plays with all his might
But worry not, he won't bite!™

My record

(Beanies are the #1 collectible in American collecting history. A complete, detailed record will vastly increase the value of this Beanie, if and when you ever appraise, trade, re-sell, gift, or bequeath it.)

Description *(which version do you have?):*

Gift from:

Date received/purchased:

Purchased from:

NAME OF PERSON OR RETAILER

ADDRESS

CITY/STATE/ZIP

PHONE

Qty. purchased: **Cost ea.**
(check one)   ❏ *Cash*   ❏ *Check*   ❏ *Charge*

Reason(s) for purchase(s):

Traded to:

NAME

ADDRESS

CITY/STATE/ZIP

PHONE

TRADED FOR

Re-sold to:

NAME

ADDRESS

CITY/STATE/ZIP

PHONE

PRICE RE-SOLD FOR

Your feelings about and/or experiences with this Beanie:

Scottie™

Type:	Male Scottish terrier	**Categories:**	Black, dog	**Style no.:**	4102

Birthday: June 15, 1996   **Released:** 6/15/96   **Retired:** 5/1/98

Position: Standing   **Tags:** 4th & 5th generation   **Teenie:**

Description: Black napped body, black plastic eyes & nose, short ears & stubby tail, hang tag left ear, tush tag left back leg

Replaces: None

Variations: None

Oddities: Born & released on same date; Scottie has second birthday (6/3/96) erroneously listed on some tags

Commentary: In circulation only 23 months, making it one of the shortest-lived Beanies, hence, hard to find & pricey; like all napped Beanies, very popular

Poem: Scottie is a friendly sort
Even though his legs are short
He is always happy as can be
His best friends are you and me!™

My record

(Beanies are the #1 collectible in American collecting history. A complete, detailed record will vastly increase the value of this Beanie, if and when you ever appraise, trade, re-sell, gift, or bequeath it.)

Description *(which version do you have?):*

Gift from:

Date received/purchased:

Purchased from:

NAME OF PERSON OR RETAILER

ADDRESS

CITY/STATE/ZIP

PHONE

Qty. purchased: **Cost ea.**
(check one)   ❏ *Cash*   ❏ *Check*   ❏ *Charge*

Reason(s) for purchase(s):

Traded to:

NAME

ADDRESS

CITY/STATE/ZIP

PHONE

TRADED FOR

Re-sold to:

NAME

ADDRESS

CITY/STATE/ZIP

PHONE

PRICE RE-SOLD FOR

Your feelings about and/or experiences with this Beanie:

Squealer™

1 of the original 9 Beanies

Type:	Male pig	***Categories:***	Farm, pink	***Style no.:***	4005

Birthday:	April 23, 1993	***Released:***	1/8/94	***Retired:***	5/1/98

Position:	Laying down	***Tags:*** 1st-5th generation	***Teenie:***	

Description: Light pink plush body; darker pink snout, ears, tail; black plastic eyes; dark pink thread nostrils; knotted tail; hang tag left ear; tush tag left back leg

Replaces: None

Variations: Two versions of last line of poem

Oddities: None

Commentary: Released nine months after birth; in circulation 48 months, making it one of the longest-running Beanies; 1of the original 9 Beanies, hence, very popular; immediately scarce & pricey upon retirement; one of few Beanies w/ all 5 generations of tags

Poem: Squealer likes to joke around
He is known as class clown
Listen to his stories for awhile
There is no doubt he will make you smile!™

My record

(Beanies are the #1 collectible in American collecting history. A complete, detailed record will vastly increase the value of this Beanie, if and when you ever appraise, trade, re-sell, gift, or bequeath it.)

Description *(which version do you have?):*

Gift from:

Date received/purchased:

Purchased from:

NAME OF PERSON OR RETAILER

ADDRESS

CITY/STATE/ZIP

PHONE

Qty. purchased: **Cost ea.**
(check one)   ❑ *Cash*   ❑ *Check*   ❑ *Charge*

Reason(s) for purchase(s):

Traded to:

NAME

ADDRESS

CITY/STATE/ZIP

PHONE

TRADED FOR

Re-sold to:

NAME

ADDRESS

CITY/STATE/ZIP

PHONE

PRICE RE-SOLD FOR

Your feelings about and/or experiences with this Beanie:

Stripes™

Type: Male tiger **Categories:** Big cat, jungle, striped **Style no.:** 4065

Birthday: June 11, 1995 **Released:** 6/3/96 **Retired:** 5/1/98

Position: Laying down **Tags:** 4th & 5th generation **Teenie:**

Description: Gold plush body w/ black stripes, black plastic eyes ringed w/ gold, flesh velvet nose, black thread whiskers, hang tag left ear, tush tag left back leg

Replaces: Stripes w/ thin stripes, style no. 4065, birthday 6/11/95, released 1/7/96, retired 6/3/96, extremely rare & expensive

Variations: Some early Stripes had fuzzy bellies, extremely rare & expensive; two versions of third line of poem

Oddities: Both have same style no. & birthday

Commentary: Released one year after birth, in circulation almost two years

Poem: Stripes was never fierce nor strong
So with tigers, he didn't get along
Jungle life was hard getting by
So he came to his friends at Ty!™

22

My record

(Beanies are the #1 collectible in American collecting history. A complete, detailed record will vastly increase the value of this Beanie, if and when you ever appraise, trade, re-sell, gift, or bequeath it.)

Description *(which version do you have?):*

Gift from:

Date received/purchased:

Purchased from:

NAME OF PERSON OR RETAILER

ADDRESS

CITY/STATE/ZIP

PHONE

Qty. purchased: **Cost ea.**
(check one)   ❏ *Cash*   ❏ *Check*   ❏ *Charge*

Reason(s) for purchase(s):

Traded to:

NAME

ADDRESS

CITY/STATE/ZIP

PHONE

TRADED FOR

Re-sold to:

NAME

ADDRESS

CITY/STATE/ZIP

PHONE

PRICE RE-SOLD FOR

Your feelings about and/or experiences with this Beanie:

Twigs™

Type:	Male giraffe	*Categories:* Jungle, spotted	*Style no.:* 4068

Birthday: May 19, 1995   *Released:* 1/7/96   *Retired:* 5/1/98

Position: Sitting   *Tags:* 3rd-5th generation   *Teenie:* 5/98

Description: Pale yellow plush body w/ orange spots; brown inner ears, mane & hooves; black plastic eyes; hang tag left ear; tush tag left back leg

Replaces: None

Variations: None

Oddities: None

Commentary: Released eight months after birth; in circulation only 17 months before retirement, making it one of the shortest-lived Beanies, hence, hard to find & pricey

Poem: Twigs has his head in the clouds
He stands tall, he stands proud
With legs so skinny they wobble and shake
What an unusual friend he will make!™

My record

(Beanies are the #1 collectible in American collecting history. A complete, detailed record will vastly increase the value of this Beanie, if and when you ever appraise, trade, re-sell, gift, or bequeath it.)

Description *(which version do you have?):*

Gift from:

Date received/purchased:

Purchased from:

NAME OF PERSON OR RETAILER

ADDRESS

CITY/STATE/ZIP

PHONE

Qty. purchased: **Cost ea.**
(check one)   ❏ *Cash*   ❏ *Check*   ❏ *Charge*

Reason(s) for purchase(s):

Traded to:

NAME

ADDRESS

CITY/STATE/ZIP

PHONE

TRADED FOR

Re-sold to:

NAME

ADDRESS

CITY/STATE/ZIP

PHONE

PRICE RE-SOLD FOR

Your feelings about and/or experiences with this Beanie:

Waddle™

Type: Male penguin   **Categories:** Arctic, bird   **Style no.:** 4075

Birthday: December 19, 1995   **Released:** 6/3/95   **Retired:** 5/1/98

Position: Standing   **Tags:** 3rd-5th generation   **Teenie:** 5/98

Description: Black plush body, white belly & under wings, orange beak & feet, yellow collar, black plastic eyes, hang tag left wing, tush tag bottom

Replaces: None

Variations: None

Oddities: Released six months before birth

Commentary: In circulation nearly three years; one of the most handsome Beanies, hence, very popular; immediately scarce & pricey upon retirement

Poem: Waddle the penguin likes to dress up
Every night he wears his tux
When Waddle walks, it never fails
He always trips over his tails!™

My record

(Beanies are the #1 collectible in American collecting history. A complete, detailed record will vastly increase the value of this Beanie, if and when you ever appraise, trade, re-sell, gift, or bequeath it.)

Description *(which version do you have?):*

Gift from:

Date received/purchased:

Purchased from:

NAME OF PERSON OR RETAILER

ADDRESS

CITY/STATE/ZIP

PHONE

Qty. purchased: **Cost ea.**
(check one)   ❏ *Cash*   ❏ *Check*   ❏ *Charge*

Reason(s) for purchase(s):

Traded to:

NAME

ADDRESS

CITY/STATE/ZIP

PHONE

TRADED FOR

Re-sold to:

NAME

ADDRESS

CITY/STATE/ZIP

PHONE

PRICE RE-SOLD FOR

Your feelings about and/or experiences with this Beanie:

Waves™

Type:	Male whale	*Categories:*	Black & white, sea	*Style no.:*	4084

Birthday: December 8, 1996   *Released:* 5/11/97   *Retired:* 5/1/98

Position: Leaping   *Tags:* 4th & 5th generation   *Teenie:*

Description: Black plush body, white belly, black plastic eyes, three sets of fins, hang tag left fin, tush tag back

Replaces: Splash the whale, style no. 4022, birthday 7/8/93, released 1/8/94, retired 5/11/97, rare & expensive

Variations: None

Oddities: Waves released same day Splash retired, originally released w/ Echo tag

Commentary: Released five months after birth; in circulation only one year, making it one of the shortest-lived Beanies, hence, hard to find & pricey

Poem: Join him today on the Internet
Don't be afraid to get your feet wet
He taught all the Beanies how to surf
Our web page is his home turf!™

My record

(Beanies are the #1 collectible in American collecting history. A complete, detailed record will vastly increase the value of this Beanie, if and when you ever appraise, trade, re-sell, gift, or bequeath it.)

Description *(which version do you have?):*

Gift from:

Date received/purchased:

Purchased from:

NAME OF PERSON OR RETAILER

ADDRESS

CITY/STATE/ZIP

PHONE

Qty. purchased: **Cost ea.**

(check one)   ❏ *Cash*   ❏ *Check*   ❏ *Charge*

Reason(s) for purchase(s):

Traded to:

NAME

ADDRESS

CITY/STATE/ZIP

PHONE

TRADED FOR

Re-sold to:

NAME

ADDRESS

CITY/STATE/ZIP

PHONE

PRICE RE-SOLD FOR

Your feelings about and/or experiences with this Beanie:

Weenie™

Type:	Male dachshund	*Categories:* Brown, dog	*Style no.:* 4013
Birthday:	July 20, 1995	*Released:* 1/7/96	*Retired:* 5/1/98
Position:	Standing	*Tags:* 3rd-5th generation	*Teenie:*

Description: Brown plush body, black plastic eyes ringed w/ brown, black plastic nose, short legs, long ears, stubby tail, hang tag left ear, tush tag left back leg

Replaces: None

Variations: None

Oddities: Weenie shares the same style no. w/ Peking

Commentary: Released six months after birth, in circulation 28 months before retiring, immediately scarce & pricey upon retirement

Poem: Weenie the dog is quite a sight
Long of body and short of height
He perches himself high on a log
And considers himself to be top dog!™

My record

(Beanies are the #1 collectible in American collecting history. A complete, detailed record will vastly increase the value of this Beanie, if and when you ever appraise, trade, re-sell, gift, or bequeath it.)

Description *(which version do you have?):*

Gift from:

Date received/purchased:

Purchased from:

NAME OF PERSON OR RETAILER

ADDRESS

CITY/STATE/ZIP

PHONE

Qty. purchased: **Cost ea.**
(check one)   ❏ *Cash*   ❏ *Check*   ❏ *Charge*

Reason(s) for purchase(s):

Traded to:

NAME

ADDRESS

CITY/STATE/ZIP

PHONE

TRADED FOR

Re-sold to:

NAME

ADDRESS

CITY/STATE/ZIP

PHONE

PRICE RE-SOLD FOR

Your feelings about and/or experiences with this Beanie:

Ziggy™

Type:	Male zebra	*Categories:* Jungle, striped	*Style no.:* 4063
Birthday:	December 24, 1995	*Released:* 6/3/95	*Retired:* 5/1/98
Position:	Laying down	*Tags:* 3rd-5th generation	*Teenie:*

Description: White plush body w/ black stripes, black inner ears, black yarn mane & tail, black plastic eyes, hang tag left ear, tush tag left back leg

Replaces: None

Variations: None

Oddities: Released six months before birth

Commentary: In circulation almost three years before retiring, one of the most popular jungle Beanies

Poem: Ziggy likes soccer—he's a referee
That way he watches the games for free
The other Beanies don't think it's fair
But Ziggy the zebra doesn't care!™

My record

(Beanies are the #1 collectible in American collecting history. A complete, detailed record will vastly increase the value of this Beanie, if and when you ever appraise, trade, re-sell, gift, or bequeath it.)

Description *(which version do you have?):*

Gift from:

Date received/purchased:

Purchased from:

NAME OF PERSON OR RETAILER

ADDRESS

CITY/STATE/ZIP

PHONE

Qty. purchased: **Cost ea.**
(check one)   ❏ *Cash*   ❏ *Check*   ❏ *Charge*

Reason(s) for purchase(s):

Traded to:

NAME

ADDRESS

CITY/STATE/ZIP

PHONE

TRADED FOR

Re-sold to:

NAME

ADDRESS

CITY/STATE/ZIP

PHONE

PRICE RE-SOLD FOR

Your feelings about and/or experiences with this Beanie:

Zip™

Type:	Cat *Categories:* Black & white, cats *Style no.:* 4004	

Birthday: March 28, 1994   **Released:** 3/10/96   **Retired:** 5/1/98

Position: Laying down   **Tags:** 3rd-5th generation   **Teenie:** 5/98

Description: Black plush body, white inner ears & socks, black plastic eyes ringed w/ green, pink plastic nose, white thread whiskers & mouth, hang tag left ear, tush tag left back leg

Replaces: Zip the black cat w/ white face & belly, style no. 4004, birthday 3/28/94, released 1/7/95, retired 1/7/96; Zip the all black cat, style no. 4004, birthday 3/28/94, released 1/7/96, retired 3/10/96; both extremely rare & expensive

Variations: None

Oddities: One of few Beanies w/ no gender indicated, all have same style no. & birthdays, Zip w/ white socks released same day all black Zip retired

Commentary: Released two years after birthday, in circulation 26 months before retiring, immediately scarce & pricey upon retirement

Poem: Keep Zip by your side all the day through
Zip is good luck, you'll see it's true
When you have something you need to do
Zip will always believe in you!™

My record

(Beanies are the #1 collectible in American collecting history. A complete, detailed record will vastly increase the value of this Beanie, if and when you ever appraise, trade, re-sell, gift, or bequeath it.)

Description *(which version do you have?):*

Gift from:

Date received/purchased:

Purchased from:

NAME OF PERSON OR RETAILER

ADDRESS

CITY/STATE/ZIP

PHONE

Qty. purchased:　　　**Cost ea.**
(check one)　　　❑ *Cash*　　　❑ *Check*　　　❑ *Charge*

Reason(s) for purchase(s):

Traded to:

NAME

ADDRESS

CITY/STATE/ZIP

PHONE

TRADED FOR

Re-sold to:

NAME

ADDRESS

CITY/STATE/ZIP

PHONE

PRICE RE-SOLD FOR

Your feelings about and/or experiences with this Beanie:

Teddy Brown™

(old face)

Type:	Bear	***Categories:***	Bear, brown	***Style no.:***	4050

Birthday: None   ***Released:*** 6/25/94   ***Retired:*** 1/7/95

Position: Sitting up   ***Tags:*** 1st & 2nd generation   ***Teenie:***

Description: Brown plush body, black plastic eyes & nose, hang tag left ear, tush tag left bottom

Replaces: None

Variations: None

Oddities: Like all '95-'96 Retired Beanies, no gender indicated, no birthday & no poem; same style no. as Teddy Brown (new face); all old-faced Teddies released & retired same dates; one of few bears w/ no ribbon tied around neck

Commentary: In circulation only seven months before retiring, making it one of the shortest-lived Beanies ever; one of the rarest, most valued, most expensive Beanies ever; replaced by Teddy Brown w/ new face & ribbon

Poem: None

My record

(Beanies are the #1 collectible in American collecting history. A complete, detailed record will vastly increase the value of this Beanie, if and when you ever appraise, trade, re-sell, gift, or bequeath it.)

Description *(which version do you have?):*

_____

_____

_____

Gift from: _____

Date received/purchased: _____

Purchased from: _____

NAME OF PERSON OR RETAILER

ADDRESS

CITY/STATE/ZIP

PHONE

Qty. purchased: **Cost ea.**

(check one)   ❏ *Cash*   ❏ *Check*   ❏ *Charge*

Reason(s) for purchase(s): _____

_____

_____

_____

Traded to: _____

NAME

ADDRESS

CITY/STATE/ZIP

PHONE

TRADED FOR

Re-sold to: _____

NAME

ADDRESS

CITY/STATE/ZIP

PHONE

PRICE RE-SOLD FOR

Your feelings about and/or experiences with this Beanie:

_____

_____

_____

12/31/97 Retireds

Place behind this tab
the following Beanie Babies®:

1997 Holiday Teddy
Bucky   *Magic*
Cubbie   *Nip*
Goldie   *Snowball*
Lizzy   *Spooky*

1997 Holiday Teddy™

Type: Bear   ***Categories:*** Bear, brown, holiday   ***Style no.:*** 4200

Birthday: December 25, 1996   ***Released:*** 10/1/97   ***Retired:*** 12/31/97

Position: Sitting up   ***Tags:*** 4th generation   ***Teenie:***

Description: Brown plush body, red plush cap w/ white trim & ball covering right ear, red felt scarf w/ white trim, black plastic eyes, brown plastic nose, hang tag left ear, tush tag left bottom

Replaces: None

Variations: None

Oddities: One of few Beanies w/ no gender indicated, one of few holiday Beanies

Commentary: Released 10 months after birth; in circulation only three months before retiring, hence, very hard to find & very expensive; special 1997 holiday release; popular holiday gift/decoration

Poem: Beanie Babies are special no doubt
All filled with love—inside and out
Wishes for fun times filled with joy
Ty's holiday teddy is a magical toy!™

My record

(Beanies are the #1 collectible in American collecting history. A complete, detailed record will vastly increase the value of this Beanie, if and when you ever appraise, trade, re-sell, gift, or bequeath it.)

Description *(which version do you have?)*:

Gift from:

Date received/purchased:

Purchased from:

NAME OF PERSON OR RETAILER

ADDRESS

CITY/STATE/ZIP

PHONE

Qty. purchased: **Cost ea.**
(check one)   ❏ *Cash*   ❏ *Check*   ❏ *Charge*

Reason(s) for purchase(s):

Traded to:

NAME

ADDRESS

CITY/STATE/ZIP

PHONE

TRADED FOR

Re-sold to:

NAME

ADDRESS

CITY/STATE/ZIP

PHONE

PRICE RE-SOLD FOR

Your feelings about and/or experiences with this Beanie:

Bucky™

Type:	Male beaver	*Categories:* Brown, woodland	*Style no.:* 4016
Birthday:	June 8, 1995	*Released:* 1/7/96	*Retired:* 12/31/97
Position:	Laying down	*Tags:* 3rd & 4th generation	*Teenie:*

Description: Brown plush body, darker brown ears & tail, black plastic eyes & nose, black thread whiskers, white felt buck teeth, hang tag left ear, tush tag left back leg

Replaces: None

Variations: None

Oddities: Bucky shares same birthday w/ Manny

Commentary: Released six months after birth, in circulation two years before retiring, one of the most authentic-looking Beanies

Poem: Bucky's teeth are shiny as can be
Often used for cutting trees
He hides in his dam night and day
Maybe for you he will come out and play!™

My record

(Beanies are the #1 collectible in American collecting history. A complete, detailed record will vastly increase the value of this Beanie, if and when you ever appraise, trade, re-sell, gift, or bequeath it.)

Description *(which version do you have?):*

Gift from:

Date received/purchased:

Purchased from:

NAME OF PERSON OR RETAILER

ADDRESS

CITY/STATE/ZIP

PHONE

Qty. purchased: **Cost ea.**

(check one)   ❏ *Cash*   ❏ *Check*   ❏ *Charge*

Reason(s) for purchase(s):

Traded to:

NAME

ADDRESS

CITY/STATE/ZIP

PHONE

TRADED FOR

Re-sold to:

NAME

ADDRESS

CITY/STATE/ZIP

PHONE

PRICE RE-SOLD FOR

Your feelings about and/or experiences with this Beanie:

Cubbie™

1 of the original 9 Beanies

Type:	Male bear *Categories:* Bear, brown *Style no.:* 4010
Birthday:	November 14, 1993 *Released:* 1/8/94 *Retired:* 12/31/97
Position:	Laying down *Tags:* 1st-4th generation *Teenie:*
Description:	Brown plush body, lighter brown snout, black plastic eyes, brown plastic nose, hang tag left ear, tush tag left back leg
Replaces:	Previously named Brownie, extremely rare & expensive
Variations:	Name changed to Cubbie in 1994, Chicago Cubs special edition w/ commemorative card
Oddities:	Cubbie shares same birthday w/ Goldie
Commentary:	Released two months after birth; in circulation four years before retiring, making it one of the longest-running Beanies; like all Beanie bears, very popular, very hard to find, very expensive
Poem:	Cubbie used to eat crackers and honey And what happened to him was funny He was stung by fourteen bees Now Cubbie eats broccoli and cheese!™

My record

(Beanies are the #1 collectible in American collecting history. A complete, detailed record will vastly increase the value of this Beanie, if and when you ever appraise, trade, re-sell, gift, or bequeath it.)

Description (which version do you have?):

_____

_____

_____

Gift from: _____

Date received/purchased: _____

Purchased from: _____

NAME OF PERSON OR RETAILER _____

ADDRESS _____

CITY/STATE/ZIP _____

PHONE _____

Qty. purchased: **Cost ea.**

(check one)   ❏ _Cash_   ❏ _Check_   ❏ _Charge_

Reason(s) for purchase(s): _____

_____

_____

_____

Traded to:

NAME _____

ADDRESS _____

CITY/STATE/ZIP _____

PHONE _____

TRADED FOR _____

Re-sold to:

NAME _____

ADDRESS _____

CITY/STATE/ZIP _____

PHONE _____

PRICE RE-SOLD FOR _____

Your feelings about and/or experiences with this Beanie: _____

_____

_____

_____

_____

Goldie™

Type:	Female goldfish *Categories:* Fish, orange, sea *Style no.:* 4023
Birthday:	November 14, 1994 *Released:* 6/25/94 *Retired:* 12/31/97
Position:	Swimming *Tags:* 1st-5th generation *Teenie:* 4/97
Description:	Orange plush body w/ orange detail stitching front & top fins, black plastic eyes, hang tag left front fin, tush tag lower back fin
Replaces:	None
Variations:	None
Oddities:	Released four months before birth; Goldie shares same birthday w/ Cubbie
Commentary:	In circulation 3 1/2 years before retiring, making it one of the longest-running Beanies; very popular w/ kids
Poem:	She's got rhythm, she's got soul What more to like in a fish bowl? Through sound waves Goldie swam Because this goldfish likes to jam!™

4

My record

(Beanies are the #1 collectible in American collecting history. A complete, detailed record will vastly increase the value of this Beanie, if and when you ever appraise, trade, re-sell, gift, or bequeath it.)

Description *(which version do you have?):*

Gift from:

Date received/purchased:

Purchased from:

NAME OF PERSON OR RETAILER

ADDRESS

CITY/STATE/ZIP

PHONE

Qty. purchased: **Cost ea.**
(check one)   ❑ *Cash*   ❑ *Check*   ❑ *Charge*

Reason(s) for purchase(s):

Traded to:

NAME

ADDRESS

CITY/STATE/ZIP

PHONE

TRADED FOR

Re-sold to:

NAME

ADDRESS

CITY/STATE/ZIP

PHONE

PRICE RE-SOLD FOR

Your feelings about and/or experiences with this Beanie:

Lizzy®

Type:	Female lizard **Categories:** Blue, reptile, spotted **Style no.:** 4033
Birthday:	May 11, 1995 **Released:** 1/7/96 **Retired:** 12/31/97
Position:	Crawling **Tags:** 3rd-5th generation **Teenie:** 4/97
Description:	Blue plush body topside w/ black spots, pale yellow belly w/ orange spots, black plastic eyes, red felt forked tongue, long tail, hang tag left front claw, tush tag left back side
Replaces:	Tie-dyed Lizzy, style no. 4033, birthday 5/11/95, released 6/3/95, retired 1/7/96, extremely rare & expensive
Variations:	None
Oddities:	Both have same style no. & birthday; one of three Beanies w/ two different poems
Commentary:	Released eight months after birth, in circulation 24 months before retiring, one of the most colorful Beanies, very popular w/ boys
Poem:	Lizzy loves Legs the frog She hides with him under logs Both of them search for flies Underneath the clear blue skies!™

My record

(Beanies are the #1 collectible in American collecting history. A complete, detailed record will vastly increase the value of this Beanie, if and when you ever appraise, trade, re-sell, gift, or bequeath it.)

Description *(which version do you have?):*

Gift from:

Date received/purchased:

Purchased from:

NAME OF PERSON OR RETAILER

ADDRESS

CITY/STATE/ZIP

PHONE

Qty. purchased: **Cost ea.**
(check one)   ❏ *Cash*   ❏ *Check*   ❏ *Charge*

Reason(s) for purchase(s):

Traded to:

NAME

ADDRESS

CITY/STATE/ZIP

PHONE

TRADED FOR

Re-sold to:

NAME

ADDRESS

CITY/STATE/ZIP

PHONE

PRICE RE-SOLD FOR

Your feelings about and/or experiences with this Beanie:

Magic™

Type:	Female dragon	*Categories:* Fantasy, white	*Style no.:* 4088

Birthday: September 5, 1995   *Released:* 6/3/95   *Retired:* 12/31/97

Position: Standing   *Tags:* 3rd & 4th generation   *Teenie:*

Description: White plush body, white iridescent scales & wings w/ pale pink detail stitching, black plastic eyes, pink thread nostrils, curled tail, hang tag left wing, tush tag tail

Replaces: None

Variations: First, pale pink stitching; then, hot pink stitching (hard to find & expensive); then, pale pink stitching again

Oddities: Released three months prior to birth

Commentary: In circulation only 18 months before retiring, hence, very hard to find & very expensive; one of the most beautiful, fanciful Beanies, hence, very popular

Poem: Magic the dragon lives in a dream
The most beautiful that you have ever seen
Through Magic lands she likes to fly
Look up and watch her, way up high!™

My record

(Beanies are the #1 collectible in American collecting history. A complete, detailed record will vastly increase the value of this Beanie, if and when you ever appraise, trade, re-sell, gift, or bequeath it.)

Description *(which version do you have?):*

Gift from:

Date received/purchased:

Purchased from:

NAME OF PERSON OR RETAILER

ADDRESS

CITY/STATE/ZIP

PHONE

Qty. purchased: **Cost ea.**
(check one)   ❏ *Cash*   ❏ *Check*   ❏ *Charge*

Reason(s) for purchase(s):

Traded to:

NAME

ADDRESS

CITY/STATE/ZIP

PHONE

TRADED FOR

Re-sold to:

NAME

ADDRESS

CITY/STATE/ZIP

PHONE

PRICE RE-SOLD FOR

Your feelings about and/or experiences with this Beanie:

Nip™

Type:	Male cat	***Categories:*** Brown, cat	***Style no.:*** 4003
Birthday:	March 6, 1994	***Released:*** 3/10/96	***Retired:*** 12/31/97
Position:	Laying down	***Tags:*** 3rd-5th generation	***Teenie:***

Description: Golden brown plush body, white inner ears & paws, black plastic eyes ringed w/ gold, pink plastic nose, white thread mouth & whiskers, hang tag left ear, tush tag left back leg

Replaces: Gold w/ white face & belly, style no. 4003, birthday 3/6/94, released 1/7/95, retired 1/7/96; all gold, style no. 4003, birthday 3/6/94, released 1/7/96, retired 3/10/96; both extremely rare & expensive

Variations: None

Oddities: All three have same style no. & birthday

Commentary: Released two years after birth; in circulation only 21 months before retiring, hence, very hard to find & very expensive

Poem: His name is Nipper, but we call him Nip
His best friend is a black cat named Zip
Nip likes to run in races for fun
He runs so fast he's always number one!™

My record

(Beanies are the #1 collectible in American collecting history. A complete, detailed record will vastly increase the value of this Beanie, if and when you ever appraise, trade, re-sell, gift, or bequeath it.)

Description *(which version do you have?):*

Gift from:

Date received/purchased:

Purchased from:

NAME OF PERSON OR RETAILER

ADDRESS

CITY/STATE/ZIP

PHONE

Qty. purchased: **Cost ea.**
(check one)   ❏ *Cash*   ❏ *Check*   ❏ *Charge*

Reason(s) for purchase(s):

Traded to:

NAME

ADDRESS

CITY/STATE/ZIP

PHONE

TRADED FOR

Re-sold to:

NAME

ADDRESS

CITY/STATE/ZIP

PHONE

PRICE RE-SOLD FOR

Your feelings about and/or experiences with this Beanie:

Snowball™

Type: Male snowman **Categories:** Holiday, white **Style no.:** 4201

Birthday: December 22, 1996 **Released:** 10/1/97 **Retired:** 12/31/97

Position: Standing **Tags:** 4th generation **Teenie:**

Description: White plush body, black felt hat w/ red band, shiny black plastic eyes, pointed orange felt nose, black v-shaped thread mouth, red felt scarf w/ white tassels, matte black buttons, hands, hang tag left hand, tush tag left bottom

Replaces: None

Variations: None

Oddities: One of few holiday Beanies

Commentary: Released 10 months after birth; in circulation only three months before retiring, hence, very hard to find & very expensive; special 1997 holiday release; popular Christmas gift/decoration; one of the most detailed Beanies

Poem: There is a snowman, I've been told
That plays with Beanies out in the cold
What is better in a winter wonderland
Than a Beanie snowman in your hand!™

My record

(Beanies are the #1 collectible in American collecting history. A complete, detailed record will vastly increase the value of this Beanie, if and when you ever appraise, trade, re-sell, gift, or bequeath it.)

Description *(which version do you have?)*:

Gift from:

Date received/purchased:

Purchased from:

NAME OF PERSON OR RETAILER

ADDRESS

CITY/STATE/ZIP

PHONE

Qty. purchased: Cost ea.
(check one)   ❑ *Cash*   ❑ *Check*   ❑ *Charge*

Reason(s) for purchase(s):

Traded to:

NAME

ADDRESS

CITY/STATE/ZIP

PHONE

TRADED FOR

Re-sold to:

NAME

ADDRESS

CITY/STATE/ZIP

PHONE

PRICE RE-SOLD FOR

Your feelings about and/or experiences with this Beanie:

Spooky™

Type:	Ghost	**Categories:** Holiday, white	**Style no.:** 4090
Birthday:	October 31, 1995	**Released:** 9/1/95	**Retired:** 12/31/97
Position:	Flying	**Tags:** 3rd & 4th generation	**Teenie:**

Description: White plush body, pointed head & tail, two hands, black plastic eyes, black thread crescent-shaped smile w/ red felt mouth, orange satin ribbon tied around neck, hang tag left hand, tush tag bottom

Replaces: Previously named Spook, extremely rare & expensive

Variations: Full smile, half smile, v-shaped smile; side & bottom tush tags

Oddities: Released two months before birth, one of few Beanies w/ no gender indicated, one of few holiday Beanies; only Beanie that lists designer on hang tag

Commentary: In circulation 28 months before retiring; special 1995 holiday release; popular Halloween gift/decoration

Poem: Ghosts can be a scary sight
But don't let Spooky bring you any fright
Because when you're alone, you will see
The best friend that Spooky can be!™

9

My record

(Beanies are the #1 collectible in American collecting history. A complete, detailed record will vastly increase the value of this Beanie, if and when you ever appraise, trade, re-sell, gift, or bequeath it.)

Description *(which version do you have?):*

Gift from:

Date received/purchased:

Purchased from:

NAME OF PERSON OR RETAILER

ADDRESS

CITY/STATE/ZIP

PHONE

Qty. purchased: **Cost ea.**
(check one)   ❑ *Cash*   ❑ *Check*   ❑ *Charge*

Reason(s) for purchase(s):

Traded to:

NAME

ADDRESS

CITY/STATE/ZIP

PHONE

TRADED FOR

Re-sold to:

NAME

ADDRESS

CITY/STATE/ZIP

PHONE

PRICE RE-SOLD FOR

Your feelings about and/or experiences with this Beanie:

10/1/97 Retireds

Place behind this tab
the following Beanie Babies®:

Ally	Speedy
Bessie	Spot
Flip	Tank
Hoot	Teddy Brown
Legs	Velvet
Seamore	

Ally ™

Type: Male alligator   ***Categories:***   Green, reptile, spotted   ***Style no.:***   4032

Birthday: March 14, 1994   ***Released:***   6/25/94   ***Retired:***   10/1/97

Position: Crawling   ***Tags:***   1st-4th generation   ***Teenie:***

Description: Moss green plush body w/ brown spotted stripe from nose to tail, black plastic eyes, hang tag left front claw, tush tag right side of tail

Replaces: None

Variations: None

Oddities: None

Commentary: Released three months after birth; in circulation 40 months before retiring, making it one of the longest-running Beanies; hard to find & pricey; very popular with boys

Poem: When Ally gets out of classes
He wears a hat and dark glasses
He plays bass in a street band
He's the coolest gator in the land! ™

My record

(Beanies are the #1 collectible in American collecting history. A complete, detailed record will vastly increase the value of this Beanie, if and when you ever appraise, trade, re-sell, gift, or bequeath it.)

Description *(which version do you have?)*:
_____
_____
_____

Gift from: _____

Date received/purchased: _____

Purchased from:

NAME OF PERSON OR RETAILER _____
ADDRESS _____
CITY/STATE/ZIP _____
PHONE _____

Qty. purchased: **Cost ea.**
(check one)   ❏ *Cash*   ❏ *Check*   ❏ *Charge*

Reason(s) for purchase(s):
_____
_____
_____

Traded to:

NAME _____
ADDRESS _____
CITY/STATE/ZIP _____
PHONE _____
TRADED FOR _____

Re-sold to:

NAME _____
ADDRESS _____
CITY/STATE/ZIP _____
PHONE _____
PRICE RE-SOLD FOR _____

Your feelings about and/or experiences with this Beanie:
_____
_____
_____
_____

Bessie™

Type: Female cow	***Categories:*** Brown, farm	***Style no.:*** 4009
Birthday: June 27, 1995	***Released:*** 6/3/95	***Retired:*** 10/1/97
Position: Sitting up	***Tags:*** 3rd & 4th generation	***Teenie:***

Description: Brown plush body; white face, inner ears & hooves; tan horns; black plastic eyes; black thread nostrils; knotted tail; hang tag left ear; tush tag left bottom

Replaces: None

Variations: Shade of horns

Oddities: Released 24 days before birth

Commentary: In circulation 28 months before retiring; like all farm Beanies, very popular, very hard to find, very expensive; replaced by Daisy

Poem: Bessie the cow likes to dance and sing
Because music is her favorite thing
Every night when you are counting sheep
She'll sing you a song to help you sleep!™

My record

(Beanies are the #1 collectible in American collecting history. A complete, detailed record will vastly increase the value of this Beanie, if and when you ever appraise, trade, re-sell, gift, or bequeath it.)

Description *(which version do you have?):*

Gift from:

Date received/purchased:

Purchased from:

NAME OF PERSON OR RETAILER

ADDRESS

CITY/STATE/ZIP

PHONE

Qty. purchased: **Cost ea.**

(check one) ❏ *Cash* ❏ *Check* ❏ *Charge*

Reason(s) for purchase(s):

Traded to:

NAME

ADDRESS

CITY/STATE/ZIP

PHONE

TRADED FOR

Re-sold to:

NAME

ADDRESS

CITY/STATE/ZIP

PHONE

PRICE RE-SOLD FOR

Your feelings about and/or experiences with this Beanie:

Flip™

Type: Female cat **Categories:** Cat, white **Style no.:** 4012

Birthday: February 28, 1995 **Released:** 1/7/96 **Retired:** 10/1/97

Position: Laying down **Tags:** 3rd & 4th generation **Teenie:**

Description: White plush body, pink inner ears, black plastic eyes ringed w/ blue, pink plastic nose, pink thread mouth & whiskers, hang tag left ear, tush tag left back leg

Replaces: None

Variations: None

Oddities: Flip shares the same style no. w/ Chilly

Commentary: Released ten months after birth; in circulation only 22 months before retiring, making it one of the shortest-lived Beanies, hence, one of the hardest to find and most expensive; one of the most beautiful Beanies; like all Beanie cats, very popular

Poem: Flip the cat is an acrobat
She loves playing on her mat
This cat flips with such grace and flare
She can somersault in mid-air!™

3

My record

(Beanies are the #1 collectible in American collecting history. A complete, detailed record will vastly increase the value of this Beanie, if and when you ever appraise, trade, re-sell, gift, or bequeath it.)

Description *(which version do you have?):*

Gift from:

Date received/purchased:

Purchased from:

NAME OF PERSON OR RETAILER

ADDRESS

CITY/STATE/ZIP

PHONE

Qty. purchased: **Cost ea.**
(check one)   ❏ *Cash*   ❏ *Check*   ❏ *Charge*

Reason(s) for purchase(s):

Traded to:

NAME

ADDRESS

CITY/STATE/ZIP

PHONE

TRADED FOR

Re-sold to:

NAME

ADDRESS

CITY/STATE/ZIP

PHONE

PRICE RE-SOLD FOR

Your feelings about and/or experiences with this Beanie:

Hoot™

Type: Owl **Categories:** Bird, brown, woodland **Style no.:** 4073

Birthday: August 9, 1995 **Released:** 1/7/96 **Retired:** 10/1/97

Position: Perching **Tags:** 3rd & 4th generation **Teenie:**

Description: Dark brown plush body; lighter brown face, front, underwings & bottom; orange felt beak; black plastic eyes; hang tag left wing; tush tag left bottom

Replaces: None

Variations: Second & fourth lines of poem vary

Oddities: One of few Beanies w/ no sex indicated

Commentary: Released five months after birth; in circulation only 22 months before retiring, making it one of the shortest-lived Beanies, hence, one of the hardest to find and most expensive; cuter and smaller than later novelty owl named Wise

Poem: Late to bed, late to rise
Nevertheless, Hoot's quite wise
Studies by candlelight, nothing new
Like a president, do you know whooo?™

4

My record

(Beanies are the #1 collectible in American collecting history. A complete, detailed record will vastly increase the value of this Beanie, if and when you ever appraise, trade, re-sell, gift, or bequeath it.)

Description *(which version do you have?):*

Gift from:

Date received/purchased:

Purchased from:

NAME OF PERSON OR RETAILER

ADDRESS

CITY/STATE/ZIP

PHONE

Qty. purchased: **Cost ea.**
(check one)   ❏ *Cash*   ❏ *Check*   ❏ *Charge*

Reason(s) for purchase(s):

Traded to:

NAME

ADDRESS

CITY/STATE/ZIP

PHONE

TRADED FOR

Re-sold to:

NAME

ADDRESS

CITY/STATE/ZIP

PHONE

PRICE RE-SOLD FOR

Your feelings about and/or experiences with this Beanie:

Legs™

Type:	Frog	Categories:	Green, reptile	Style no.:	4020

Birthday: April 25, 1993   **Released:** 1/8/94   **Retired:** 10/1/97

Position: Laying down   **Tags:** 1st-4th generation   **Teenie:**

Description: Bright green plush body, black plastic eyes ringed in green, hang tag front left leg, tush tag back left leg

Replaces: None

Variations: Fourth line of poem varies

Oddities: One of few Beanies w/ no sex indicated

Commentary: Released eight months after birth; in circulation 46 months before retiring, making it one of the longest-running Beanies; hard to find & pricey; very popular with boys; replaced by Smoochy

Poem:
Legs lives in a hollow log
Legs likes to play leap frog
If you like to hang out at the lake
Legs will be the new friend you'll make!™

My record

(Beanies are the #1 collectible in American collecting history. A complete, detailed record will vastly increase the value of this Beanie, if and when you ever appraise, trade, re-sell, gift, or bequeath it.)

Description *(which version do you have?):*

Gift from:

Date received/purchased:

Purchased from:

NAME OF PERSON OR RETAILER

ADDRESS

CITY/STATE/ZIP

PHONE

Qty. purchased: **Cost ea.**
(check one)   ❏ *Cash*   ❏ *Check*   ❏ *Charge*

Reason(s) for purchase(s):

Traded to:

NAME

ADDRESS

CITY/STATE/ZIP

PHONE

TRADED FOR

Re-sold to:

NAME

ADDRESS

CITY/STATE/ZIP

PHONE

PRICE RE-SOLD FOR

Your feelings about and/or experiences with this Beanie:

Seamore

Type: Baby female seal **Categories:** Sea, white **Style no.:** 4029

Birthday: December 14, 1996 **Released:** 6/25/94 **Retired:** 10/1/97

Position: Crawling **Tags:** 1st-4th generation **Teenie:** 4/97

Description: White plush body, black plastic eyes & nose, black thread eyebrows & whiskers, hang tag left front flipper, tush tag left back side

Replaces: None

Variations: None

Oddities: Released 2 1/2 years before birth

Commentary: In circulation 40 months before retiring, making it one of the longest-running Beanies; one of the most beautiful and popular Beanies, hence, very hard to find and very expensive

Poem: Seamore is a little white seal
Fish and clams are her favorite meal
Playing and laughing in the sand
She's the happiest seal in the land!™

My record

(Beanies are the #1 collectible in American collecting history. A complete, detailed record will vastly increase the value of this Beanie, if and when you ever appraise, trade, re-sell, gift, or bequeath it.)

Description (which version do you have?):

Gift from:

Date received/purchased:

Purchased from:

NAME OF PERSON OR RETAILER

ADDRESS

CITY/STATE/ZIP

PHONE

Qty. purchased: **Cost ea.**
(check one) ❏ Cash ❏ Check ❏ Charge

Reason(s) for purchase(s):

Traded to:

NAME

ADDRESS

CITY/STATE/ZIP

PHONE

TRADED FOR

Re-sold to:

NAME

ADDRESS

CITY/STATE/ZIP

PHONE

PRICE RE-SOLD FOR

Your feelings about and/or experiences with this Beanie:

Speedy®

Type:	Male turtle	*Categories:* Green, reptile *Style no.:* 4030

Birthday:	August 14, 1994 *Released:* 6/25/94 *Retired:* 10/1/97
Position:	Crawling *Tags:* 1st-4th generation *Teenie:* 4/97
Description:	Bright green plush body, brown spotted shell, black plastic eyes, hang tag left front leg, tush tag back left leg
Replaces:	None
Variations:	None
Oddities:	Released two months before birth
Commentary:	In circulation 40 months before retiring, making it one of the longest-running Beanies; hard to find & pricey; very popular with boys
Poem:	Speedy ran marathons in the past Such a shame, always last Now Speedy is a big star After he bought a racing car!™

My record

(Beanies are the #1 collectible in American collecting history. A complete, detailed record will vastly increase the value of this Beanie, if and when you ever appraise, trade, re-sell, gift, or bequeath it.)

Description *(which version do you have?):*

Gift from:

Date received/purchased:

Purchased from:

NAME OF PERSON OR RETAILER

ADDRESS

CITY/STATE/ZIP

PHONE

Qty. purchased: Cost ea.
(check one)   ❏ *Cash*   ❏ *Check*   ❏ *Charge*

Reason(s) for purchase(s):

Traded to:

NAME

ADDRESS

CITY/STATE/ZIP

PHONE

TRADED FOR

Re-sold to:

NAME

ADDRESS

CITY/STATE/ZIP

PHONE

PRICE RE-SOLD FOR

Your feelings about and/or experiences with this Beanie:

Spot™

1 of the original 9 Beanies

Type:	Male dog ***Categories:*** Black & white, dog ***Style no.:*** 4000
Birthday:	January 1, 1993 ***Released:*** 4/13/94 ***Retired:*** 10/1/97
Position:	Laying down ***Tags:*** 2nd-4th generation ***Teenie:***
Description:	White plush body w/ black left eye, ears, tail & spot on back; black plastic eyes & nose; hang tag left ear; tush tag left back leg
Replaces:	Spot w/o a spot, style no. 4000, birthday 1/3/93, released 1/8/94, retired 4/13/94, extremely rare & expensive
Variations:	None
Oddities:	Both Spots have same style no. & birthday
Commentary:	Released 16 months after birth; in circulation 41 months before retiring, making it one of the longest-running Beanies; like all Beanie dogs, very popular, very hard to find, very expensive
Poem:	See Spot sprint, see Spot run You and Spot will have lots of fun Watch out now, because he's not slow Just stand back and watch him go!™

My record

(Beanies are the #1 collectible in American collecting history. A complete, detailed record will vastly increase the value of this Beanie, if and when you ever appraise, trade, re-sell, gift, or bequeath it.)

Description *(which version do you have?):*

Gift from:

Date received/purchased:

Purchased from:

NAME OF PERSON OR RETAILER

ADDRESS

CITY/STATE/ZIP

PHONE

Qty. purchased: **Cost ea.**
(check one)   ❏ *Cash*   ❏ *Check*   ❏ *Charge*

Reason(s) for purchase(s):

Traded to:

NAME

ADDRESS

CITY/STATE/ZIP

PHONE

TRADED FOR

Re-sold to:

NAME

ADDRESS

CITY/STATE/ZIP

PHONE

PRICE RE-SOLD FOR

Your feelings about and/or experiences with this Beanie:

Tank™

Type:	Male armadillo	***Categories:*** Gray, reptile	***Style no.:*** 4031	
Birthday:	February 22, 1995	***Released:*** 1/7/96	***Retired:*** 10/1/97	
Position:	Crawling	***Tags:*** 4th generation	***Teenie:***	

Description: Gray plush body, darker gray ears, gray thread detailing on shell, black plastic eyes, hang tag left ear, tush tag left bottom

Replaces: Tank w/o shell, style no. 4031, birthday 2/22/95, released 1/7/95, retired 1/7/96, extremely rare & expensive

Variations: 6 plates w/o shell, 8 plates w/o shell, 8 plates w/ shell

Oddities: Both Tanks have same style no. & birthday, Tank shares the same style no. w/ Slither

Commentary: Released 11 months after birth; in circulation only 22 months before retiring, making it one of the shortest-lived Beanies, hence, one of the hardest to find and most expensive; very popular with boys

Poem: This armadillo lives in the south
Shoving Tex-Mex in his mouth
He sure loves it south of the border
Keeping his friends in good order!™

My record

(Beanies are the #1 collectible in American collecting history. A complete, detailed record will vastly increase the value of this Beanie, if and when you ever appraise, trade, re-sell, gift, or bequeath it.)

Description *(which version do you have?):*

Gift from:

Date received/purchased:

Purchased from:

NAME OF PERSON OR RETAILER

ADDRESS

CITY/STATE/ZIP

PHONE

Qty. purchased: **Cost ea.**
(check one)   ❏ *Cash*   ❏ *Check*   ❏ *Charge*

Reason(s) for purchase(s):

Traded to:

NAME

ADDRESS

CITY/STATE/ZIP

PHONE

TRADED FOR

Re-sold to:

NAME

ADDRESS

CITY/STATE/ZIP

PHONE

PRICE RE-SOLD FOR

Your feelings about and/or experiences with this Beanie:

Teddy Brown™

(new face)

Type:	Male bear	**Categories:** Bear, brown		**Style no.:** 4050

Birthday: November 28, 1995   **Released:** 1/7/95 **Retired:** 10/1/97

Position: Sitting up   **Tags:** 2nd-4th generation   **Teenie:**

Description: Brown plush body, black plastic eyes & nose, wine-colored satin ribbon tied around neck, hang tag left ear, tush tag left cheek

Replaces: Teddy Brown (old face), style no. 4050, birthday unknown, released 6/25/94, retired 1/7/95, extremely rare & expensive

Variations: Second line of poem varies

Oddities: Both Teddys have same style no., released ten months before birth

Commentary: In circulation 34 months before retiring; the bear after whom all subsequent sit-up bears are styled; like all Beanie bears, very popular, very hard to find, very expensive

Poem: Teddy wanted to go out today
All of his friends went out to play
But he'd rather help whatever you do
After all, his best friend is you!™

My record

(Beanies are the #1 collectible in American collecting history. A complete, detailed record will vastly increase the value of this Beanie, if and when you ever appraise, trade, re-sell, gift, or bequeath it.)

Description *(which version do you have?):*

Gift from:

Date received/purchased:

Purchased from:

NAME OF PERSON OR RETAILER

ADDRESS

CITY/STATE/ZIP

PHONE

Qty. purchased: **Cost ea.**
(check one)   ❏ *Cash*   ❏ *Check*   ❏ *Charge*

Reason(s) for purchase(s):

Traded to:

NAME

ADDRESS

CITY/STATE/ZIP

PHONE

TRADED FOR

Re-sold to:

NAME

ADDRESS

CITY/STATE/ZIP

PHONE

PRICE RE-SOLD FOR

Your feelings about and/or experiences with this Beanie:

Velvet™

Type:	Female panther **Categories:** Big cat, black, jungle **Style no.:** 4064
Birthday:	December 16, 1995 **Released:** 6/3/95 **Retired:** 10/1/97
Position:	Laying down **Tags:** 3rd & 4th generation **Teenie:**
Description:	Black plush body, black plastic eyes ringed w/ gold, flesh velvet nose, black thread whiskers, hang tag left ear, tush tag left back leg
Replaces:	None
Variations:	None
Oddities:	Released six months before birth
Commentary:	In circulation 28 months before retiring; one of the most dramatic Beanies; very popular, very hard to find, very expensive
Poem:	Velvet loves to sleep in the trees Lulled to dreams by the buzz of the bees She snoozes all day and plays all night Running and jumping in the moonlight!™

My record

(Beanies are the #1 collectible in American collecting history. A complete, detailed record will vastly increase the value of this Beanie, if and when you ever appraise, trade, re-sell, gift, or bequeath it.)

Description *(which version do you have?):*

Gift from:

Date received/purchased:

Purchased from:

NAME OF PERSON OR RETAILER

ADDRESS

CITY/STATE/ZIP

PHONE

Qty. purchased: **Cost ea.**
(check one)   ❏ *Cash*   ❏ *Check*   ❏ *Charge*

Reason(s) for purchase(s):

Traded to:

NAME

ADDRESS

CITY/STATE/ZIP

PHONE

TRADED FOR

Re-sold to:

NAME

ADDRESS

CITY/STATE/ZIP

PHONE

PRICE RE-SOLD FOR

Your feelings about and/or experiences with this Beanie:

5/11/97 Retireds

Place behind this tab
the following Beanie Babies®:

Bubbles   Manny
Digger   Radar
Flash   Sparky
Garcia   Splash
Grunt

Bubbles™

Type:	Female fish *Categories:* Fish, sea, striped *Style no.:* 4078
Birthday:	July 2, 1995 *Released:* 6/3/95 *Retired:* 5/11/97
Position:	Swimming *Tags:* 3rd & 4th generation *Teenie:*
Description:	Yellow & black striped plush body, black plastic eyes, three sets of fins, hang tag left fin, tush tag bottom
Replaces:	None
Variations:	None
Oddities:	Released one month before birth
Commentary:	In circulation 23 months before retiring; one of the most beautiful Beanies, hence, very popular, very hard to find, very expensive; replaced by Goldie
Poem:	All day long Bubbles likes to swim She never gets tired of flapping her fins Bubbles lived in a sea of blue Now she's ready to come home with you!™

1

My record

(Beanies are the #1 collectible in American collecting history. A complete, detailed record will vastly increase the value of this Beanie, if and when you ever appraise, trade, re-sell, gift, or bequeath it.)

Description *(which version do you have?):*

Gift from:

Date received/purchased:

Purchased from:

NAME OF PERSON OR RETAILER

ADDRESS

CITY/STATE/ZIP

PHONE

Qty. purchased: **Cost ea.**
(check one) ❏ *Cash* ❏ *Check* ❏ *Charge*

Reason(s) for purchase(s):

Traded to:

NAME

ADDRESS

CITY/STATE/ZIP

PHONE

TRADED FOR

Re-sold to:

NAME

ADDRESS

CITY/STATE/ZIP

PHONE

PRICE RE-SOLD FOR

Your feelings about and/or experiences with this Beanie:

Digger™

Type:	Female crab **Categories:** Red, sea **Style no.:** 4027
Birthday:	August 23, 1995 **Released:** 6/3/95 **Retired:** 5/11/97
Position:	Crawling **Tags:** 3rd & 4th generation **Teenie:**
Description:	Red plush body, black plastic eyes, black thread whiskers, two pinchers, eight legs, hang tag left pincher, tush tag back
Replaces:	Digger the orange crab, style no. 4027, birthday 8/23/95, released 6/25/94, retired 6/3/95, very rare & expensive
Variations:	None
Oddities:	Both have same style no. & birthday, red released same day orange retired, red released two months before birth
Commentary:	In circulation 23 months before retiring; one of the most popular retired Beanies, hence, very hard to find & very expensive; replaced by Claude
Poem:	Digging in the sand and walking sideways That's how Digger spends her days Hard on the outside but sweet deep inside Basking in the sun, riding the tide!™

My record

(Beanies are the #1 collectible in American collecting history. A complete, detailed record will vastly increase the value of this Beanie, if and when you ever appraise, trade, re-sell, gift, or bequeath it.)

Description *(which version do you have?)*:

Gift from:

Date received/purchased:

Purchased from:

NAME OF PERSON OR RETAILER

ADDRESS

CITY/STATE/ZIP

PHONE

Qty. purchased: **Cost ea.**
(check one)   ❏ *Cash*   ❏ *Check*   ❏ *Charge*

Reason(s) for purchase(s):

Traded to:

NAME

ADDRESS

CITY/STATE/ZIP

PHONE

TRADED FOR

Re-sold to:

NAME

ADDRESS

CITY/STATE/ZIP

PHONE

PRICE RE-SOLD FOR

Your feelings about and/or experiences with this Beanie:

Flash™

1 of the original 9 Beanies

Type: Female dolphin **Categories:** Gray, sea **Style no.:** 4021

Birthday: May 13, 1993 **Released:** 1/8/94 **Retired:** 5/11/97

Position: Swimming **Tags:** 1st-4th generation **Teenie:**

Description: Light gray plush body, white under side, black plastic eyes, three sets of fins, hang tag left fin, tush tag left back

Replaces: None

Variations: One of three Beanies w/ two poems

Oddities: None

Commentary: Released eight months after birth, in circulation 40 months before retiring, making it one of the longest-running Beanies; 1 of the original 9 Beanies, hence, very popular, very hard to find, very expensive; replaced by Echo

Poem: You know dolphins are a smart breed
Our friend Flash knows how to read
Splash the whale is the one who taught her
Although reading is difficult under the water!™

My record

(Beanies are the #1 collectible in American collecting history. A complete, detailed record will vastly increase the value of this Beanie, if and when you ever appraise, trade, re-sell, gift, or bequeath it.)

Description *(which version do you have?):*

Gift from:

Date received/purchased:

Purchased from:

NAME OF PERSON OR RETAILER

ADDRESS

CITY/STATE/ZIP

PHONE

Qty. purchased: **Cost ea.**
(check one)   ❏ *Cash*   ❏ *Check*   ❏ *Charge*

Reason(s) for purchase(s):

Traded to:

NAME

ADDRESS

CITY/STATE/ZIP

PHONE

TRADED FOR

Re-sold to:

NAME

ADDRESS

CITY/STATE/ZIP

PHONE

PRICE RE-SOLD FOR

Your feelings about and/or experiences with this Beanie:

Garcia

Type: Male bear   **Categories:** Bear, tie-dyed   **Style no.:** 4051

Birthday: August 1, 1995   **Released:** 1/7/96   **Retired:** 5/11/97

Position: Sitting up   **Tags:** 3rd & 4th generation   **Teenie:**

Description: Tie-dyed plush body, black plastic eyes & nose, hang tag left ear, tush tag left bottom

Replaces: None

Variations: Tie-dye varies from cool to warm colors

Oddities: May have Peace hang or tush tags

Commentary: Released five months after birth; in circulation only 16 months before retiring, making it one of the shortest-lived Beanies, hence, very hard to find & very expensive; like all Beanie bears, very popular; retired due to flack from Jerry Garcia estate; replaced by Peace

Poem: The Beanies used to follow him around
Because Garcia traveled from town to town
He's pretty popular as you can see
Some even say he's legendary!™

4

My record

(Beanies are the #1 collectible in American collecting history. A complete, detailed record will vastly increase the value of this Beanie, if and when you ever appraise, trade, re-sell, gift, or bequeath it.)

Description *(which version do you have?):*

Gift from:

Date received/purchased:

Purchased from:

NAME OF PERSON OR RETAILER

ADDRESS

CITY/STATE/ZIP

PHONE

Qty. purchased: **Cost ea.**
(check one)   ❏ *Cash*   ❏ *Check*   ❏ *Charge*

Reason(s) for purchase(s):

Traded to:

NAME

ADDRESS

CITY/STATE/ZIP

PHONE

TRADED FOR

Re-sold to:

NAME

ADDRESS

CITY/STATE/ZIP

PHONE

PRICE RE-SOLD FOR

Your feelings about and/or experiences with this Beanie:

Grunt™

Type:	Male razorback hog	**Categories:** Red	**Style no.:** 4092	

Birthday: July 19, 1995 **Released:** 1/7/96 **Retired:** 5/11/97

Position: Laying down **Tags:** 3rd & 4th generation **Teenie:**

Description: Red plush body, red felt ears & spikes, white feet & fangs, black plastic eyes, black thread eyebrows, knotted tail, hang tag left ear, tush tag left back leg

Replaces: None

Variations: None

Oddities: None

Commentary: Released six months after birth; in circulation only 16 months before retiring, making it one of the shortest-lived Beanies, hence, very hard to find & very expensive; one of the meanest-looking Beanies; very popular w/ boys

Poem: Some Beanies think Grunt is tough
No surprise, he's scary enough
But if you take him home you'll see
Grunt is the sweetest Beanie Baby!™

My record

(Beanies are the #1 collectible in American collecting history. A complete, detailed record will vastly increase the value of this Beanie, if and when you ever appraise, trade, re-sell, gift, or bequeath it.)

Description *(which version do you have?):*

Gift from:

Date received/purchased:

Purchased from:

NAME OF PERSON OR RETAILER

ADDRESS

CITY/STATE/ZIP

PHONE

Qty. purchased: **Cost ea.**

(check one)   ❏ *Cash*   ❏ *Check*   ❏ *Charge*

Reason(s) for purchase(s):

Traded to:

NAME

ADDRESS

CITY/STATE/ZIP

PHONE

TRADED FOR

Re-sold to:

NAME

ADDRESS

CITY/STATE/ZIP

PHONE

PRICE RE-SOLD FOR

Your feelings about and/or experiences with this Beanie:

Manny™

Type:	Female manatee	*Categories:*	Gray, sea	*Style no.:*	4081	
Birthday:	June 8, 1995	*Released:*	1/7/96	*Retired:*	5/11/97	
Position:	Swimming	*Tags:*	3rd & 4th generation	*Teenie:*		

Description: Light gray plush body, black plastic eyes, black thread nostrils, two flippers, hang tag left flipper, tush tag left back side

Replaces: None

Variations: None

Oddities: Odd animal to turn into a Beanie; Manny shares same birthday w/ Bucky

Commentary: Released seven months after birth; in circulation only 16 months before retiring, making it one of the shortest-lived Beanies, hence, very hard to find & very expensive

Poem: Manny is sometimes called a sea cow
She likes to twirl and likes to bow
Manny sure is glad you bought her
Because it's so lonely under water!™

My record

(Beanies are the #1 collectible in American collecting history. A complete, detailed record will vastly increase the value of this Beanie, if and when you ever appraise, trade, re-sell, gift, or bequeath it.)

Description *(which version do you have?):*

Gift from:

Date received/purchased:

Purchased from:

NAME OF PERSON OR RETAILER

ADDRESS

CITY/STATE/ZIP

PHONE

Qty. purchased: Cost ea.
(check one)   ❏ *Cash*   ❏ *Check*   ❏ *Charge*

Reason(s) for purchase(s):

Traded to:

NAME

ADDRESS

CITY/STATE/ZIP

PHONE

TRADED FOR

Re-sold to:

NAME

ADDRESS

CITY/STATE/ZIP

PHONE

PRICE RE-SOLD FOR

Your feelings about and/or experiences with this Beanie:

Radar™

Type:	Male bat	*Categories:* Black, creepie crawlie	*Style no.:* 4091
Birthday:	October 30, 1995	*Released:* 9/1/95	*Retired:* 5/11/97
Position:	Flying	*Tags:* 3rd & 4th generation	*Teenie:*

Description: Black plush body, black felt hands & feet, white inner ears, black thread detailing on wings, red plastic eyes, black plastic nose, hang tag left ear, tush tag left wing

Replaces: None

Variations: None

Oddities: Released nearly two months before birth

Commentary: In circulation only 20 months before retiring, making it one of the shortest-lived Beanies, hence, very hard to find & very expensive; very popular with boys; replaced by Batty

Poem: Radar the bat flies late at night
He can soar to an amazing height
If you see something as high as a star
Take a good look, it might be Radar!™

My record

(Beanies are the #1 collectible in American collecting history. A complete, detailed record will vastly increase the value of this Beanie, if and when you ever appraise, trade, re-sell, gift, or bequeath it.)

Description *(which version do you have?):*

Gift from:

Date received/purchased:

Purchased from:

NAME OF PERSON OR RETAILER
ADDRESS
CITY/STATE/ZIP
PHONE

Qty. purchased: **Cost ea.**
(check one)   ❏ *Cash*   ❏ *Check*   ❏ *Charge*

Reason(s) for purchase(s):

Traded to:

NAME
ADDRESS
CITY/STATE/ZIP
PHONE
TRADED FOR

Re-sold to:

NAME
ADDRESS
CITY/STATE/ZIP
PHONE
PRICE RE-SOLD FOR

Your feelings about and/or experiences with this Beanie:

Sparky

Type:	Male dalmatian	*Categories:* Black & white, dog	*Style no.:* 4100
Birthday:	February 27, 1996	*Released:* 6/15/96	*Retired:* 5/11/97
Position:	Laying down	*Tags:* 4th generation	*Teenie:*

Description: White plush body w/ black spots, black plastic eyes & nose, black thread mouth, stubby tail, hang tag left ear, tush tag left back leg

Replaces: None

Variations: Three versions of fourth line of poem

Oddities: Some tush tags read "Dotty"

Commentary: Released four months after birth; in circulation only 11 months before retiring, making it one of the shortest-lived Beanies, hence, very hard to find & very expensive; retired due to flack from firemen's association whose dalmatian mascot is named Sparky; one of few Beanies w/ only one generation of tags; replaced by Dotty

Poem: Sparky rides proud on the firetruck
Ringing the bell and pushing his luck
He gets under foot when trying to help
He often gets stepped on and lets out a yelp!™

My record

(Beanies are the #1 collectible in American collecting history. A complete, detailed record will vastly increase the value of this Beanie, if and when you ever appraise, trade, re-sell, gift, or bequeath it.)

Description *(which version do you have?):*

Gift from:

Date received/purchased:

Purchased from:

NAME OF PERSON OR RETAILER

ADDRESS

CITY/STATE/ZIP

PHONE

Qty. purchased: **Cost ea.**
(check one) ❏ *Cash* ❏ *Check* ❏ *Charge*

Reason(s) for purchase(s):

Traded to:

NAME

ADDRESS

CITY/STATE/ZIP

PHONE

TRADED FOR

Re-sold to:

NAME

ADDRESS

CITY/STATE/ZIP

PHONE

PRICE RE-SOLD FOR

Your feelings about and/or experiences with this Beanie:

Splash™

1 of the original 9 Beanies

Type:	Male whale	***Categories:***	Black & white, sea	***Style no.:***	4022
Birthday:	July 8, 1993	***Released:***	1/8/94	***Retired:***	5/11/97
Position:	Swimming	***Tags:***	1st-4th generation	***Teenie:***	

Description: Black plush body, white under side, black plastic eyes, three sets of fins, hang tag left fin, tush tag left back side

Replaces: None

Variations: One of three Beanies w/ two poems

Oddities: Gender changes in two poems

Commentary: Released six months after birth; in circulation 40 months before retiring, making it one of the longest-running Beanies; 1 of the original 9 Beanies, hence, very popular, very hard to find, very expensive; replaced by Waves

Poem: Splash loves to jump and dive
He's the fastest whale alive
He always wins the 100 yard-dash
With a victory jump, he'll make a splash!™

My record

(Beanies are the #1 collectible in American collecting history. A complete, detailed record will vastly increase the value of this Beanie, if and when you ever appraise, trade, re-sell, gift, or bequeath it.)

Description *(which version do you have?):*

Gift from:

Date received/purchased:

Purchased from:

NAME OF PERSON OR RETAILER

ADDRESS

CITY/STATE/ZIP

PHONE

Qty. purchased: **Cost ea.**
(check one)   ❑ *Cash*   ❑ *Check*   ❑ *Charge*

Reason(s) for purchase(s):

Traded to:

NAME

ADDRESS

CITY/STATE/ZIP

PHONE

TRADED FOR

Re-sold to:

NAME

ADDRESS

CITY/STATE/ZIP

PHONE

PRICE RE-SOLD FOR

Your feelings about and/or experiences with this Beanie:

1/1/97 Retireds

Place behind this tab
the following Beanie Babies®:

Chops   Righty
Coral   Sting
Kiwi   Tabasco
Lefty   Tusk
Libearty

Chops®

Type:	Lamb	**Categories:** Cream, farm		**Style no.:** 4019
Birthday:	May 3, 1996	**Released:** 1/7/96		**Retired:** 1/1/97
Position:	Laying down	**Tags:** 3rd & 4th generation		**Teenie:** 4/97

Description: Cream-colored plush body, black face & inner ears, black plastic eyes, pink plastic nose, pink thread mouth, stubby tail, hang tag left ear, tush tag left back leg

Replaces: None

Variations: None

Oddities: Released four months before birth; one of few Beanies w/ no gender indicated

Commentary: In circulation only 16 months before retiring, making it one of the shortest-lived Beanies, hence, very hard to find & very expensive; one of the most sought-after Beanies; replaced by Fleece

Poem: Chops is a little lamb
This lamb you'll surely know
Because every path that you may take
This lamb is sure to go!™

1

My record

(Beanies are the #1 collectible in American collecting history. A complete, detailed record will vastly increase the value of this Beanie, if and when you ever appraise, trade, re-sell, gift, or bequeath it.)

Description *(which version do you have?):*

Gift from:

Date received/purchased:

Purchased from:

NAME OF PERSON OR RETAILER

ADDRESS

CITY/STATE/ZIP

PHONE

Qty. purchased: **Cost ea.**
(check one)   ❏ *Cash*   ❏ *Check*   ❏ *Charge*

Reason(s) for purchase(s):

Traded to:

NAME

ADDRESS

CITY/STATE/ZIP

PHONE

TRADED FOR

Re-sold to:

NAME

ADDRESS

CITY/STATE/ZIP

PHONE

PRICE RE-SOLD FOR

Your feelings about and/or experiences with this Beanie:

Coral™

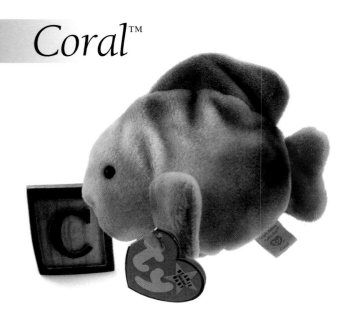

Type:	Fish	**Categories:** Sea, tie-dyed	**Style no.:** 4079	
Birthday:	March 2, 1995	**Released:** 6/3/95	**Retired:** 1/1/97	
Position:	Swimming	**Tags:** 3rd & 4th generation	**Teenie:**	

Description: Tie-dyed plush body, black plastic eyes, three sets of fins, hang tag left fin, tush tag bottom

Replaces: None

Variations: Tie-dye varies from cool to warm colors

Oddities: Released same day as Bubbles; one of few Beanies w/ no gender indicated

Commentary: Released three months after birth; in circulation only 19 months before retiring, making it one of the shortest-lived Beanies, hence, very hard to find & very expensive; one of the prettiest Beanies, hence, very popular; replaced by Goldie

Poem: Coral is beautiful, as you know
Made of colors in the rainbow
Whether it's pink, yellow or blue
These colors were chosen just for you!™

2

My record

(Beanies are the #1 collectible in American collecting history. A complete, detailed record will vastly increase the value of this Beanie, if and when you ever appraise, trade, re-sell, gift, or bequeath it.)

Description *(which version do you have?):*

Gift from:

Date received/purchased:

Purchased from:

NAME OF PERSON OR RETAILER

ADDRESS

CITY/STATE/ZIP

PHONE

Qty. purchased: **Cost ea.**
(check one)   ❏ *Cash*   ❏ *Check*   ❏ *Charge*

Reason(s) for purchase(s):

Traded to:

NAME

ADDRESS

CITY/STATE/ZIP

PHONE

TRADED FOR

Re-sold to:

NAME

ADDRESS

CITY/STATE/ZIP

PHONE

PRICE RE-SOLD FOR

Your feelings about and/or experiences with this Beanie:

Kiwi™

Type: Male toucan   **Categories:** Birds, jungle   **Style no.:** 4070

Birthday: September 16, 1995   **Released:** 6/3/95   **Retired:** 1/1/97

Position: Perching   **Tags:** 3rd & 4th generation   **Teenie:**

Description: Black plush body, royal blue beak & feet, red belly & under wings, yellow throat, black plastic eyes, three-pronged tail, hang tag left wing, tush tag bottom

Replaces: None

Variations: None

Oddities: Released three months before birth; Kiwi shares same birthday w/ Derby

Commentary: In circulation only 19 months before retiring, making it one of the shortest-lived Beanies, hence, very hard to find & very expensive; one of the most colorful Beanies, hence, very popular

Poem: Kiwi waits for the April showers
Watching a garden bloom with flowers
There trees grow with fruit that's sweet
I'm sure you'll guess his favorite treat!™

3

My record

(Beanies are the #1 collectible in American collecting history. A complete, detailed record will vastly increase the value of this Beanie, if and when you ever appraise, trade, re-sell, gift, or bequeath it.)

Description *(which version do you have?)*:

Gift from:

Date received/purchased:

Purchased from:

NAME OF PERSON OR RETAILER

ADDRESS

CITY/STATE/ZIP

PHONE

Qty. purchased: **Cost ea.**
(check one)   ❏ *Cash*   ❏ *Check*   ❏ *Charge*

Reason(s) for purchase(s):

Traded to:

NAME

ADDRESS

CITY/STATE/ZIP

PHONE

TRADED FOR

Re-sold to:

NAME

ADDRESS

CITY/STATE/ZIP

PHONE

PRICE RE-SOLD FOR

Your feelings about and/or experiences with this Beanie:

Lefty™

Type:	Donkey	*Categories:* Blue, flag, political	*Style no.:* 4086

Birthday:	July 4, 1996	*Released:* 6/15/96	*Retired:* 1/1/97

Position:	Laying down	*Tags:* 4th generation	*Teenie:*

Description: Steel blue plush body; black nose, inner ears & hooves; black yarn mane & tail; red, white & blue embroidered U.S. flag stitched w/ white thread on left back side; hang tag left ear; tush tag back left leg

Replaces: None

Variations: Placement of flag

Oddities: Like Righty, born on the 4th of July; released one month before birth; one of few Beanies w/ no gender indicated; same poem as Righty

Commentary: In circulation only six months before retiring, making it one of the shortest-lived Beanies ever, hence, very hard to find & very expensive; one of the most sought-after Beanies ever; one of only two political Beanies; one of few Beanies w/ only one generation of tags

Poem: Donkeys to the left, elephants to the right
Often seems like a crazy sight
This whole game seems very funny
Until you realize they're spending your money!™

4

My record

(Beanies are the #1 collectible in American collecting history. A complete, detailed record will vastly increase the value of this Beanie, if and when you ever appraise, trade, re-sell, gift, or bequeath it.)

Description *(which version do you have?):*

Gift from:

Date received/purchased:

Purchased from:

NAME OF PERSON OR RETAILER

ADDRESS

CITY/STATE/ZIP

PHONE

Qty. purchased: **Cost ea.**
(check one)   ❏ *Cash*   ❏ *Check*   ❏ *Charge*

Reason(s) for purchase(s):

Traded to:

NAME

ADDRESS

CITY/STATE/ZIP

PHONE

TRADED FOR

Re-sold to:

NAME

ADDRESS

CITY/STATE/ZIP

PHONE

PRICE RE-SOLD FOR

Your feelings about and/or experiences with this Beanie:

Libearty™

Type: Bear	***Categories:*** Bear, flag, white	***Style no.:*** 4057
Birthday: Summer '96	***Released:*** 6/15/96	***Retired:*** 1/1/97
Position: Sitting up	***Tags:*** 4th generation	***Teenie:***

Description: White plush body; black plastic eyes; brown plastic nose; red, white & blue embroidered U.S. flag stitched w/ white thread over heart; red & blue satin ribbon tied around neck; hang tag left ear; tush tag left bottom

Replaces: None

Variations: Special Atlanta Summer Olympics '96 edition w/ commemorative card, extremely rare & expensive

Oddities: No specific birthday; released same day as Lefty & Righty; one of few Beanies w/ no gender indicated; one of few poems written in first person; flag upside down or missing

Commentary: In circulation only six months before retiring, making it one of the shortest-lived Beanies ever, hence, very hard to find & very expensive; one of the most beautiful & sought-after Beanies ever

Poem: I am called Libearty
I wear the flag for all to see
Hope and freedom is my way
That's why I wear flag USA!™

My record

(Beanies are the #1 collectible in American collecting history. A complete, detailed record will vastly increase the value of this Beanie, if and when you ever appraise, trade, re-sell, gift, or bequeath it.)

Description *(which version do you have?)*:

Gift from:

Date received/purchased:

Purchased from:

NAME OF PERSON OR RETAILER

ADDRESS

CITY/STATE/ZIP

PHONE

Qty. purchased: **Cost ea.**
(check one)   ❏ *Cash*   ❏ *Check*   ❏ *Charge*

Reason(s) for purchase(s):

Traded to:

NAME

ADDRESS

CITY/STATE/ZIP

PHONE

TRADED FOR

Re-sold to:

NAME

ADDRESS

CITY/STATE/ZIP

PHONE

PRICE RE-SOLD FOR

Your feelings about and/or experiences with this Beanie:

Righty™

Type:	Elephant	***Categories:*** Flag, gray, political		***Style no.:***	4086

Birthday: July 4, 1996   ***Released:*** 6/15/96   ***Retired:*** 1/1/97

Position: Laying down   ***Tags:*** 4th generation   ***Teenie:***

Description: Light gray plush body; pink inner ears; black plastic eyes; trunk; knotted tail; red, white & blue embroidered U.S. flag stitched w/ white thread on left back side; hang tag left ear; tush tag left back leg

Replaces: None

Variations: Placement of flag

Oddities: Like Lefty, born on the 4th of July; released one month before birth; one of few Beanies w/ no gender indicated; same poem as Lefty

Commentary: In circulation only six months before retiring, making it one of the shortest-lived Beanies ever, hence, very hard to find & very expensive; one of the most sought-after Beanies ever; one of only two political Beanies; one of few Beanies w/ only one generation of tags

Poem: Donkeys to the left, elephants to the right
Often seems like a crazy sight
This whole game seems very funny
Until you realize they're spending your money!™

6

My record

(Beanies are the #1 collectible in American collecting history. A complete, detailed record will vastly increase the value of this Beanie, if and when you ever appraise, trade, re-sell, gift, or bequeath it.)

Description *(which version do you have?):*

Gift from:

Date received/purchased:

Purchased from:

NAME OF PERSON OR RETAILER

ADDRESS

CITY/STATE/ZIP

PHONE

Qty. purchased: **Cost ea.**
(check one)   ❏ *Cash*   ❏ *Check*   ❏ *Charge*

Reason(s) for purchase(s):

Traded to:

NAME

ADDRESS

CITY/STATE/ZIP

PHONE

TRADED FOR

Re-sold to:

NAME

ADDRESS

CITY/STATE/ZIP

PHONE

PRICE RE-SOLD FOR

Your feelings about and/or experiences with this Beanie:

Sting™

Type:	Manta ray	**Categories:** Tie-dyed, sea	**Style no.:** 4077

Birthday: August 27, 1995   **Released:** 6/3/95   **Retired:** 1/1/97

Position: Swimming   **Tags:** 3rd & 4th generation   **Teenie:**

Description: Blue-green tie-dyed plush body, black plastic eyes, long tail, hang tag left front ray, tush tag left back ray

Replaces: None

Variations: Tie-dye varies in colors from blue to green

Oddities: Odd animal to turn into a Beanie; released more than two months before birth; one of few Beanies w/ no gender indicated; one of few poems written in first person; manta rays are gray to black, not blue

Commentary: In circulation only 19 months before retiring, making it one of the shortest-lived Beanies, hence, very hard to find & very expensive; one of few Beanies w/ unrealistic coloring; very popular with boys

Poem: I'm a manta ray and my name is Sting
I'm quite unusual and this is the thing
Under the water I glide like a bird
Have you ever seen something so absurd?™

My record

(Beanies are the #1 collectible in American collecting history. A complete, detailed record will vastly increase the value of this Beanie, if and when you ever appraise, trade, re-sell, gift, or bequeath it.)

Description *(which version do you have?):*

Gift from:

Date received/purchased:

Purchased from:

NAME OF PERSON OR RETAILER

ADDRESS

CITY/STATE/ZIP

PHONE

Qty. purchased: **Cost ea.**
(check one)   ❏ *Cash*   ❏ *Check*   ❏ *Charge*

Reason(s) for purchase(s):

Traded to:

NAME

ADDRESS

CITY/STATE/ZIP

PHONE

TRADED FOR

Re-sold to:

NAME

ADDRESS

CITY/STATE/ZIP

PHONE

PRICE RE-SOLD FOR

Your feelings about and/or experiences with this Beanie:

Tabasco

Type:	Male bull	*Categories:*	Farm, red	*Style no.:*	4002	

Birthday: May 15, 1995   *Released:* 6/3/95   *Retired:* 1/1/97

Position: Laying down   *Tags:* 3rd & 4th generation   *Teenie:*

Description: Red plush body; cream-colored horns, inner ears & tip of snout; black plastic eyes; black thread nostrils; knotted tail; hang tag left ear; tush tag left back leg

Replaces: None

Variations: None

Oddities: Tabasco shares same birthday w/ Snort

Commentary: Released one month after birth; in circulation only 19 months before retiring, making it one of the shortest-lived Beanies, hence, very hard to find & very expensive; retired due to flack from hot sauce company who owns Tabasco name; one of the most sought-after Beanies; replaced by Snort

Poem: Although Tabasco is not so tall
He loves to play basketball
He is a star player in his dream
Can you guess his favorite team?™

My record

(Beanies are the #1 collectible in American collecting history. A complete, detailed record will vastly increase the value of this Beanie, if and when you ever appraise, trade, re-sell, gift, or bequeath it.)

Description *(which version do you have?):*

Gift from:

Date received/purchased:

Purchased from:

NAME OF PERSON OR RETAILER

ADDRESS

CITY/STATE/ZIP

PHONE

Qty. purchased: **Cost ea.**
(check one)   ❏ *Cash*   ❏ *Check*   ❏ *Charge*

Reason(s) for purchase(s):

Traded to:

NAME

ADDRESS

CITY/STATE/ZIP

PHONE

TRADED FOR

Re-sold to:

NAME

ADDRESS

CITY/STATE/ZIP

PHONE

PRICE RE-SOLD FOR

Your feelings about and/or experiences with this Beanie:

Tusk™

Type:	Male walrus	**Categories:**	Arctic, brown, sea	**Style no.:**	4076

Birthday: September 18, 1995   **Released:** 1/7/95   **Retired:** 1/1/97

Position: Laying down   **Tags:** 3rd & 4th generation   **Teenie:**

Description: Reddish-brown plush body, lighter brown plush beard, white felt tusks, black plastic eyes & nose, hang tag left flapper, tush tag left back side

Replaces: None

Variations: Four versions of fourth line of poem

Oddities: Released eight months before birth, only poem to encourage a good habit (brushing teeth); some hang tags read "Tuck"; some tusks upside down

Commentary: In circulation 24 months before retiring; hard to find & expensive; replaced by Jolly

Poem: Tusk brushes his teeth everyday
To keep them shiny, it's the only way
Teeth are special, so you must try
And they will sparkle when you say hi!™

My record

(Beanies are the #1 collectible in American collecting history. A complete, detailed record will vastly increase the value of this Beanie, if and when you ever appraise, trade, re-sell, gift, or bequeath it.)

Description *(which version do you have?):*

Gift from:

Date received/purchased:

Purchased from:

NAME OF PERSON OR RETAILER

ADDRESS

CITY/STATE/ZIP

PHONE

Qty. purchased: **Cost ea.**
(check one)   ❏ *Cash*   ❏ *Check*   ❏ *Charge*

Reason(s) for purchase(s):

Traded to:

NAME

ADDRESS

CITY/STATE/ZIP

PHONE

TRADED FOR

Re-sold to:

NAME

ADDRESS

CITY/STATE/ZIP

PHONE

PRICE RE-SOLD FOR

Your feelings about and/or experiences with this Beanie:

'95–'96 Retireds

Place behind this tab
the following Beanie Babies®:

1/7/95
Teddy Brown^{OF}
Teddy Cranberry^{OF}
Teddy Jade^{OF}
Teddy Magenta^{OF}
Teddy Teal^{OF}
Teddy Violet^{OF}

6/15/95
Humphrey
Slither
Trap

1/7/96
Chilly
Peking
Teddy Cranberry^{NF}
Teddy Jade^{NF}
Teddy Magenta^{NF}
Teddy Teal^{NF}
Teddy Violet^{NF}
Web

6/15/96
Bronty
Bumble
Caw
Flutter
Rex
Steg

^{OF} Old Face
^{NF} New Face

Teddy Cranberry™

(old face)

Type:	Bear	***Categories:*** Bear, red	***Style no.:*** 4052
Birthday:	None	***Released:*** 6/25/94	***Retired:*** 1/7/95
Position:	Sitting up	***Tags:*** 2nd & 3rd generation	***Teenie:***

Description: Cranberry plush body, black plastic eyes & nose, hang tag left ear, tush tag left bottom

Replaces: None

Variations: None

Oddities: Like all '95-'96 Retired Beanies, no gender indicated, no birthday & no poem; same style no. as Teddy Cranberry (new face) & Curly; all old-faced Teddies released & retired same dates; one of few bears w/ no ribbon tied around neck

Commentary: In circulation only seven months before retiring, making it one of the shortest-lived Beanies ever; one of the rarest, most valued, most expensive Beanies ever; replaced by Teddy Cranberry w/ new face & ribbon

Poem: None

2

My record

(Beanies are the #1 collectible in American collecting history. A complete, detailed record will vastly increase the value of this Beanie, if and when you ever appraise, trade, re-sell, gift, or bequeath it.)

Description *(which version do you have?):*

Gift from:

Date received/purchased:

Purchased from:

NAME OF PERSON OR RETAILER

ADDRESS

CITY/STATE/ZIP

PHONE

Qty. purchased: **Cost ea.**
(check one)   ❑ *Cash*   ❑ *Check*   ❑ *Charge*

Reason(s) for purchase(s):

Traded to:

NAME

ADDRESS

CITY/STATE/ZIP

PHONE

TRADED FOR

Re-sold to:

NAME

ADDRESS

CITY/STATE/ZIP

PHONE

PRICE RE-SOLD FOR

Your feelings about and/or experiences with this Beanie:

Teddy Jade™

(old face)

Type:	Bear	*Categories:* Bear, green	*Style no.:* 4057	

Birthday: None *Released:* 6/25/94 *Retired:* 1/7/95

Position: Sitting up *Tags:* 1st & 2nd generation *Teenie:*

Description: Jade plush body, black plastic eyes & nose, hang tag left ear, tush tag left bottom

Replaces: None

Variations: None

Oddities: Like all '95-'96 Retired Beanies, no gender indicated, no birthday & no poem; same style no. as Teddy Jade (new face) & Libearty; all old-faced Teddies released & retired same dates; one of few bears w/ no ribbon tied around neck

Commentary: In circulation only seven months before retiring, making it one of the shortest-lived Beanies ever; one of the rarest, most valued, most expensive Beanies ever; replaced by Teddy Jade w/ new face & ribbon

Poem: None

3

My record

(Beanies are the #1 collectible in American collecting history. A complete, detailed record will vastly increase the value of this Beanie, if and when you ever appraise, trade, re-sell, gift, or bequeath it.)

Description *(which version do you have?):*

Gift from:

Date received/purchased:

Purchased from:

NAME OF PERSON OR RETAILER

ADDRESS

CITY/STATE/ZIP

PHONE

Qty. purchased: **Cost ea.**
(check one)   ❏ *Cash*   ❏ *Check*   ❏ *Charge*

Reason(s) for purchase(s):

Traded to:

NAME

ADDRESS

CITY/STATE/ZIP

PHONE

TRADED FOR

Re-sold to:

NAME

ADDRESS

CITY/STATE/ZIP

PHONE

PRICE RE-SOLD FOR

Your feelings about and/or experiences with this Beanie:

Teddy Magenta™

(old face)

Type:	Bear ***Categories:*** Bear, purple	***Style no.:*** 4056	

Birthday:	None ***Released:*** 6/25/94	***Retired:*** 1/7/95

Position: Sitting up   ***Tags:*** 1st & 2nd generation   ***Teenie:***

Description: Magenta plush body, black plastic eyes & nose, hang tag left ear, tush tag left bottom

Replaces: None

Variations: None

Oddities: Like all '95-'96 Retired Beanies, no gender indicated, no birthday & no poem; same style no. as Teddy Magenta (new face); all old-faced Teddies released & retired same dates; one of few bears w/ no ribbon tied around neck

Commentary: In circulation only seven months before retiring, making it one of the shortest-lived Beanies ever; one of the rarest, most valued, most expensive Beanies ever; replaced by Teddy Magenta w/ new face & ribbon

Poem: None

4

My record

(Beanies are the #1 collectible in American collecting history. A complete, detailed record will vastly increase the value of this Beanie, if and when you ever appraise, trade, re-sell, gift, or bequeath it.)

Description *(which version do you have?):*

Gift from:

Date received/purchased:

Purchased from:

NAME OF PERSON OR RETAILER

ADDRESS

CITY/STATE/ZIP

PHONE

Qty. purchased: **Cost ea.**

(check one)   ❑ *Cash*   ❑ *Check*   ❑ *Charge*

Reason(s) for purchase(s):

Traded to:

NAME

ADDRESS

CITY/STATE/ZIP

PHONE

TRADED FOR

Re-sold to:

NAME

ADDRESS

CITY/STATE/ZIP

PHONE

PRICE RE-SOLD FOR

Your feelings about and/or experiences with this Beanie:

Teddy Teal™

(old face)

Type:	Bear	***Categories:*** Bear, green	***Style no.:*** 4051

Birthday:	None	***Released:*** 6/25/94	***Retired:*** 1/7/95

Position:	Sitting up	***Tags:*** 1st & 2nd generation	***Teenie:***

Description: Teal plush body, black plastic eyes & nose, hang tag left ear, tush tag left bottom

Replaces: None

Variations: None

Oddities: Like all '95-'96 Retired Beanies, no gender indicated, no birthday & no poem; same style no. as Teddy Teal (new face) & Garcia; all old-faced Teddies released & retired same dates; one of few bears w/ no ribbon tied around neck

Commentary: In circulation only seven months before retiring, making it one of the shortest-lived Beanies ever; one of the rarest, most valued, most expensive Beanies ever; replaced by Teddy Teal w/ new face & ribbon

Poem: None

5

My record

(Beanies are the #1 collectible in American collecting history. A complete, detailed record will vastly increase the value of this Beanie, if and when you ever appraise, trade, re-sell, gift, or bequeath it.)

Description *(which version do you have?):*

Gift from:

Date received/purchased:

Purchased from:

NAME OF PERSON OR RETAILER

ADDRESS

CITY/STATE/ZIP

PHONE

Qty. purchased: **Cost ea.**
(check one)   ❏ *Cash*   ❏ *Check*   ❏ *Charge*

Reason(s) for purchase(s):

Traded to:

NAME

ADDRESS

CITY/STATE/ZIP

PHONE

TRADED FOR

Re-sold to:

NAME

ADDRESS

CITY/STATE/ZIP

PHONE

PRICE RE-SOLD FOR

Your feelings about and/or experiences with this Beanie:

Teddy Violet™

(old face)

Type: Bear   **Categories:** Bear, purple   **Style no.:** 4055

Birthday: None   **Released:** 6/25/94   **Retired:** 1/7/95

Position: Sitting up   **Tags:** 1st & 2nd generation   **Teenie:**

Description: Violet plush body, black plastic eyes & nose, hang tag left ear, tush tag left bottom

Replaces: None

Variations: None

Oddities: Like all '95-'96 Retired Beanies, no gender indicated, no birthday & no poem; same style no. as Teddy Violet (new face); all old-faced Teddies released & retired same dates; one of few bears w/ no ribbon tied around neck

Commentary: In circulation only seven months before retiring, making it one of the shortest-lived Beanies ever; one of the rarest, most valued, most expensive Beanies ever; replaced by Teddy Violet w/ new face & ribbon

Poem: None

My record

(Beanies are the #1 collectible in American collecting history. A complete, detailed record will vastly increase the value of this Beanie, if and when you ever appraise, trade, re-sell, gift, or bequeath it.)

Description *(which version do you have?):*

Gift from:

Date received/purchased:

Purchased from:

NAME OF PERSON OR RETAILER

ADDRESS

CITY/STATE/ZIP

PHONE

Qty. purchased: **Cost ea.**

(check one)   ❏ *Cash*   ❏ *Check*   ❏ *Charge*

Reason(s) for purchase(s):

Traded to:

NAME

ADDRESS

CITY/STATE/ZIP

PHONE

TRADED FOR

Re-sold to:

NAME

ADDRESS

CITY/STATE/ZIP

PHONE

PRICE RE-SOLD FOR

Your feelings about and/or experiences with this Beanie:

Humphrey™

Type:	Camel	***Categories:*** Brown, desert	***Style no.:*** 4060	
Birthday:	None	***Released:*** 6/25/94	***Retired:*** 6/15/95	
Position:	Laying down	***Tags:*** 1st-3rd generation	***Teenie:***	
Description:	Brown plush body, black plastic eyes, black thread nostrils, one hump, knotted tail, hang tag left ear, tush tag left bottom			
Replaces:	None			
Variations:	None			
Oddities:	Like all '95-'96 Retired Beanies, no gender indicated, no birthday & no poem; Humphrey shares same style no. w/ Spike			
Commentary:	In circulation only one year before retiring, making it one of the shortest-lived Beanies; one of the rarest, most valued, most expensive Beanies ever			
Poem:	None			

My record

(Beanies are the #1 collectible in American collecting history. A complete, detailed record will vastly increase the value of this Beanie, if and when you ever appraise, trade, re-sell, gift, or bequeath it.)

Description *(which version do you have?):*

Gift from:

Date received/purchased:

Purchased from:

NAME OF PERSON OR RETAILER

ADDRESS

CITY/STATE/ZIP

PHONE

Qty. purchased: **Cost ea.**
(check one)   ❏ *Cash*   ❏ *Check*   ❏ *Charge*

Reason(s) for purchase(s):

Traded to:

NAME

ADDRESS

CITY/STATE/ZIP

PHONE

TRADED FOR

Re-sold to:

NAME

ADDRESS

CITY/STATE/ZIP

PHONE

PRICE RE-SOLD FOR

Your feelings about and/or experiences with this Beanie:

Slither ™

| **Type:** | Snake | **Categories:** | Brown, reptile | **Style no.:** | 4031 |

Birthday: None   **Released:** 6/25/94   **Retired:** 6/15/95

Position: Slithering   **Tags:** 1st-3rd generation   **Teenie:**

Description: Moss green top side w/ brown spots, yellow bottom side, red felt forked tongue, black plastic eyes, hang tag left front, tush tag left back

Replaces: None

Variations: None

Oddities: Like all '95-'96 Retired Beanies, no gender indicated, no birthday & no poem; Slither shares same style no. w/ Tank; tongue easily fell out, hard to find w/ tongue

Commentary: In circulation only one year before retiring, making it one of the shortest-lived Beanies, hence; one of the rarest, most valued, most expensive Beanies ever; very popular w/ boys; replaced by Hissy

Poem: None

My record

(Beanies are the #1 collectible in American collecting history. A complete, detailed record will vastly increase the value of this Beanie, if and when you ever appraise, trade, re-sell, gift, or bequeath it.)

Description *(which version do you have?):*

Gift from:

Date received/purchased:

Purchased from:

NAME OF PERSON OR RETAILER

ADDRESS

CITY/STATE/ZIP

PHONE

Qty. purchased: **Cost ea.**
(check one)   ❏ *Cash*   ❏ *Check*   ❏ *Charge*

Reason(s) for purchase(s):

Traded to:

NAME

ADDRESS

CITY/STATE/ZIP

PHONE

TRADED FOR

Re-sold to:

NAME

ADDRESS

CITY/STATE/ZIP

PHONE

PRICE RE-SOLD FOR

Your feelings about and/or experiences with this Beanie:

Trap™

Type:	Mouse	*Categories:* Creepie crawlie, gray	*Style no.:* 4042
Birthday:	None	*Released:* 6/25/94	*Retired:* 6/15/95
Position:	Crawling	*Tags:* 1st-3rd generation	*Teenie:*

Description: Light gray plush body; pink inner ears, feet & tail; black plastic eyes; pink plastic nose; black thread whiskers; knotted tail; hang tag left ear; tush tag left back

Replaces: None

Variations: None

Oddities: Like all '95-'96 Retired Beanies, no gender indicated, no birthday & no poem

Commentary: In circulation only one year before retiring, making it one of the shortest-lived Beanies, hence, extremely rare & expensive; very popular w/ boys

Poem: None

My record

(Beanies are the #1 collectible in American collecting history. A complete, detailed record will vastly increase the value of this Beanie, if and when you ever appraise, trade, re-sell, gift, or bequeath it.)

Description *(which version do you have?):*

Gift from:

Date received/purchased:

Purchased from:

NAME OF PERSON OR RETAILER

ADDRESS

CITY/STATE/ZIP

PHONE

Qty. purchased: **Cost ea.**
(check one)   ❏ *Cash*   ❏ *Check*   ❏ *Charge*

Reason(s) for purchase(s):

Traded to:

NAME

ADDRESS

CITY/STATE/ZIP

PHONE

TRADED FOR

Re-sold to:

NAME

ADDRESS

CITY/STATE/ZIP

PHONE

PRICE RE-SOLD FOR

Your feelings about and/or experiences with this Beanie:

Chilly™

Type:	Polar bear	**Categories:** Arctic, bear, white	**Style no.:** 4012
Birthday:	None	**Released:** 6/25/94	**Retired:** 1/7/96
Position:	Laying down	**Tags:** 1st-3rd generation	**Teenie:**

Description: White plush body, black plastic eyes & nose, stubby tail, hang tag left ear, tush tag left bottom

Replaces: None

Variations: None

Oddities: Like all '95-'96 Retired Beanies, no gender indicated, no birthday & no poem; Chilly shares same style no. w/ Flip

Commentary: In circulation only 19 months before retiring, making it one of the shortest-lived Beanies; one of the rarest, most valued, most expensive Beanies ever

Poem: None

My record

(Beanies are the #1 collectible in American collecting history. A complete, detailed record will vastly increase the value of this Beanie, if and when you ever appraise, trade, re-sell, gift, or bequeath it.)

Description *(which version do you have?):*

Gift from:

Date received/purchased:

Purchased from:

NAME OF PERSON OR RETAILER

ADDRESS

CITY/STATE/ZIP

PHONE

Qty. purchased: **Cost ea.**
(check one)   ❏ *Cash*   ❏ *Check*   ❏ *Charge*

Reason(s) for purchase(s):

Traded to:

NAME

ADDRESS

CITY/STATE/ZIP

PHONE

TRADED FOR

Re-sold to:

NAME

ADDRESS

CITY/STATE/ZIP

PHONE

PRICE RE-SOLD FOR

Your feelings about and/or experiences with this Beanie:

Peking™

Type: Panda   **Categories:** Bear, black & white   **Style no.:** 4013

Birthday: None   **Released:** 6/25/94   **Retired:** 1/7/96

Position: Laying down   **Tags:** 1st-3rd generation   **Teenie:**

Description: White plush body; black ears, shoulders, legs & tail; black plastic eyes & nose; black felt droopies under eyes; stubby tail; hang tag left ear; tush tag left back leg

Replaces: None

Variations: None

Oddities: Like all '95-'96 Retired Beanies, no gender indicated, no birthday & no poem; Peking shares same style no. w/ Weenie

Commentary: In circulation only 19 months before retiring, making it one of the shortest-lived Beanies; one of the rarest, most valued, most expensive Beanies ever; replaced by Fortune

Poem: None

My record

(Beanies are the #1 collectible in American collecting history. A complete, detailed record will vastly increase the value of this Beanie, if and when you ever appraise, trade, re-sell, gift, or bequeath it.)

Description *(which version do you have?):*

Gift from:

Date received/purchased:

Purchased from:

NAME OF PERSON OR RETAILER

ADDRESS

CITY/STATE/ZIP

PHONE

Qty. purchased: **Cost ea.**
(check one)   ❑ *Cash*   ❑ *Check*   ❑ *Charge*

Reason(s) for purchase(s):

Traded to:

NAME

ADDRESS

CITY/STATE/ZIP

PHONE

TRADED FOR

Re-sold to:

NAME

ADDRESS

CITY/STATE/ZIP

PHONE

PRICE RE-SOLD FOR

Your feelings about and/or experiences with this Beanie:

Teddy Cranberry™

(new face)

Type:	Bear	**Categories:** Bear, red	**Style no.:** 4052	
Birthday:	None	**Released:** 1/7/95	**Retired:** 1/7/96	
Position:	Sitting up	**Tags:** 2nd & 3rd generation	**Teenie:**	

Description: Cranberry plush body, black plastic eyes & nose, green satin ribbon tied around neck, hang tag left ear, tush tag left bottom

Replaces: Teddy Cranberry (old face), style no. 4052, birthday unknown, released 6/25/94, retired 1/7/95, extremely rare & expensive

Variations: None

Oddities: Like all '95-'96 Retired Beanies, no gender indicated, no birthday & no poem; same style no. as Teddy Cranberry (old face) & Curly; old retired same date new released; all new-faced Teddies released same date; all new-faced Teddies (except brown) retired same date

Commentary: In circulation only one year before retiring, making it one of the shortest-lived Beanies; one of the rarest, most valued, most expensive Beanies ever

Poem: None

My record

(Beanies are the #1 collectible in American collecting history. A complete, detailed record will vastly increase the value of this Beanie, if and when you ever appraise, trade, re-sell, gift, or bequeath it.)

Description *(which version do you have?)*:

Gift from:

Date received/purchased:

Purchased from:

NAME OF PERSON OR RETAILER

ADDRESS

CITY/STATE/ZIP

PHONE

Qty. purchased: **Cost ea.**
(check one)   ❏ *Cash*   ❏ *Check*   ❏ *Charge*

Reason(s) for purchase(s):

Traded to:

NAME

ADDRESS

CITY/STATE/ZIP

PHONE

TRADED FOR

Re-sold to:

NAME

ADDRESS

CITY/STATE/ZIP

PHONE

PRICE RE-SOLD FOR

Your feelings about and/or experiences with this Beanie:

Teddy Jade™

(new face)

Type:	Bear	*Categories:* Bear, green	*Style no.:* 4057
Birthday:	None	*Released:* 1/7/95	*Retired:* 1/7/96
Position:	Sitting up	*Tags:* 2nd & 3rd generation	*Teenie:*

Description: Jade plush body, black plastic eyes & nose, cranberry satin ribbon tied around neck, hang tag left ear, tush tag left bottom

Replaces: Teddy Jade (old face), style no. 4057, birthday unknown, released 6/25/94, retired 1/7/95, extremely rare & expensive

Variations: None

Oddities: Like all '95-'96 Retired Beanies, no gender indicated, no birthday & no poem; same style no. as Teddy Jade (old face) & Libearty; old retired same date new released; all new-faced Teddies released same date; all new-faced Teddies (except brown) retired same date

Commentary: In circulation only one year before retiring, making it one of the shortest-lived Beanies; one of the rarest, most valued, most expensive Beanies ever

Poem: None

My record

(Beanies are the #1 collectible in American collecting history. A complete, detailed record will vastly increase the value of this Beanie, if and when you ever appraise, trade, re-sell, gift, or bequeath it.)

Description *(which version do you have?):*

Gift from:

Date received/purchased:

Purchased from:

NAME OF PERSON OR RETAILER

ADDRESS

CITY/STATE/ZIP

PHONE

Qty. purchased: **Cost ea.**
(check one)   ❑ *Cash*   ❑ *Check*   ❑ *Charge*

Reason(s) for purchase(s):

Traded to:

NAME

ADDRESS

CITY/STATE/ZIP

PHONE

TRADED FOR

Re-sold to:

NAME

ADDRESS

CITY/STATE/ZIP

PHONE

PRICE RE-SOLD FOR

Your feelings about and/or experiences with this Beanie:

Teddy Magenta™

(new face)

Type:	Bear	**Categories:** Bear, purple	**Style no.:** 4056
Birthday:	None	**Released:** 1/7/95	**Retired:** 1/7/96
Position:	Sitting up	**Tags:** 2nd & 3rd generation	**Teenie:**

Description: Magenta plush body, black plastic eyes & nose, pale pink satin ribbon tied around neck, hang tag left ear, tush tag left bottom

Replaces: Teddy Magenta (old face), style no. 4056, birthday unknown, released 6/25/94, retired 1/7/95, extremely rare & expensive

Variations: None

Oddities: Like all '95-'96 Retired Beanies, no gender indicated, no birthday & no poem; same style no. as Teddy Magenta (old face); old retired same date new released; all new-faced Teddies released same date; all new-faced Teddies (except brown) retired same date

Commentary: In circulation only one year before retiring, making it one of the shortest-lived Beanies; one of the rarest, most valued, most expensive Beanies ever

Poem: None

My record

(Beanies are the #1 collectible in American collecting history. A complete, detailed record will vastly increase the value of this Beanie, if and when you ever appraise, trade, re-sell, gift, or bequeath it.)

Description *(which version do you have?):*

Gift from:

Date received/purchased:

Purchased from:

NAME OF PERSON OR RETAILER

ADDRESS

CITY/STATE/ZIP

PHONE

Qty. purchased: **Cost ea.**
(check one)   ❏ *Cash*   ❏ *Check*   ❏ *Charge*

Reason(s) for purchase(s):

Traded to:

NAME

ADDRESS

CITY/STATE/ZIP

PHONE

TRADED FOR

Re-sold to:

NAME

ADDRESS

CITY/STATE/ZIP

PHONE

PRICE RE-SOLD FOR

Your feelings about and/or experiences with this Beanie:

Teddy Teal™

(new face)

Type: Bear   *Categories:* Bear, green   *Style no.:* 4051

Birthday: None   *Released:* 1/7/95   *Retired:* 1/7/96

Position: Sitting up   *Tags:* 2nd & 3rd generation   *Teenie:*

Description: Teal plush body, black plastic eyes & nose, violet satin ribbon tied around neck, hang tag left ear, tush tag left bottom

Replaces: Teddy Teal (old face), style no. 4051, birthday unknown, released 6/25/94, retired 1/7/95, extremely rare & expensive

Variations: None

Oddities: Like all '95-'96 Retired Beanies, no gender indicated, no birthday & no poem; same style no. as Teddy Teal (old face) & Garcia; old retired same date new released; all new-faced Teddies released same date; all new-faced Teddies (except brown) retired same date

Commentary: In circulation only one year before retiring, making it one of the shortest-lived Beanies; one of the rarest, most valued, most expensive Beanies ever

Poem: None

My record

(Beanies are the #1 collectible in American collecting history. A complete, detailed record will vastly increase the value of this Beanie, if and when you ever appraise, trade, re-sell, gift, or bequeath it.)

Description *(which version do you have?):*

Gift from:

Date received/purchased:

Purchased from:

NAME OF PERSON OR RETAILER

ADDRESS

CITY/STATE/ZIP

PHONE

Qty. purchased: **Cost ea.**
(check one)   ❏ *Cash*   ❏ *Check*   ❏ *Charge*

Reason(s) for purchase(s):

Traded to:

NAME

ADDRESS

CITY/STATE/ZIP

PHONE

TRADED FOR

Re-sold to:

NAME

ADDRESS

CITY/STATE/ZIP

PHONE

PRICE RE-SOLD FOR

Your feelings about and/or experiences with this Beanie:

Teddy Violet™

(new face)

Type:	Bear	*Categories:*	Bear, purple	*Style no.:*	4055
Birthday:	None	*Released:*	1/7/95	*Retired:*	1/7/96
Position:	Sitting up	*Tags:*	2nd & 3rd generation	*Teenie:*	

Description: Violet plush body, black plastic eyes & nose, green satin ribbon tied around neck, hang tag left ear, tush tag left bottom

Replaces: Teddy Violet (old face), style no. 4055, birthday unknown, released 6/25/94, retired 1/7/95, extremely rare & expensive

Variations: Special 1997 Christmas employee edition w/ red & green ribbons, no hang tag, tush tag w/ no details

Oddities: Like all '95-'96 Retired Beanies, no gender indicated, no birthday & no poem; same style no. as Teddy Violet (old face); old retired same date new released; all new-faced Teddies released same date; all new-faced Teddies (except brown) retired same date

Commentary: In circulation only one year before retiring, making it one of the shortest-lived Beanies; one of the rarest, most valued, most expensive Beanies ever

Poem: None

My record

(Beanies are the #1 collectible in American collecting history. A complete, detailed record will vastly increase the value of this Beanie, if and when you ever appraise, trade, re-sell, gift, or bequeath it.)

Description *(which version do you have?):*

Gift from:

Date received/purchased:

Purchased from:

NAME OF PERSON OR RETAILER

ADDRESS

CITY/STATE/ZIP

PHONE

Qty. purchased: **Cost ea.**
(check one)   ❏ *Cash*   ❏ *Check*   ❏ *Charge*

Reason(s) for purchase(s):

Traded to:

NAME

ADDRESS

CITY/STATE/ZIP

PHONE

TRADED FOR

Re-sold to:

NAME

ADDRESS

CITY/STATE/ZIP

PHONE

PRICE RE-SOLD FOR

Your feelings about and/or experiences with this Beanie:

Web™

Type:	Spider	*Categories:* Black, creepie crawlie	*Style no.:* 4041
Birthday:	None	*Released:* 6/25/94	*Retired:* 1/7/96
Position:	Crawling	*Tags:* 1st-3rd generation	*Teenie:*

Description: Black plush body, red plush underside, black plastic eyes, eight legs, hang tag left front leg, tush tag left back

Replaces: None

Variations: None

Oddities: Like all '95-'96 Retired Beanies, no gender indicated, no birthday & no poem

Commentary: In circulation only 19 months before retiring, making it one of the shortest-lived Beanies; one of the rarest, most valued, most expensive Beanies ever; very popular w/ boys; replaced by Spinner

Poem: None

17

My record

(Beanies are the #1 collectible in American collecting history. A complete, detailed record will vastly increase the value of this Beanie, if and when you ever appraise, trade, re-sell, gift, or bequeath it.)

Description *(which version do you have?):* _____

_____

_____

Gift from: _____

Date received/purchased: _____

Purchased from: _____

NAME OF PERSON OR RETAILER

ADDRESS

CITY/STATE/ZIP

PHONE

Qty. purchased: **Cost ea.**
(check one)   ❏ *Cash*   ❏ *Check*   ❏ *Charge*

Reason(s) for purchase(s): _____

_____

_____

Traded to: _____

NAME

ADDRESS

CITY/STATE/ZIP

PHONE

TRADED FOR

Re-sold to: _____

NAME

ADDRESS

CITY/STATE/ZIP

PHONE

PRICE RE-SOLD FOR

Your feelings about and/or experiences with this Beanie: _____

_____

_____

_____

Bronty™

Type:	Brontosaurus	*Categories:*	Dinosaur, tie-dyed	*Style no.:*	4085
Birthday:	None	*Released:*	6/3/95	*Retired:*	6/15/96
Position:	Standing	*Tags:*	3rd generation	*Teenie:*	

Description: Blue-green tie-dyed plush body, black plastic eyes, hang tag left front leg, tush tag left bottom

Replaces: None

Variations: Tie-dye varies in colors from cool to warm

Oddities: Like all '95-'96 Retired Beanies, no gender indicated, no birthday & no poem; Bronty shares same style no. w/ Righty; dinosaurs are not tie-dyed

Commentary: In circulation only one year before retiring, making it one of the shortest-lived Beanies, hence, extremely rare & expensive; one of few Beanies w/ unrealistic coloring; very popular w/ boys

Poem: None

My record

(Beanies are the #1 collectible in American collecting history. A complete, detailed record will vastly increase the value of this Beanie, if and when you ever appraise, trade, re-sell, gift, or bequeath it.)

Description *(which version do you have?)*:

Gift from:

Date received/purchased:

Purchased from:

NAME OF PERSON OR RETAILER

ADDRESS

CITY/STATE/ZIP

PHONE

Qty. purchased: **Cost ea.**
(check one)   ❏ *Cash*   ❏ *Check*   ❏ *Charge*

Reason(s) for purchase(s):

Traded to:

NAME

ADDRESS

CITY/STATE/ZIP

PHONE

TRADED FOR

Re-sold to:

NAME

ADDRESS

CITY/STATE/ZIP

PHONE

PRICE RE-SOLD FOR

Your feelings about and/or experiences with this Beanie:

Bumble™

Type:	Bee	*Categories:*	Insect, striped	*Style no.:*	4045
Birthday:	October 16, 1995	*Released:*	6/3/95	*Retired:*	6/15/96
Position:	Flying	*Tags:*	3rd-4th generation	*Teenie:*	

Description: Black & yellow striped plush body, black head & wings, black plastic eyes, black thread antennae, hang tag left wing, tush tag left bottom

Replaces: Third generation w/o birthday & poem

Variations: None

Oddities: Fourth generation tag has birthday & poem, hence, more valuable than third generation

Commentary: In circulation only one year before retiring, making it one of the shortest-lived Beanies, hence, extremely rare & expensive

Poem: Bumble the bee will not sting you
It is only love that this bee will bring you
So don't be afraid to give this bee a hug
Because Bumlbe the bee is a love-bug.™

19

My record

(Beanies are the #1 collectible in American collecting history. A complete, detailed record will vastly increase the value of this Beanie, if and when you ever appraise, trade, re-sell, gift, or bequeath it.)

Description *(which version do you have?):*

_____

_____

_____

_____

Gift from:

Date received/purchased:

Purchased from:

NAME OF PERSON OR RETAILER

ADDRESS

CITY/STATE/ZIP

PHONE

Qty. purchased: **Cost ea.**
(check one) ❏ *Cash* ❏ *Check* ❏ *Charge*

Reason(s) for purchase(s):

_____

_____

_____

Traded to:

NAME

ADDRESS

CITY/STATE/ZIP

PHONE

TRADED FOR

Re-sold to:

NAME

ADDRESS

CITY/STATE/ZIP

PHONE

PRICE RE-SOLD FOR

Your feelings about and/or experiences with this Beanie:

_____

_____

_____

_____

Caw™

Type:	Crow	**Categories:** Bird, black	**Style no.:** 4071
Birthday:	None	**Released:** 6/3/95	**Retired:** 6/15/96
Position:	Perching	**Tags:** 3rd generation	**Teenie:**

Description: Black plush body, orange beak & feet, black plastic eyes, three-pronged tail, hang tag left wing, tush tag bottom

Replaces: None

Variations: None

Oddities: Like all '95-'96 Retired Beanies, no gender indicated, no birthday & no poem

Commentary: In circulation only one year before retiring, making it one of the shortest-lived Beanies, hence, extremely rare & expensive

Poem: None

My record

(Beanies are the #1 collectible in American collecting history. A complete, detailed record will vastly increase the value of this Beanie, if and when you ever appraise, trade, re-sell, gift, or bequeath it.)

Description *(which version do you have?):*

_____

_____

_____

Gift from:

Date received/purchased:

Purchased from:

NAME OF PERSON OR RETAILER

ADDRESS

CITY/STATE/ZIP

PHONE

Qty. purchased: **Cost ea.**
(check one)   ❏ *Cash*   ❏ *Check*   ❏ *Charge*

Reason(s) for purchase(s):

_____

_____

_____

Traded to:

NAME

ADDRESS

CITY/STATE/ZIP

PHONE

TRADED FOR

Re-sold to:

NAME

ADDRESS

CITY/STATE/ZIP

PHONE

PRICE RE-SOLD FOR

Your feelings about and/or experiences with this Beanie:

_____

_____

_____

Flutter™

Type:	Butterfly	*Categories:* Insect, tie-dyed	*Style no.:* 4043
Birthday:	None	*Released:* 6/3/95	*Retired:* 6/15/96
Position:	Flying	*Tags:* 3rd generation	*Teenie:*

Description: Black plush body, tie-dyed wings w/ detail stitching, black plastic eyes, black thread antennae, hang tag left top wing, tush tag left bottom wing

Replaces: None

Variations: Tie-dye varies in colors from cool to warm

Oddities: Like all '95-'96 Retired Beanies, no gender indicated, no birthday & no poem

Commentary: In circulation only one year before retiring, making it one of the shortest-lived Beanies, hence, extremely rare & expensive; very popular w/ girls

Poem: None

My record

(Beanies are the #1 collectible in American collecting history. A complete, detailed record will vastly increase the value of this Beanie, if and when you ever appraise, trade, re-sell, gift, or bequeath it.)

Description *(which version do you have?):*

Gift from:

Date received/purchased:

Purchased from:

NAME OF PERSON OR RETAILER

ADDRESS

CITY/STATE/ZIP

PHONE

Qty. purchased: **Cost ea.**
(check one)   ❑ *Cash*   ❑ *Check*   ❑ *Charge*

Reason(s) for purchase(s):

Traded to:

NAME

ADDRESS

CITY/STATE/ZIP

PHONE

TRADED FOR

Re-sold to:

NAME

ADDRESS

CITY/STATE/ZIP

PHONE

PRICE RE-SOLD FOR

Your feelings about and/or experiences with this Beanie:

Rex™

Type:	Tyrannosaurus	*Categories:* Dinosaur, tie-dyed	*Style no.:* 4086
Birthday:	None	*Released:* 6/3/95	*Retired:* 6/15/96
Position:	Standing up	*Tags:* 3rd generation	*Teenie:*

Description: Red-purple tie-dyed plush body, black plastic eyes, long tail, hang tag left arm, tush tag left side of tail

Replaces: None

Variations: Tie-dye varies in colors from cool to warm

Oddities: Like all '95-'96 Retired Beanies, no gender indicated, no birthday & no poem; Rex shares same style no. w/ Lefty; dinosaurs are not tie-dyed

Commentary: In circulation only one year before retiring, making it one of the shortest-lived Beanies, hence, extremely rare & expensive; one of few Beanies w/ unrealistic coloring; very popular w/ boys

Poem: None

My record

(Beanies are the #1 collectible in American collecting history. A complete, detailed record will vastly increase the value of this Beanie, if and when you ever appraise, trade, re-sell, gift, or bequeath it.)

Description *(which version do you have?):*

Gift from:

Date received/purchased:

Purchased from:

NAME OF PERSON OR RETAILER

ADDRESS

CITY/STATE/ZIP

PHONE

Qty. purchased: **Cost ea.**
(check one)   ❏ *Cash*   ❏ *Check*   ❏ *Charge*

Reason(s) for purchase(s):

Traded to:

NAME

ADDRESS

CITY/STATE/ZIP

PHONE

TRADED FOR

Re-sold to:

NAME

ADDRESS

CITY/STATE/ZIP

PHONE

PRICE RE-SOLD FOR

Your feelings about and/or experiences with this Beanie:

Steg™

Type:	Stegosaurus	***Categories:*** Dinosaur, tie-dyed	***Style no.:*** 4087

Birthday: None ***Released:*** 6/3/95 ***Retired:*** 6/15/96

Position: Standing up ***Tags:*** 3rd generation ***Teenie:***

Description: Green-brown tie-dyed plush body, black plastic eyes, spikes, long tail, hang tag left front leg, tush tag left side of tail

Replaces: None

Variations: Tie-dye varies in colors from cool to warm

Oddities: Like all '95-'96 Retired Beanies, no gender indicated, no birthday & no poem; dinosaurs are not tie-dyed

Commentary: In circulation only one year before retiring, making it one of the shortest-lived Beanies, hence, extremely rare & expensive; one of few Beanies w/ unrealistic coloring; very popular w/ boys

Poem: None

My record

(Beanies are the #1 collectible in American collecting history. A complete, detailed record will vastly increase the value of this Beanie, if and when you ever appraise, trade, re-sell, gift, or bequeath it.)

Description *(which version do you have?):*

Gift from:

Date received/purchased:

Purchased from:

NAME OF PERSON OR RETAILER

ADDRESS

CITY/STATE/ZIP

PHONE

Qty. purchased: **Cost ea.**
(check one)   ❏ *Cash*   ❏ *Check*   ❏ *Charge*

Reason(s) for purchase(s):

Traded to:

NAME

ADDRESS

CITY/STATE/ZIP

PHONE

TRADED FOR

Re-sold to:

NAME

ADDRESS

CITY/STATE/ZIP

PHONE

PRICE RE-SOLD FOR

Your feelings about and/or experiences with this Beanie:

Teenies & Buddies

Place behind this tab all the
McDonald's Teenie Beanie Babies™ pages
& Beanie Buddies® pages

Lists & Forms

Place behind this tab
all the BBB lists & forms

My Beanie Baby™ Binder Spring '99 Update Pak

Table of Contents & Instructions

New tab

(1) Spring '99 Retireds

Place this tab (& the pages listed on the tab) after the Current tab & pages

2 New Beanie Babies® pages

(missing from Dec-Jan Update Pak)

(1) Fuzz™
(2) Germania™

Place these 2 pages behind the Current tab

15 New Release Beanie Babies® pages

(listed in order of release date)

(1) Eucalyptus™	(6) Knuckles™	(11) Almond™
(2) Neon™	(7) Swirly™	(12) Amber™
(3) Pecan™	(8) Tiptoe™	(13) Silver™
(4) Schweetheart™	(9) Cheeks™	(14) Wiser™
(5) Paul™	(10) Osito™	(15) Spangle™

Place these 15 pages behind the New Release tab

3 New Release Teenies™ pages

(listed in order of release date)

(1) Freckles™	(9) Claude™
(2) Antsy™	(10) Stretchy™
(3) Smoochy™	(11) 'Nook™
(4) Spunky™	(12) Chip™
(5) Rocket™	(13) Britannia™
(6) Iggy™	(14) Glory™
(7) Strut®	(15) Erin™
(8) Nuts™	(16) Maple™

Place these 3 pages behind the Teenies & Buddies tab

New International Bears page

(listed in order of release date)

(1) Glory™
(2) Britannia™
(3) Erin™
(4) Maple™

Place this page behind the Teenies & Buddies tab

4 New Release Beanie Buddies® pages

(listed in order of release date)

(1) Fuzz™
(2) Jabber™
(3) Hope™
(4) Millennium™
(5) Princess™

Place these 4 pages behind the Teenies & Buddies tab

Revised Shopping/Collecting Lists

Place these pages behind the Lists & Forms tab & discard
previous lists pages

Current Beanie Babies®

(1) 1999 Signature Bear™	(15) Goochy™	(29) Nibbler™
(2) Beak™	(16) Halo™	(30) Nibbly™
(3) Britannia™	(17) Hippie™	(31) Peace™
(4) Butch™	(18) Hope™	(32) Prickles™
(5) Canyon™	(19) Jabber™	(33) Roam™
(6) Clubby II™	(20) Jake™	(34) Rocket™
(7) Early™	(21) Kicks™	(35) Sammy™
(8) Eggbert™	(22) Kuku™	(36) Scat™
(9) Ewey™	(23) Loosy™	(37) Scorch™
(10) Fortune™	(24) Luke™	(38) Slippery™
(11) Fuzz™	(25) Mac™	(39) Tiny™
(12) Germania™	(26) Maple™	(40) Tracker™
(13) Gigi™	(27) Millennium™	(41) Valentina™
(14) Goatee™	(28) Mooch™	(42) Whisper™

(With the exception of Clubby II™ [which is included in this Pak], you already have these pages; this is the
new line-up behind your Current tab)

Thank You for your business!
Peg et. al.
"My Beanie Baby™ Binder"
Vine Street Publishing, Inc.
Box 97
Orem, UT 84059
(801) 222-9670; 9680 fax
pegfugal@aol.com
www.mybeaniebabybinder.com

Fuzz™

Type: Male bear   **Categories:** Bears, brown, napped   **Style no.:** 4237

Birthday: July 23, 1998   **Released:** 1/1/99   **Retired:**

Position: Sitting up   **Tags:** 5th/7th   **Teenie:**   **Buddy:** 4/1/99

Description: Golden brown, silky, napped fabric, black plastic eyes & nose, navy blue satin ribbon tied around neck, hang tag left ear, tush tag left bottom

Replaces: Curly™

Variations: Golden highlights vary

Oddities: None

Commentary: Released six months after birth; one of eight bears this release; new silky, napped fabric; similar to Curly™ & Germania™ w/ finer, softer nap; initially hard to find & pricey; destined to become one of the most popular bears ever

Poem: Look closely at this handsome bear
His texture is really quite rare
With golden highlights in his hair
He has class, style and flair!™

My record

(Beanies are the #1 collectible in American collecting history. A complete, detailed record will vastly increase the value of this Beanie, if & when you ever appraise, trade, re-sell, gift, or bequeath it.)

Description *(which version do you have?):*

_____
_____
_____

Gift from: _____

Date received/purchased: _____

Purchased from: _____

NAME OF PERSON OR RETAILER
ADDRESS
CITY/STATE/ZIP
PHONE

Qty. purchased: **Cost ea.**
(check one)   ❏ *Cash*   ❏ *Check*   ❏ *Charge*

Reason(s) for purchase(s): _____

_____
_____

Traded to:

NAME
ADDRESS
CITY/STATE/ZIP
PHONE
TRADED FOR

Re-sold to:

NAME
ADDRESS
CITY/STATE/ZIP
PHONE
PRICE RE-SOLD FOR

Your feelings about &/or experiences w/ this Beanie:

_____
_____
_____

Germania™

Type:	Bear	*Categories:* Bear, brown, napped	*Style no.:* 4236

Birthday: Oktober 3, 1990   *Released:* 1/1/99   *Retired:*

Position: Sitting up   *Tags:* 5th/7th   *Teenie:*   *Buddy:*

Description: Golden brown, napped fabric, black plastic eyes & nose, red & yellow satin ribbons tied around neck, embroidered German flag inset over heart, hang tag left ear, tush tag left bottom

Replaces: None

Variations: None

Oddities: No gender indicated; released nine years after birth! (Birthdate reads: Oktober 3, 1990—three years after first Ty® Beanie Babies® were produced!) Birthday & poem in German; one of few Beanie Babies® w/ double ribbons; flag inset rather than stitched

Commentary: Similar to Curly™ & Fuzz™ in color & texture; one of eight bears this release; fourth international bear; exclusive German release; available only via secondary market, hence, hard to find & pricey

Poem: Einigkeit und Recht und Freiheit   Unity and Justice and Freedom
ist der Deutschen Einheislied   is the song of German unity
Allen Kindern brav un fein   All good little girls and boys
soll dieser Bar das liebste sein!™   should love this little German bear!™

My record

(Beanies are the #1 collectible in American collecting history. A complete, detailed record will vastly increase the value of this Beanie, ifand when you ever appraise, trade, re-sell, gift, or bequeath it.)

Description *(which version do you have?)*:

Gift from:

Date received/purchased:

Purchased from:

NAME OF PERSON OR RETAILER

ADDRESS

CITY/STATE/ZIP

PHONE

Qty. purchased: **Cost ea.**
(check one)   ❑ *Cash*   ❑ *Check*   ❑ *Charge*

Reason(s) for purchase(s):

Traded to:

NAME

ADDRESS

CITY/STATE/ZIP

PHONE

TRADED FOR

Re-sold to:

NAME

ADDRESS

CITY/STATE/ZIP

PHONE

PRICE RE-SOLD FOR

Your feelings about &/or experiences w/ this Beanie:

Eucalyptus™

Type: Bear   **Categories:** Bears, heather   **Style no.:** 4240

Birthday: April 28, 1999   **Released:** 4/8/99   **Retired:**

Position: Sitting up   **Tags:** 5th/7th   **Teenie:**   **Buddy:**

Description: Blue-green heather plush body; cream plush inner ears, belly & paw pads; shiny black plastic eyes; big black matte plastic nose; black thread mouth & detailing on paws; big ears; hang tag left ear; tush tag left bottom

Replaces: Mel™

Variations: Heather coloring varies

Oddities: No gender indicated, released twenty days before birth, one of three bears this release, & the first bears, that can both stand on all four legs or sit on hind haunches, odd coloring for koala

Commentary: The second koala; one of five bears this release; one of six Beanie Babies® this release designed to sit up on hind haunches; one of six heather Beanie Babies® this release; like all bears, popular, hard to find, pricey & will surge in value upon retirement

Poem: Koalas climb with grace and ease
To the top branches of the trees
Sleeping by day under a gentle breeze
Feeding at night on two pounds of leaves!™

My record

(Beanies are the #1 collectible in American collecting history. A complete, detailed record will vastly increase the value of this Beanie, if & when you ever appraise, trade, re-sell, gift, or bequeath it.)

Description *(which version do you have?):*

Gift from:

Date received/purchased:

Purchased from:

NAME OF PERSON OR RETAILER

ADDRESS

CITY/STATE/ZIP

PHONE

Qty. purchased: **Cost ea.**
(check one)   ❏ *Cash*   ❏ *Check*   ❏ *Charge*

Reason(s) for purchase(s):

Traded to:

NAME

ADDRESS

CITY/STATE/ZIP

PHONE

TRADED FOR

Re-sold to:

NAME

ADDRESS

CITY/STATE/ZIP

PHONE

PRICE RE-SOLD FOR

Your feelings about &/or experiences w/ this Beanie:

Neon™

Type:	Seahorse	**Categories:** Sea, tie-dyed	**Style no.:** 4239
Birthday:	April 1, 1999	**Released:** 4/8/99	**Retired:**
Position:	Swimming	**Tags:** 5th/7th	**Teenie:** **Buddy:**

Description: Iridescent, tie-dyed, pastel plush body w/ ears, fin & curly tail; black plastic eyes ringed w/ gold; hang tag left side; tush tag left bottom

Replaces: None

Variations: Tie-dye varies in colors

Oddities: No gender indicated, head & body seem too large for tail, tail hangs limp

Commentary: Released seven days after birth, first seahorse, one of three sea creatures this release, one of two pastel tie-dyes this release

Poem: Born in shallow water in a sea grass bay
Their eyes can swivel and look every way
Walk down the beach on a bright sunny day
Jump into the sea and watch them play!™

My record

(Beanies are the #1 collectible in American collecting history. A complete, detailed record will vastly increase the value of this Beanie, if & when you ever appraise, trade, re-sell, gift, or bequeath it.)

Description *(which version do you have?):*

_____
_____
_____

Gift from: _____

Date received/purchased: _____

Purchased from:

NAME OF PERSON OR RETAILER
_____
ADDRESS
_____
CITY/STATE/ZIP
_____
PHONE

Qty. purchased: **Cost ea.**
(check one)   ❏ *Cash*   ❏ *Check*   ❏ *Charge*

Reason(s) for purchase(s): _____

_____
_____
_____

Traded to:

NAME
_____
ADDRESS
_____
CITY/STATE/ZIP
_____
PHONE
_____
TRADED FOR

Re-sold to:

NAME
_____
ADDRESS
_____
CITY/STATE/ZIP
_____
PHONE
_____
PRICE RE-SOLD FOR

Your feelings about &/or experiences w/ this Beanie:

_____
_____
_____
_____
_____

Pecan™

Type:	Female bear	*Categories:* Bears, heather	*Style no.:* 4251

Birthday: April 15, 1999   *Released:* 4/8/99   *Retired:*

Position: Sitting   *Tags:* 5th/7th   *Teenie:*   *Buddy:*

Description: Reddish-brown heather plush body, light brown plush paw pads, shiny black plastic eyes, black matte plastic nose, black thread mouth & detailing on paws, stubby tail, hang tag left ear, tush tag left bottom

Replaces: None

Variations: Heather coloring varies

Oddities: Released eight days before birth; one of three bears this release, & the first bears, that can both stand on all four legs or sit on hind haunches

Commentary: One of five bears this release; one of six Beanie Babies® this release designed to sit up on hind haunches; one of six heather Beanie Babies® this release; companion to Almond™; like all bears, popular, hard to find, pricey & will surge in value upon retirement

Poem: In late fall, as wind gusts blow
Pecan hibernates before winter snow
In early spring, sweet scent of a flower
Wakes her up to take a shower!™

My record

(Beanies are the #1 collectible in American collecting history. A complete, detailed record will vastly increase the value of this Beanie, if & when you ever appraise, trade, re-sell, gift, or bequeath it.)

Description *(which version do you have?):*

Gift from:

Date received/purchased:

Purchased from:

NAME OF PERSON OR RETAILER
ADDRESS
CITY/STATE/ZIP
PHONE

Qty. purchased: **Cost ea.**
(check one)   ❏ *Cash*   ❏ *Check*   ❏ *Charge*

Reason(s) for purchase(s):

Traded to:

NAME
ADDRESS
CITY/STATE/ZIP
PHONE
TRADED FOR

Re-sold to:

NAME
ADDRESS
CITY/STATE/ZIP
PHONE
PRICE RE-SOLD FOR

Your feelings about &/or experiences w/ this Beanie:

Schweetheart™

Type: Orang-Utan   **Categories:** Monkeys, heather   **Style no.:** 4252

Birthday: January 23, 1999   **Released:** 4/11/99   **Retired:**

Position: Sitting up   **Tags:** 5th/7th   **Teenie:**   **Buddy:**

Description: Rusty brown heather plush body; tan plush hands, feet, ears & snout; brown plush face; brown hairy bangs; black plastic almond-shaped eyes w/ tan eyelids; black thread nose & mouth; long arms & legs; hang tag left ear; tush tag bottom

Replaces: Bongo™

Variations: Heather coloring varies

Oddities: No gender indicated; first Beanie Baby™ w/ almond-shaped eyes & lids; one of few Beanie Baby™ poems written in first person; first "love" poem

Commentary: Released three months after birth; one of two "monkeys" this release; one of six heather Beanie Babies® this release; like Bongo™, will become popular & surge in value upon retirement

Poem: Of all the jungles filled with vines
Traveling about, you came to mine
Because of all the things you said
I can't seem to get you out of my head!™

My record

(Beanies are the #1 collectible in American collecting history. A complete, detailed record will vastly increase the value of this Beanie, if & when you ever appraise, trade, re-sell, gift, or bequeath it.)

Description *(which version do you have?):*

Gift from:

Date received/purchased:

Purchased from:

NAME OF PERSON OR RETAILER

ADDRESS

CITY/STATE/ZIP

PHONE

Qty. purchased: **Cost ea.**
(check one)   ❏ *Cash*   ❏ *Check*   ❏ *Charge*

Reason(s) for purchase(s):

Traded to:

NAME

ADDRESS

CITY/STATE/ZIP

PHONE

TRADED FOR

Re-sold to:

NAME

ADDRESS

CITY/STATE/ZIP

PHONE

PRICE RE-SOLD FOR

Your feelings about &/or experiences w/ this Beanie:

Paul™

Type: Male walrus   **Categories:** Brown, sea   **Style no.:** 4248

Birthday: February 23, 1999   **Released:** 4/12/99   **Retired:**

Position: Standing   **Tags:** 5th/7th   **Teenie:**   **Buddy:**

Description: Brown plush body w/ an iridescent sheen, brown & gray hairy beard, cream plush tusks, black plastic eyes, pink plastic nose, brown thread detailing on webbed feet, hang tag left front foot, tush tag left side

Replaces: Tusk™ & Jolly™

Variations: None

Oddities: Sheen to plush, strange choice of name

Commentary: Released two months after birth; third walrus; one of three sea creatures this release; while Tusk™ had tusks & Jolly™ had a beard, Paul™ has both; sheen makes Paul™ look like he just slipped out of the water

Poem: Traveling the ocean in a submarine
Singing and playing a tambourine
One day hoping to lead a band
First he needs to find dry land!™

My record

(Beanies are the #1 collectible in American collecting history. A complete, detailed record will vastly increase the value of this Beanie, if & when you ever appraise, trade, re-sell, gift, or bequeath it.)

Description *(which version do you have?):*

Gift from:

Date received/purchased:

Purchased from:

NAME OF PERSON OR RETAILER

ADDRESS

CITY/STATE/ZIP

PHONE

Qty. purchased: **Cost ea.**
(check one)   ❏ *Cash*   ❏ *Check*   ❏ *Charge*

Reason(s) for purchase(s):

Traded to:

NAME

ADDRESS

CITY/STATE/ZIP

PHONE

TRADED FOR

Re-sold to:

NAME

ADDRESS

CITY/STATE/ZIP

PHONE

PRICE RE-SOLD FOR

Your feelings about &/or experiences w/ this Beanie:

Knuckles™

Type: Female pig   **Categories:** Farm   **Style no.:** 4247

Birthday: March 25, 1999   **Released:** 4/14/99   **Retired:**

Position: Sitting   **Tags:** 5th/7th   **Teenie:**   **Buddy:**

Description: Flesh-colored plush body; brown plush snout & hooves; beige flannel inner ears & knotted tail; black plastic eyes; dark pink thread nostrils & detailing on hooves; royal blue ribbon tied around neck; hang tag left ear; tush tag left back

Replaces: Squealer™

Variations: None

Oddities: Unlike Squealer™, can stand on four legs or sit on hind haunches; strange choice of name for pig; one of few non-bear Beanie Babies® w/ ribbon

Commentary: Released one month after birth; only farm animal this release; one of six Beanie Babies® this release designed to sit up on hind haunches; more detailed & cuter than Squealer™; bound to become as popular as all Beanie Baby™ farm animals

Poem: In the kitchen working hard
Using ingredients from the yard
No one will eat it, can you guess why?
Her favorite recipe is for mud pie!™

My record

(Beanies are the #1 collectible in American collecting history. A complete, detailed record will vastly increase the value of this Beanie, if & when you ever appraise, trade, re-sell, gift, or bequeath it.)

Description *(which version do you have?)*: _____

_____

_____

Gift from: _____

Date received/purchased: _____

Purchased from: _____

NAME OF PERSON OR RETAILER

ADDRESS

CITY/STATE/ZIP

PHONE

Qty. purchased: **Cost ea.** _____
(check one)   ❏ *Cash*   ❏ *Check*   ❏ *Charge*

Reason(s) for purchase(s): _____

_____

_____

Traded to:

NAME

ADDRESS

CITY/STATE/ZIP

PHONE

TRADED FOR

Re-sold to:

NAME

ADDRESS

CITY/STATE/ZIP

PHONE

PRICE RE-SOLD FOR

Your feelings about &/or experiences w/ this Beanie: _____

_____

_____

_____

Swirly™

Type: Snail   **Categories:** Sea, tie-dyed   **Style no.:** 4249

Birthday: March 10, 1999   **Released:** 4/14/99   **Retired:**

Position: Crawling   **Tags:** 5th/7th   **Teenie:**   **Buddy:**

Description: Pale pink plush body; iridescent, tie-dyed, pastel plush shell w/ red thread detailing; iridescent, pale pink, metallic antennae; black plastic eyes ringed w/ blue; pink thread antennae; hang & tush tags left side

Replaces: None

Variations: Tie-dye varies in colors

Oddities: No gender indicated, snail body not in proportion to snail shell, poem written in first person

Commentary: Released one month after birth, first snail, one of three sea creatures this release, one of two pastel tie-dyes this release

Poem: Carefully traveling, leaving a trail
I'm not very fast, for I am a snail
Although I go my own plodding pace
Slow and steady, wins the race!™

My record

(Beanies are the #1 collectible in American collecting history. A complete, detailed record will vastly increase the value of this Beanie, if & when you ever appraise, trade, re-sell, gift, or bequeath it.)

Description *(which version do you have?):*

Gift from:

Date received/purchased:

Purchased from:

NAME OF PERSON OR RETAILER

ADDRESS

CITY/STATE/ZIP

PHONE

Qty. purchased: **Cost ea.**
(check one)   ❏ *Cash*   ❏ *Check*   ❏ *Charge*

Reason(s) for purchase(s):

Traded to:

NAME

ADDRESS

CITY/STATE/ZIP

PHONE

TRADED FOR

Re-sold to:

NAME

ADDRESS

CITY/STATE/ZIP

PHONE

PRICE RE-SOLD FOR

Your feelings about &/or experiences w/ this Beanie:

Tiptoe™

Type:	Mouse	*Categories:* Brown, mice	*Style no.:* 4241

Birthday: January 8, 1999   *Released:* 4/16/99   *Retired:*

Position: Sneaking   *Tags:* 5th/7th   *Teenie:*   *Buddy:*

Description: Brown & gray heather plush body; flesh-colored, felt ears & feet; black plastic eyes; black thread whiskers & mouth; long tail; hang tag left front leg; tush tag left back leg

Replaces: Trap™

Variations: Heather coloring varies

Oddities: No gender indicated; while Trap™ looked like a sweet little mouse, Tiptoe™ looks like a big, fat rat!

Commentary: Released three months after birth; one of six heather Beanie Babies® this release; will surely become popular w/ boys to terrorize girls

Poem: Creeping quietly along the wall
Little foot prints fast and small
Tiptoeing through the house with ease
Searching for a piece of cheese!™

My record

(Beanies are the #1 collectible in American collecting history. A complete, detailed record will vastly increase the value of this Beanie, if & when you ever appraise, trade, re-sell, gift, or bequeath it.)

Description *(which version do you have?)*:

Gift from:

Date received/purchased:

Purchased from:

NAME OF PERSON OR RETAILER

ADDRESS

CITY/STATE/ZIP

PHONE

Qty. purchased: **Cost ea.**
(check one)   ❑ *Cash*   ❑ *Check*   ❑ *Charge*

Reason(s) for purchase(s):

Traded to:

NAME

ADDRESS

CITY/STATE/ZIP

PHONE

TRADED FOR

Re-sold to:

NAME

ADDRESS

CITY/STATE/ZIP

PHONE

PRICE RE-SOLD FOR

Your feelings about &/or experiences w/ this Beanie:

Cheeks™

Type: Baboon   **Categories:** Monkeys, heather   **Style no.:** 4250

Birthday: May 18, 1999   **Released:** 4/17/99   **Retired:**

Position: Sitting up   **Tags:** 5th/7th   **Teenie:**   **Buddy:**

Description: Dark brown-gold heather plush body; dark brown hands, feet, ears, eyebrows & chin; bright red snout w/ pink plastic nose; turquoise & black-striped cheeks; yellow-green tie-dyed bottom; plastic eyes ringed w/ gold; black thread mouth; stubby tail; hang tag left ear; tush tag left bottom

Replaces: Congo™

Variations: Heather coloring & tie-dye varies

Oddities: No gender indicated; released one month before birth; one of few Beanie Baby™ poems written in first person; poem refers to"ty-dyed red cheeks" & bottom, which Cheeks™ does not have

Commentary: One of two "monkeys" this release; one of six heather Beanie Babies® this release; one of the most detailed Beanie Babies® ever; like baboons, mean-looking

Poem: Don't confuse me with an ape
I have a most unusual shape
My cheeks are round and ty-died red
On my behind as well as my head!™

My record

(Beanies are the #1 collectible in American collecting history. A complete, detailed record will vastly increase the value of this Beanie, if & when you ever appraise, trade, re-sell, gift, or bequeath it.)

Description *(which version do you have?):*

Gift from:

Date received/purchased:

Purchased from:

NAME OF PERSON OR RETAILER

ADDRESS

CITY/STATE/ZIP

PHONE

Qty. purchased: **Cost ea.**
(check one)   ❏ *Cash*   ❏ *Check*   ❏ *Charge*

Reason(s) for purchase(s):

Traded to:

NAME

ADDRESS

CITY/STATE/ZIP

PHONE

TRADED FOR

Re-sold to:

NAME

ADDRESS

CITY/STATE/ZIP

PHONE

PRICE RE-SOLD FOR

Your feelings about &/or experiences w/ this Beanie:

Osito™

Type: Bear   **Categories:** Bears, red   **Style no.:** 4244

Birthday: February 5, 1999   **Released:** 4/17/99   **Retired:**

Position: Sitting up   **Tags:** 5th/7th   **Teenie:**   **Buddy:**

Description: Bright red plush body, black plastic eyes & nose, green & white satin ribbons tied around neck, embroidered Mexican flag stitched over heart, hang tag left ear, tush tag left bottom

Replaces: None

Variations: None

Oddities: No gender indicated, one of only two international bears not exclusive to country it represents, one of few Beanie Babies® w/ double ribbons

Commentary: Released two months after birth; one of five international bears; one of five bears this release; unlike some international bears, available in U.S., but still hard to find & pricey; will sky-rocket in value upon retirement

Poem: Across the waters of the Rio Grande
Lies a beautiful mystic land
A place we all should plan to go
Known by all as Mexico!™

My record

(Beanies are the #1 collectible in American collecting history. A complete, detailed record will vastly increase the value of this Beanie, if & when you ever appraise, trade, re-sell, gift, or bequeath it.)

Description *(which version do you have?):*

Gift from:

Date received/purchased:

Purchased from:

NAME OF PERSON OR RETAILER

ADDRESS

CITY/STATE/ZIP

PHONE

Qty. purchased: **Cost ea.**
(check one)   ❏ *Cash*   ❏ *Check*   ❏ *Charge*

Reason(s) for purchase(s):

Traded to:

NAME

ADDRESS

CITY/STATE/ZIP

PHONE

TRADED FOR

Re-sold to:

NAME

ADDRESS

CITY/STATE/ZIP

PHONE

PRICE RE-SOLD FOR

Your feelings about &/or experiences w/ this Beanie:

Almond™

Type: Female bear   **Categories:** Bears, heather   **Style no.:** 4246

Birthday: April 14, 1999   **Released:** 4/19/99   **Retired:**

Position: Sitting up   **Tags:** 5th/7th   **Teenie:**   **Buddy:**

Description: Almond heather plush body, cream plush paw pads, black shiny plastic eyes, black matte plastic nose, black thread mouth & detailing on paws, stubby tail, hang tag left ear, tush tag left bottom

Replaces: None

Variations: Heather coloring varies

Oddities: One of three bears this release, & the first bears, that can both stand on all four legs or sit on hind haunches

Commentary: Released only five days after birth; one of five bears this release; one of six Beanie Babies® this release designed to sit up on hind haunches; one of six heather Beanie Babies® this release; companion to Pecan™; like all Beanie Baby™ bears, popular, hard to find, pricey & will surge in value upon retirement

Poem: Leaving her den in early spring
So very hungry, she'll eat anything
Nuts, fruit, berries and fish
Mixed together make a great dish!™

My record

(Beanies are the #1 collectible in American collecting history. A complete, detailed record will vastly increase the value of this Beanie, if & when you ever appraise, trade, re-sell, gift, or bequeath it.)

Description *(which version do you have?):*

_____
_____
_____

Gift from:

Date received/purchased:

Purchased from:

NAME OF PERSON OR RETAILER
ADDRESS
CITY/STATE/ZIP
PHONE

Qty. purchased: **Cost ea.**
(check one)   ❏ *Cash*   ❏ *Check*   ❏ *Charge*

Reason(s) for purchase(s):

_____
_____
_____

Traded to:

NAME
ADDRESS
CITY/STATE/ZIP
PHONE
TRADED FOR

Re-sold to:

NAME
ADDRESS
CITY/STATE/ZIP
PHONE
PRICE RE-SOLD FOR

Your feelings about &/or experiences w/ this Beanie:

_____
_____
_____

Amber™

Type: Female cat   **Categories:** Cats, striped   **Style no.:** 4243

Birthday: February 21, 1999   **Released:** 4/20/99   **Retired:**

Position: Sitting up   **Tags:** 5th/7th   **Teenie:**   **Buddy:**

Description: Gold & cream striped plush body; cream plush inner ears, chin & paws; black plastic eyes ringed w/ gold; pink plastic nose; pink thread whiskers, mouth & detailing on paws; long tail; hang tag left ear; tush tag left bottom

Replaces: None

Variations: Striping varies

Oddities: Unlike new bears, cannot stand up on long legs

Commentary: Released two months after birth; introduces new syle of Beanie Baby™ cat w/ more cat-like features; one of six Beanie Babies® this release designed to sit up on hind haunches; companion to Silver™; like all Beanie Baby™ cats, will become popular & surge in value upon retirement

Poem: Sleeping all day and all night
Waiting to pounce and give you a fright
She means no harm, just playing a game
She's very lovable and quite tame!™

My record

(Beanies are the #1 collectible in American collecting history. A complete, detailed record will vastly increase the value of this Beanie, if & when you ever appraise, trade, re-sell, gift, or bequeath it.)

Description *(which version do you have?):*

Gift from:

Date received/purchased:

Purchased from:

NAME OF PERSON OR RETAILER

ADDRESS

CITY/STATE/ZIP

PHONE

Qty. purchased: **Cost ea.**

(check one)   ❏ *Cash*   ❏ *Check*   ❏ *Charge*

Reason(s) for purchase(s):

Traded to:

NAME

ADDRESS

CITY/STATE/ZIP

PHONE

TRADED FOR

Re-sold to:

NAME

ADDRESS

CITY/STATE/ZIP

PHONE

PRICE RE-SOLD FOR

Your feelings about &/or experiences w/ this Beanie:

Silver™

Type:	Male cat	**Categories:** Cats, striped	**Style no.:** 4242
Birthday:	February 11, 1999	**Released:** 4/21/99	**Retired:**
Position:	Sitting up	**Tags:** 5th/7th	**Teenie:** **Buddy:**

Description: Silver & cream striped plush body; cream plush inner ears, chin & paws; black plastic eyes ringed w/ blue; pink plastic nose; pink thread mouth & detailing on paws; long tail; hang tag left ear; tush tag left bottom

Replaces: Prance™

Variations: Striping varies

Oddities: Unlike new bears, cannot stand up on long legs; so similar to retired Prance™, collectors might wonder why Silver™; same fabric as Wiser™/Class of '99

Commentary: Released two months after birth; introduces new syle of Beanie Baby™ cat w/ more cat-like features; one of six Beanie Babies® this release designed to sit up on hind haunches; companion to Amber™; like all cats, will surge in value upon retirement

Poem: Curled up, sleeping in the sun
He's worn out from having fun
Chasing dust specks in the sunrays
This is how he spends his days!™

My record

(Beanies are the #1 collectible in American collecting history. A complete, detailed record will vastly increase the value of this Beanie, if & when you ever appraise, trade, re-sell, gift, or bequeath it.)

Description *(which version do you have?)*:

Gift from:

Date received/purchased:

Purchased from:

NAME OF PERSON OR RETAILER

ADDRESS

CITY/STATE/ZIP

PHONE

Qty. purchased: Cost ea.
(check one)   ❑ Cash   ❑ Check   ❑ Charge

Reason(s) for purchase(s):

Traded to:

NAME

ADDRESS

CITY/STATE/ZIP

PHONE

TRADED FOR

Re-sold to:

NAME

ADDRESS

CITY/STATE/ZIP

PHONE

PRICE RE-SOLD FOR

Your feelings about &/or experiences w/ this Beanie:

Wiser™

Type: Owl   **Categories:** Gray, striped   **Style no.:** 4238

Birthday: June 4, 1999   **Released:** 4/22/99   **Retired:**

Position: Perching   **Tags:** 5th/7th   **Teenie:**   **Buddy:**

Description: Dark & light gray striped plush back; white plush face, belly, under-wings & under-tail; dark gray plush feet; black felt beak; black plastic eyes ringed w/ gold; black felt mortar board w/ orange tassle, inscribed "Class of '99"; hang tag left wing; tush tag bottom

Replaces: Hoot™ & Wise™

Variations: Striping varies

Oddities: Unlike Wise™, no gender indicated; released two months before birth; along w/ Wise™, only the second dated Beanie Baby™; same fabric as Silver™

Commentary: The second of two "graduation" owls: Wise™ & Wiser™; whereas Wise™ was solid brown, Wiser™ is gray striped; popular graduation decoration/gift; like Wise™, will retire soon & become scarce & pricey; "Wisest" likely to follow

Poem: Waking daily to the morning sun
Learning makes school so much fun
Looking great and feeling fine
The newest graduate, "Class of '99!"™

My record

(Beanies are the #1 collectible in American collecting history. A complete, detailed record will vastly increase the value of this Beanie, if & when you ever appraise, trade, re-sell, gift, or bequeath it.)

Description *(which version do you have?):*

Gift from:

Date received/purchased:

Purchased from:

NAME OF PERSON OR RETAILER

ADDRESS

CITY/STATE/ZIP

PHONE

Qty. purchased: **Cost ea.**
(check one)   ❑ *Cash*   ❑ *Check*   ❑ *Charge*

Reason(s) for purchase(s):

Traded to:

NAME

ADDRESS

CITY/STATE/ZIP

PHONE

TRADED FOR

Re-sold to:

NAME

ADDRESS

CITY/STATE/ZIP

PHONE

PRICE RE-SOLD FOR

Your feelings about &/or experiences w/ this Beanie:

Spangle™

Type:	Male bear	***Categories:*** Bears, patriotic		***Style no.:*** 4245	

Birthday: June 14, 1999   ***Released:*** 4/24/99   ***Retired:***

Position: Sitting up   ***Tags:*** 5th/7th   ***Teenie:***   ***Buddy:***

Description: Plush body: red & white striped right arm & ear, left body & leg; blue field w/ white stars right body & leg, left arm & ear; tie-dyed pale pink head; black plastic eyes & nose, red & white satin ribbons tied around neck; hang tag left ear; tush tag left bottom

Replaces: Libearty™ & Glory™

Variations: Tie-dye varies in colors

Oddities: Tie-dyed pale pink head (one would expect a white head); released two months before birth; one of few Beanie Babies® w/ double ribbon

Commentary: One of three patriotic bears (born on Flag Day—June 14); one of five bears this release; darling patriotic pj-look will be popular w/ both children & bear collectors; like all bears, hard to find & pricey; like other patriotic bears, will sky-rocket in value

Poem: Stars and stripes he wears proudly
Everywhere he goes he says loudly
"Hip hip hooray, for the land of the free
There's no place on earth I'd rather be!"™

My record

(Beanies are the #1 collectible in American collecting history. A complete, detailed record will vastly increase the value of this Beanie, if & when you ever appraise, trade, re-sell, gift, or bequeath it.)

Description *(which version do you have?):*

Gift from:

Date received/purchased:

Purchased from:

NAME OF PERSON OR RETAILER

ADDRESS

CITY/STATE/ZIP

PHONE

Qty. purchased: **Cost ea.**
(check one)   ❑ *Cash*   ❑ *Check*   ❑ *Charge*

Reason(s) for purchase(s):

Traded to:

NAME

ADDRESS

CITY/STATE/ZIP

PHONE

TRADED FOR

Re-sold to:

NAME

ADDRESS

CITY/STATE/ZIP

PHONE

PRICE RE-SOLD FOR

Your feelings about &/or experiences w/ this Beanie:

Clubby II™

Type:	Bear	**Categories:** Bear, heather	**Style no.:** None	

Birthday: March 9, 1999   **Released:** Spring '99   **Retired:**

Position: Sitting up   **Tags:** 5th/7th   **Teenie:**   **Buddy:**

Description: Orchid-blue heather plush body, silver metallic ribbon tied around neck, black plastic eyes & nose, hang tag left ear, tush tag left bottom

Replaces: Clubby™

Variations: Heather varies in color

Oddities: No gender indicated, no style no., backside of hang tag different from other 5th generation hang tags

Commentary: Unlike the first Clubby™—which was available only to collectors who bought the Beanie Babies® Official Club Kit (paper case) and mailed in the order form for the bear—Clubby II™ comes *inside* the Platinum Beanie Babies® Official Club Kit (clear plastic zippered case), along with a membership card, collector's coin, collector's cards, newsletter, and pocket checklist; spectacular color; destined to become as popular & pricey as Clubby™

Poem: A proud member, named Clubby II
My color is special, a purplish hue
Take me along to your favorite place
Carry me in my platinum case!™

My record

(Beanies are the #1 collectible in American collecting history. A complete, detailed record will vastly increase the value of this Beanie, if and when you ever appraise, trade, re-sell, gift, or bequeath it.)

Description *(which version do you have?):*

Gift from:

Date received/purchased:

Purchased from:

NAME OF PERSON OR RETAILER

ADDRESS

CITY/STATE/ZIP

PHONE

Qty. purchased: **Cost ea.**
(check one)   ❏ *Cash*   ❏ *Check*   ❏ *Charge*

Reason(s) for purchase(s):

Traded to:

NAME

ADDRESS

CITY/STATE/ZIP

PHONE

TRADED FOR

Re-sold to:

NAME

ADDRESS

CITY/STATE/ZIP

PHONE

PRICE RE-SOLD FOR

Your feelings about and/or experiences with this Beanie:

Clubby™

Type: Male bear **Categories:** Bears, blue **Style no.:** None

Birthday: July 7, 1998 **Released:** Summer '98 **Retired:** 2/15/99

Position: Sitting up **Tags:** Special edition **Teenie:**

Description: Royal blue plush body, Ty Beanie Babies Official Club button over heart, multi-colored satin ribbon tied around neck, black plastic eyes & nose, hang tag left ear, tush tag left bottom.

Replaces: None

Variations: None

Oddities: Only Beanie w/ a button, special edition hang tag w/ no bar code or style no.

Commentary: Special edition Beanie bear available only through the mail to registered members of the Ty Beanie Babies Official Club; stunning royal blue color unique to Clubby: like all Beanie bears, will skyrocket in value.

Poem: Wearing his club pin for all to see
He's a proud member like you and me
Made especially with you in mind
Clubby the bear is one of a kind! ™

My record

(Beanies are the #1 collectible in American collecting history. A complete, detailed record will vastly increase the value of this Beanie, if and when you ever appraise, trade, re-sell, gift, or bequeath it.)

Description *(which version do you have?):*

Gift from:

Date received/purchased:

Purchased from:

NAME OF PERSON OR RETAILER

ADDRESS

CITY/STATE/ZIP

PHONE

Qty. purchased: **Cost ea.**
(check one)   ❏ *Cash*   ❏ *Check*   ❏ *Charge*

Reason(s) for purchase(s):

Traded to:

NAME

ADDRESS

CITY/STATE/ZIP

PHONE

TRADED FOR

Re-sold to:

NAME

ADDRESS

CITY/STATE/ZIP

PHONE

PRICE RE-SOLD FOR

Your feelings about and/or experiences with this Beanie:

Spring '99 Retireds

Place behind this tab
the following 22 Beanie Babies®:

3/15
Clubby

3/31
Batty
Chip
Gobbles
Hissy
Iggy
Mel
Nanook
Pouch
Pounce
Prance
Pugsly
Rainbow
Smoochy

Spunky
Stretch
Strut

4/13
Princess

5/18
Mystic

5/21
Erin

5/26
Derby

5/31
Stilts

Teenies™ '99

The third set of 12 Ty® Inc./McDonald's Teenie Beanie Babies® were released and retired late May, 1999 while the first set of 4 Ty®/McDonalds Teenie Beanie Babies® International Bears were released early June, 1999.

All have matching full-sized moms. Interestingly, 13 of 16 moms were retired before their Teenies™ or International Bears were released.

Three of the 16 have also been released as Beanie Buddies®.

While full-sized Beanie Babies® are made of plush, and larger Beanie Buddies®, are made of super plush, Teenies® and International Bears are made of velour.

Because they were released and retired simultaneously, all are hard to find and pricey, particularly the International Bears.

This is the first time bears have been included in a Teenie™ release, though they were considered by Ty® Inc. to be a separate promotion. Called "International Bears", they came in their own colorful packaging, illustrative of the country they represent. Because they were the first Teenie™ bears, they were even more popular than the Teenies™, disappearing within two days of release—making them very hard to find and very pricey. Proceeds to be donated by Ty® Inc. and McDonald's Corporation to Ronald McDonald House Charities®.

The McDonald's in-store Teenies™ displays are extremely hard to find and extremely pricey.

Teenie Beanie Babies®
Released 5/21/99
(1) *Teenie™ Freckles™ the leopard*
Cream velour body w/ orange spots encircled in brown, black thread eyes & whiskers, beige thread nose, long tail, hang tag left ear, tush tag left leg, originally released as a Beanie Baby™ 6/15/96, mom retired 12/9/98

(2) *Teenie™ Antsy™ the anteater*
Gray velour body w/ black & white stripes, darker gray ears, black thread
eyes, long tail, hang tag left front leg, tush tag left back, mom named
Ants™, originally released as a Beanie Baby™ 5/30/98, mom retired 12/5/98

(3) *Teenie™ Smoochy™ the frog*
Green and gold velour body, black embroidered eyes, red thread mouth,
hang tag left front leg, tush tag left back leg, originally released as a Beanie
Baby™ 12/31/97, mom retired 3/31/99, released as a Beanie Buddy™
1/1/99

(4) *Teenie™ Spunky™ the cocker spaniel*
Light brown velour body w/ curly, hairy ears; black thread eyes, nose &
mouth; stubby tail; hang tag left ear; tush tag left back leg; originally
released as a Beanie Baby™ 12/31/97; mom retired 3/31/99

Released 5/24/99
(5) *Teenie™ Rocket™ the blue jay*
Bright blue & white velour body, black velour beak and feet, black thread
eyes, long tail, hang tag left wing, tush tag bottom, originally released as a
Beanie Baby™ 5/30/98

(6) *Teenie™ Iggy™ the iguana*
Tie-dyed blue-green velour body, yellow thread eyes, fluorescent green
mouth, curly tail, hang tag left front leg, tush tag left back, originally
released as a Beanie Baby™ 12/31/97, mom retired 3/31/99, major difference between Teenie™ and Beanie Baby™: no spikes along spine

(7) *Teenie™ Strut® the rooster*
One of the most detailed Teenies: Tie-dyed pink-peach velour body, hot
pink velour wings & tail, red felt comb & wattle, orange-yellow velour beak
& feet, hang tag left wing, tush tag back, originally released as a Beanie
Baby™7/12/97, mom retired 3/31/99

(8) *Teenie™ Nuts™ the squirrel*
Brown & cream velour body; darker brown hairy, bushy tail; black thread
eyes & nose; brown thread whiskers; hang tag left ear; tush tag left bottom;
originally released as a Beanie Baby™ 1/1/97; mom retired 12/5/98

Released 5/28/99
(9) *Teenie™ Claude™ the crab*
Tie-dyed blue-brown velour body, black thread eyes & whiskers, two pinchers, six legs, hang tag left pincher, tush tag back, originally released as a
Beanie Baby™ 5/11/97, mom retired 12/4/98

(10) Teenie™ Stretchy™ the ostrich
One of the most detailed Teenies™: brown, cream & beige velour body; beige velour head, neck, legs & feet; white hairy collar; black thread eyes & nostrils; beige thread detailing; hang tag left wing; tush tag left back; mom named Stretch™; originally released as a Beanie Baby™ 12/31/97; mom retired 3/31/99; released as a Beanie Buddy™ 9/30/98

(11) Teenie™ 'Nook™ the husky
Gray & white velour body, blue thread eyes, black thread nose & mouth, hang tag left ear, tush tag left back leg, mom named Nanook™, originally released as a Beanie Baby™ 5/11/97, mom retired 3/31/99

(12) Teenie™ Chip™ the calico cat
Black, brown & white velour body; brown thread eyes; pink thread nose; white thread whiskers; long tail; hang tag left ear; tush tag left back leg; originally released as a Beanie Baby™ 5/11/97; mom retired 3/31/99; released as a Beanie Buddy™ 1/1/99

Teenie Beanie Babies® International Bears
Released 6/4/99
(1) *Teenie™ Glory™ the American bear*
White velour body w/ red & blue silkscreened stars; black thread eyes &
nose; red, white & blue U.S. flag attached over heart; hang tag left ear; tush
tag left bottom; packaging features Statute of Liberty; originally released as a
Beanie Baby™ 5/30/98; mom retired 12/10/98

(2) *Teenie™ Britannia™ the British bear*
Brown velour body; brown thread eyes; black thread nose; red satin ribbon
tied around neck; red, white & blue British flag attached over heart; hang
tag left ear; tush tag left bottom; packaging features Big Ben; originally
released as a Beanie Baby™ 12/31/97

Released 6/9/99
(3) *Teenie™ Erin™ the Irish bear*
Kelly green velour body, black thread eyes & nose, white shamrock attached
over heart, hang tag left ear, tush tag left bottom, packaging features Irish
castle and countryside, originally released as a Beanie Baby™ 1/31/98, mom
retired 5/21/99, released as a Beanie Buddy™ 1/1/99

(4) *Teenie™ Maple™ the Canadian bear*
White velour body, black thread eyes, brown thread nose, red satin ribbon
tied around neck, red & white Canadian flag attached over heart, hang tag
left ear, tush tag left bottom, packaging features Canadian Rockies and
frozen lake, originally released as a Beanie Baby™ 1/1/97

Buddies®

4/99

The third set of 5 Beanie Buddies® were released throughout April, 1999. Four of the five are bears—and, like all Beanie Baby™ bears, they will be in great demand, hard to find, and pricey.

Made of a new super plush fabric called Tylon® (designed by Ty Warner himself, and exclusive to Ty® Inc.), Beanie Buddies® surely hold the distinction of being the softest, most beautiful, most huggable plush animals in the marketplace—and, hence, are destined to become as collectible as their Beanie Baby™ counter-parts.

It is interesting to note that three of the five new release Beanie Buddies® were released as Beanie Babies® 1/1/99, and only one was retired as a Beanie Baby™ prior to being released as a Beanie Buddy™.

The four bears in this release bring the total number of Beanie Buddy™ bears to eight.

The one bird in this release brings the total number of Beanie Buddy™ birds to seven.

The five Beanie Buddies® in this release bring the total number of Beanie Buddies® to 28.

Released 4/1/99

(1) *Fuzz™ the napped bear*
Fuzz™, the napped bear, was originally released as a Beanie Baby™ 1/1/99—and instantly became a favorite due to its unique, silky, napped fabric—assuring it a place in Beanie Buddy™-dom! Made of golden brown Tylon® that is crimped under extremely high temperature (resembling natty

raw silk), Fuzz™ the Beanie Buddy™ also resembles the first (now antique) teddy bears introduced and popularized during the Teddy Roosevelt era. Like it's Beanie Baby™ counter-part, Fuzz™ the Beanie Buddy™ has black plastic eyes and nose, as well as a navy blue satin ribbon tied around its neck. Unlike its Beanie Baby™ counter-part, Fuzz the Beanie Buddy™ has golden brown plush pads on its paws.

Date & place purchased_____Amt. pd._____

Released 4/16/99
(2) *Jabber™ the parrot*
Jabber™, the multi-colored parrot, was originally released as a Beanie Baby™ 5/31/98. Because it is one of the most colorful, detailed Beanie Babies® ever, Jabber™ was destined to become a Beanie Buddy™ as well. With six colors and 17 pattern pieces, Jabber™ the Beanie Baby™, as well as Jabber™ the Beanie Buddy™, are two of Ty®'s most difficult productions. Jabber™ is the only non-bear Beanie Buddy™ this release, and one of seven Beanie Buddy™ birds.

Date & place purchased_____Amt. pd._____

Released 4/19/99
(3) *Hope™ the praying bear*
Hope™, the praying bear, was originally released as a Beanie Baby™ 1/1/99. Hope™ is the first Beanie Baby™ modeled after one of Ty™'s plush bears—which, no doubt, contributed to its choice as a Beanie Buddy™. Unique in both color (butterscotch) and position (praying), Hope™ is destined to become a favorite bedtime Beanie Buddy™ with both children (who need a reminder to say their prayers) and parents (who provide the reminder).

Date & place purchased_____Amt. pd._____

(4) *Millennium™ the magenta bear*
Millennium™, the magenta bear, was originally released as a Beanie Baby™ 1/1/99. One of the brightest, most beautiful Beanie Baby™ bears ever—and symbol of the new millennium with its sun-globe-2000 insignia—Millennium™ was a shoo-in as a Beanie Buddy™. (The misspelling of Millennium the Beanie Baby™ has been corrected on Millennium the Beanie Buddy™.)

Date & place purchased_____Amt. pd._____

Released 4/23/99

(5) Princess™ the royal purple bear

Princess™, the royal purple bear, was originally released 10/27/97 and retired 4/13/99. Designed to commemorate the late Diana, Princess of Wales, Princess™ instantly became the most beloved and sought-after Beanie Baby™ ever—which is surely why it is now a Beanie Buddy™. Like Princess™ the Beanie Baby™, proceeds from Princess™ the Beanie Buddy™ will be donated by Ty® Inc. to the Diana, Princess of Wales Memorial Fund. The hang tag, unique to this Beanie Buddy™ alone, features both the memorial fund's distinctive logo and the hallmark of the Estate of Diana, Princess of Wales, which will surely make it the most valuable Beanie Buddy™ ever. This is the only Beanie Buddy™ this release that was retired as a Beanie Baby™ before it appeared as a Beanie Buddy™.

Date & place purchased_____Amt. pd._____

3rd generation Beanie Buddy™ tush tag reads "SHELL 100% TYLON"

List #1:

Current Beanie Babies®

As of 5/30/99

Following is a list of all Current Beanie Babies® to date, listed alphabetically by name, with descriptions, for your information and shopping/collecting convenience.

New Releases

4/8/99
(1) Eucalyptus (blue-green heather koala)
(2) Neon (tie-dyed seahorse)
(3) Pecan (brown heather bear)

4/11/99
(4) Schweetheart (red orang-utan)

4/12/99
(5) Paul (brown walrus)

4/14/99
(6) Knuckles (flesh-colored pig)
(7) Swirly (tie-dyed snail)

4/16/99
(8) Tiptoe (brown mouse)

4/17/99
(9) Cheeks (brown heather baboon)
(10) Osito (red bear w/ Mexican flag)

4/19/99
(11) Almond (almond heather bear)

4/20/99
(12) Amber (gold striped cat)

4/21/99
(13) Silver (silver striped cat)

4/22/99
(14) Wiser (gray striped "Class of '99" owl)

4/24/99
(15) Spangle (bear in U.S. flag pjs)

Currents

(1) 1999 Signature Bear (heather w/ Ty insignia)
(2) Beak (brown, napped kiwi)
(3) Britannia (brown bear w/ British flag)
(4) Butch (brown/white bull terrier)
(5) Canyon (brown cougar)
(6) Early (brown robin w/ red breast)
(7) Eggbert (yellow chick in white shell)
(8) Ewey (cream, napped lamb)
(9) Fortune (black & white panda)
(10) Fuzz (brown, napped bear)
(11) Germania (bear w/ German flag)
(12) Gigi (black, napped poodle)
(13) Goatee (heather goat)
(14) Goochy (tie-dyed, iridescent jellyfish)
(15) Halo (white bear w/ iridescent halo & wings)
(16) Hippie (tie dyed, sit up bunny)
(17) Hope (butterscotch praying bear)
(18) Jabber (parrot)
(19) Jake (mallard duck)
(20) Kicks (lime green bear w/ soccer ball insignia)
(21) Kuku (white cockatoo)
(22) Loosy (black & white Canadian goose)

(23) Luke (black lab w/ b&w checkered ribbon)
(24) Mac (red cardinal)
(25) Maple (white bear w/ Canadian flag)
(26) Millennium (magenta bear w/ globe insignia)
(27) Mooch (spider monkey)
(28) Nibbler (cream bunny)
(29) Nibbly (brown heather bunny)
(30) Peace (tie-dyed bear w/ peace symbol, bright & pastel)
(31) Prickles (brown hedgehog)
(32) Roam (brown napped buffalo)
(33) Rocket (blue jay)
(34) Sammy (tie-dyed, lay down bear)
(35) Scat (heather cat)
(36) Scorch (brown dragon w/ red iridescent wings)
(37) Slippery (gray seal)
(38) Tiny (brown chihuahua)
(39) Tracker (brown basset hound)
(40) Valentina (hot pink bear w/ white heart)
(41) Whisper (brown deer)

(56 total New Releases & Currents to date)

Retired Beanie Babies® & values
As of 5/30/99

Following is a list of all Retired Beanie Babies® to date, followed by their current value, per J.C. at Collector's Mall in Orem, Utah.

5/31/99
(1) Stilts (white stork) $8

5/26/99
(1) Derby (brown horse)
(w/o diamond, coarse mane) $20
(w/o diamond, fine mane) $1,500
(w/ diamond, fine mane) $7
(w/ diamond, hairy mane) $11

5/21/99
(1) Erin (green bear w/ white shamrock) $18

5/18/99
(1) Mystic (white unicorn)
(gold horn, coarse mane) $30
(gold horn, fine mane) $175
(iridescent horn, fine mane) $7
(iridescent horn, hairy rainbow mane) $7

4/13/99
(1) Princess (royal purple bear w/ white rose) $20

3/31/99
(1) Batty
(brown) $7
(tie-dyed) $12
(2) Chip (calico cat) $7
(3) Gobbles (multi-colored turkey) $7
(4) Hissy (blue coiled snake) $7

(5) Iggy (tie-dyed iguana)
(wrong fabric) $12
(correct fabric) $7
(6) Mel (gray koala) $7
(7) Nanook (gray huskie) $7
(8) Pouch (brown kangaroo) $7
(9) Pounce (brown cat) $7
(10) Prance (gray striped cat) $7
(11) Pugsly (tan pug) $7
(12) Rainbow (tie-dyed chameleon)
(wrong fabric) $12
(correct fabric) $7
(13) Smoochy (green frog)
(thread mouth) $12
(felt mouth) $7
(14) Spunky (tan cocker spaniel) $7
(15) Stretch (brown ostrich) $7
(16) Strut (tie-dyed rooster)
(Doodles) $35
(Strut) $7

3/15/99
(1) Clubby (royal blue bear, BBOC mascot) $40

12/10/98
(1) Chocolate (brown moose) $10
(2) Roary (brown lion) $10
(3) Glory (white bear w/ red & blue stars) $25

12/9/98
(1) Bongo (brown monkey) $10
(2) Freckles (spotted leopard) $15

12/8/98
(1) Congo (black gorilla) $10

(2)   Pinky (pink flamingo) $10

(3)   Spike (gray rhino) $10

12/7/98

(1)   Fleece (white, napped lamb) $10

(2)   Snip (Siamese cat) $10

12/6/98

(1)   Curly (brown, napped bear) $18

12/5/98

(1)   Ants (gray anteater) $10

(2)   Doby (doberman) $10

(3)   Dotty (dalmatian) $10

(4)   Nuts (brown squirrel) $10

(5)   Tuffy (brown, napped terrier) $10

12/4/98

(1)   Claude (tie-dyed crab) $10 (tie-dyed crab w/ name in all caps) $18

(2)   Pumkin (w/ green arms & legs) $25

(3)   Wise (brown "Class of '98"owl w/ mortarboard & tassel) $15

12/3/98

(1)   Valentino (white bear w/ red heart) $18

12/2/98

(1)   Fetch (golden lab) $10

(2)   Scoop (blue pelican) $18

(3)   Stinger (gray scorpion) $8

12/1/98

(1)   1998 Holiday Teddy (white bear w/ holly & berries) $50

(2)   Santa (w/ green mittens) $30

(3)   Zero (penguin w/ red cap) $20

9/28/98

(1)   Stinky (black & white skunk) $10

9/24/98

(1)   Crunch (blue shark) $10

9/22/98

(1)   Bernie (St. Bernard) $10

(2)   Sly (brown fox) $10

(3)   Wrinkles (tan bulldog) $8

9/19/98

(1)   Seaweed (brown otter) $18

(2)   Spinner (black & brown spider) $10

9/18/98

(1)   Bruno (brown & white bull terrier) $8

(2)   Puffer (puffin) $12

9/16/98

(1)   Ringo (raccoon) $10

9/15/98

(1)   Blackie (black bear) $12

(2)   Daisy (black & white cow) $10

(3)   Snort (red bull) $10

5/1/98

(1)   Baldy (eagle) $20

(2)   Blizzard (white tiger) $18

(3)   Bones (brown hound dog) $15

(4)   Ears (brown bunny) $15

(5)   Echo (blue dolphin) $20

(6)   Floppity (lavender bunny) $20

(7)   Gracie (white swan) $15

(8)   Happy (purple hippo) $20

(9)   Hippity (mint green bunny) $25

(10) Hoppity (pink bunny) $20

(11) Inch (multi-colored inch worm) $20
(12) Inky (pink octopus) $25
(13) Jolly (brown walrus) $18
(14) Lucky (ladybug) $25
(15) Patti (magenta platypus) $25
(16) Peanut (blue elephant) $20
(17) Pinchers (red lobster) $20
(18) Quackers (yellow duck) $18
(19) Rover (red hound dog) $29
(20) Scottie (black, napped terrier) $30
(21) Squealer (pink pig) $25
(22) Stripes (gold tiger) $18
(23) Twigs (giraffe) $18
(24) Waddle (penguin) $25
(25) Waves (black & white whale) $20
(26) Weenie (brown dachshund) $30
(27) Ziggy (zebra) $20
(28) Zip (black cat) $35

12/31/97
(1) 1997 Holiday Teddy (brown bear w/ red hat & scarf) $50
(2) Bucky (brown beaver) $40
(3) Cubbie (brown bear) $25
(4) Goldie (goldfish) $45
(5) Lizzy (multi-colored lizard) $25
(6) Magic (white dragon) $45
(7) Nip (gold cat) $25
(8) Snowball (snowman) $40
(9) Spooky (ghost) $40

12/15/97
(1) Derby (brown horse w/o diamond) $20

10/23/97
(1) Mystic (w/ brown horn) $30

10/15/97
(1) Inch (w/ felt antennae) $150

10/1/97
(1) Ally (alligator) $45
(2) Bessie (brown & white cow) $65
(3) Flip (white cat) $35
(4) Hoot (owl) $35
(5) Legs (green frog) $25
(6) Seamore (white seal) $150
(7) Speedy (turtle) $30
(8) Spot (white dog, black spot) $50
(9) Tank (gray armadillo) $65
(10) Teddy Brown (new face) $100
(11) Velvet (black panther) $35

5/11/97
(1) Bubbles (yellow & black fish) $135
(2) Digger (red crab) $100
(3) Flash (gray & white dolphin) $100
(4) Garcia (tie-dyed bear) $165
(5) Grunt (red razorback hog) $160
(6) Manny (gray manatee) $150
(7) Radar (black bat) $100
(8) Sparky (dalmatian) $125
(9) Splash (black & white whale) $110

1/1/97
(1) Chops (cream lamb) $140
(2) Coral (tie-dyed fish) $175
(3) Kiwi (toucan) $165
(4) Lefty (blue Democratic donkey w/ U.S. flag) $250
(5) Libearty (white bear w/ U.S. flag) $275
(6) Righty (gray Republican elephant w/ U.S. flag) $250
(7) Sting (tie-dyed manta ray) $175
(8) Tabasco (red bull) $160
(9) Tusk (brown walrus) $130

8/6/96
- (1) Sly (brown-bellied fox) $135

6/29/96
- (1) Bongo (brown monkey w/ brown tail) $60

6/15/96
- (1) Bronty (tie-dyed brontosaurus) $800
- (2) Bumble (bumblebee) $500
- (3) Caw (crow) $600
- (4) Flutter (tie-dyed butterfly) $900
- (5) Rex (tie-dyed tyrannosaurus rex) $800
- (6) Steg (tie-dyed stegosaurus) $850
- (7) Web (black spider) $1,100

6/3/96
- (1) Stripes (tiger w/ thin stripes) $400

3/10/96
- (1) Nip (all gold cat) $900
- (2) Zip (all black cat) $950

2/27/96
- (1) Lucky (lady bug w/ felt spots) $225

1/7/96
- (1) Chilly (polar bear) $1,700
- (2) Lizzy (tie-dyed lizard) $900
- (3) Nip (gold cat w/ white face) $400
- (4) Peking (panda) $1,200
- (5) Tank (w/o shell) $170
- (6) Teddy Cranberry (new face) $1,500
- (7) Teddy Jade (new face) $1,500
- (8) Teddy Magenta (new face) $1,500
- (9) Teddy Teal (new face) $1,500
- (10) Teddy Violet (new face) $1,500
- (11) Zip (black cat w/ white face) $300

10/2/95
- (1) Peanut (royal blue elephant) $4,000

6/15/95
- (1) Humphrey (camel) $2,000
- (2) Slither (multi-colored snake) $1,200
- (3) Trap (gray mouse) $1,200

6/3/95
- (1) Digger (orange crab) $650
- (2) Happy (gray hippo) $1,550
- (3) Inky (tan octopus w/ mouth) $600

2/28/95
- (1) Patti (maroon platypus) $550

1/7/95
- (1) Quackers (wingless duck) $1,600
- (2) Teddy Brown (old face) $2,000
- (3) Teddy Cranberry (old face) $1,400
- (4) Teddy Jade (old face) $1,400
- (5) Teddy Magenta (old face) $1,400
- (6) Teddy Teal (old face) $1,400
- (7) Teddy Violet (old face) $1,400

9/12/94
- (1) Inky (octopus w/o mouth) $700

4/13/94
- (1) Spot (dog w/o spot) $1,500

(171 total Retireds to date)

Beanie Babies® by date of release
As of 5/30/99

Following is a list of all Beanie Babies® to date, listed first by date of release and then alphabetically, for your information and shopping/collecting convenience. You can tell by the length of each list which were regular releases and which were special releases.

1/8/94—original 9 Beanie Babies®
(1) Chocolate
(2) Brownie, renamed Cubbie
(3) Flash
(4) Legs
(5) Patti (maroon)
(6) Puncher, renamed Pinchers
(7) Splash
(8) Spot (w/o spot)
(9) Squealer

4/13/94—replacement
(1) Spot (w/ spot)

6/25/94
(1) Ally
(2) Blackie
(3) Bones
(4) Chilly
(5) Daisy
(6) Digger (orange)
(7) Goldie
(8) Happy (gray)
(9) Humphrey
(10) Inky (tan w/o mouth)
(11) Lucky (w/ felt spots)
(12) Mystic (w/ gold horn)
(13) Peking
(14) Quackers (w/o wings)
(15) Seamore
(16) Slither
(17) Speedy
(18) Teddy Brown (old)
(19) Teddy Cranberry (old)
(20) Teddy Jade (old)
(21) Teddy Magenta (old)

(22) Teddy Teal (old)
(23) Teddy Violet (old)
(24) Trap
(25) Web

9/12/94—replacement
(1) Inky (tan w/ mouth)

1/7/95
(1) Nip (w/ white face)
(2) Quackers (w/ wings)
(3) Tank (w/o shell)
(4) Teddy Brown (new)
(5) Teddy Cranberry (new)
(6) Teddy Jade (new)
(7) Teddy Magenta (new)
(8) Teddy Teal (new)
(9) Teddy Violet (new)
(10) Tusk
(11) Valentino
(12) Zip (w/ white face)

2/28/95—replacement
(1) Patti (magenta)

6/3/95
(1) Bessie
(2) Bongo (w/ tan tail)
(3) Bronty
(4) Bubbles
(5) Bumble
(6) Caw
(7) Coral
(8) Derby (w/o diamond)
(9) Digger (red)
(10) Flutter

(11) Happy (purple)
(12) Inch (w/ felt antennae)
(13) Inky (pink)
(14) Kiwi
(15) Lizzy (tie-dyed)
(16) Magic
(17) Peanut (royal blue)
(18) Pinky
(19) Rex
(20) Steg
(21) Sting
(22) Stinky
(23) Tabasco
(24) Velvet
(25) Waddle
(26) Ziggy

9/1/95—special Halloween release
(1) Radar
(2) Spooky

10/2/95—replacement
(1) Peanut (light blue)

1/7/96
(1) Bucky
(2) Chops
(3) Ears
(4) Flip
(5) Garcia
(6) Grunt
(7) Hoot
(8) Lizzy (blue)
(9) Manny
(10) Nip (all gold)
(11) Ringo
(12) Seaweed
(13) Stripes (w/ thin stripes)
(14) Tank (w/ shell)
(15) Twigs
(16) Weenie
(17) Zip (all black)

2/6/96—replacement
(1) Bongo (w/ brown tail)

2/27/96—replacement
(1) Lucky (w/ printed spots)

3/10/96—replacements
(1) Nip (w/ white socks)
(2) Zip (w/ white socks)

6/3/96—replacement
(1) Stripes (w/ wide stripes)

6/15/96
(1) Congo
(2) Curly
(3) Freckles
(4) Lefty
(5) Libearty
(6) Righty
(7) Rover
(8) Scoop
(9) Scottie
(10) Sly (w/ brown belly)
(11) Sparky
(12) Spike
(13) Wrinkles

8/6/96—replacement
(1) Sly (w/ white belly)

1/1/97
(1) Bernie
(2) Crunch
(3) Doby
(4) Fleece
(5) Floppity
(6) Gracie
(7) Hippity
(8) Hoppity
(9) Maple
(10) Mel
(11) Nuts
(12) Pouch
(13) Snip
(14) Snort

5/11/97
(1) Baldy
(2) Blizzard
(3) Chip
(4) Claude
(5) Dotty
(6) Echo
(7) Jolly
(8) Nanook
(9) Pugsly
(10) Peace
(11) Roary
(12) Tuffy
(13) Waves

7/12/97—replacement
(1) Strut

10/1/97—special holiday release
(1) 1997 Holiday Teddy
(2) Batty
(3) Gobbles
(4) Snowball
(5) Spinner

10/15/97—replacement
(1) Inch (w/ yarn antennae)

10/23/97—replacement
(1) Mystic (w/ iridescent horn)

10/29/97—special commemorative release
(1) Princess

12/15/97—replacement
(1) Derby (w/ diamond)

12/31/97
(1) Britannia
(2) Bruno
(3) Hissy
(4) Iggy
(5) Pounce
(6) Prance

(7) Puffer
(8) Rainbow
(9) Smoochy
(10) Spunky
(11) Stretch

1/31/98—special St. Patrick's Day release
(1) Erin

5/30/98
(1) Ants
(2) Early
(3) Fetch
(4) Fortune
(5) Gigi
(6) Glory
(7) Jabber
(8) Jake
(9) Kuku
(10) Rocket
(11) Stinger
(12) Tracker
(13) Whisper
(14) Wise—special graduation release

Summer '98—special BBOC release
(1) Clubby

9/30/98
(1) 1998 Holiday Teddy
(2) Beak
(3) Canyon
(4) Halo
(5) Loosy
(6) Pumkin
(7) Roam
(8) Santa
(9) Scorch

1/1/99
(1) 1999 Signature Bear
(2) Butch
(3) Eggbert

(4) Ewey
(5) Fuzz
(6) Germania
(7) Goatee
(8) Goochy
(9) Hippie
(10) Hope
(11) Kicks
(12) Luke
(13) Mac
(14) Millennium
(15) Mooch
(16) Nibbler
(17) Nibbly
(18) Prickles
(19) Sammy
(20) Scat
(21) Slippery
(22) Stilts
(23) Tiny
(24) Valentina

1/1/99—replacements
(1) Batty (tie-dyed)
(2) Derby (w/ hairy mane)
(3) Iggy (corrected fabric)
(4) Mystic (w/ hairy rainbow mane)
(5) Rainbow (corrected fabric)

Spring '99—special BBOC release
(1) Clubby II

4/8/99
(1) Eucalyptus
(2) Neon
(3) Pecan

4/11/99
(1) Schweetheart

4/12/99
(1) Paul

4/14/99
(1) Knuckles
(2) Swirly

4/16/99
(1) Tiptoe

4/17/99
(1) Cheeks
(2) Osito

4/19/99
(1) Almond

4/20/99
(1) Amber

4/21/99
(1) Silver

4/22/99
(1) Wiser

4/24/99
(1) Spangle

Beanie Baby™ multiples

As of 5/30/99

Following is a list of Beanie Baby™ multiples to date, including same kinds of animals and same Beanie Babies® w/ changes, listed alphabetically by category and then in order of release, for your information and shopping/collecting convenience.

Bats

1-Radar the black bat 9/1/95
2-Batty the brown bat 10/1/97
3-replaced by Batty the tie-dyed bat, fall '98

Bears

(sit-up, unless otherwise indicated)
1-Brownie the brown bear 1/8/94 (1st lay-down bear)
2-Brownie renamed Cubbie, mid '94 (1st revised bear)
3-Blackie the black bear 6/25/94 (2nd lay-down bear)
4-Teddy Brown (old face) 6/25/94
5-Teddy Cranberry (old face) 6/25/94
6-Teddy Jade (old face) 6/25/94
7-Teddy Magenta (old face) 6/25/94
8-Teddy Teal (old face) 6/25/94
9-Teddy Violet (old face) 6/25/94
10-Chilly the white polar bear 6/25/94 (3rd lay-down bear)
11-Peking the black & white panda 6/25/94 (1st panda) (4th lay-down bear)
12-Teddy Brown (new face) 1/7/95
13-Teddy Cranberry (new face) 1/7/95
14-Teddy Jade (new face) 1/7/95
15-Teddy Magenta (new face) 1/7/95
16-Teddy Teal (new face) 1/7/95
17-Teddy Violet (new face) 1/7/95
18-Valentino the white bear w/ red heart 1/7/95 (1st holiday bear) (companion to Valentina)
19-Garcia the tie-dyed bear 1/7/96 (1st tie-dyed bear)
20-Curly the brown, napped bear 6/15/96 (1st napped bear)
21-Libearty the white bear w/ U.S. flag 6/15/96 (1st American bear)
22-Maple the white bear w/ Canadian flag 1/1/97 (1st foreign release)
23-Mel the gray koala 1/1/97 (5th lay-down bear)
24-Peace the bright tie-dyed bear 5/11/97 (2nd tie-dyed bear)
25-1997 Holiday Teddy (brown w/ red cap & scarf) 10/1/97 (2nd holiday bear)
26-Princess the royal purple bear 10/29/97 (1st bear to commemorate a person)
27-Britannia the brown bear w/ British flag 12/31/97 (2nd foreign release)
28-Erin the green bear w/ white shamrock 1/31/98 (3rd holiday bear)
29-Fortune the black & white panda 5/30/98 (2nd panda)
30-Glory the white bear w/ red & blue stars 5/30/98 (2nd American bear)
31-Clubby the royal blue BBOC bear, summer '98 (for club members only)

32-Peace the pastel tie-dyed bear,
summer '98 (2nd revised bear)
(3rd tie-dyed bear)
33-1998 Holiday Teddy (white w/
holly & berries) 9/30/98 (4th
holiday bear)
34-Halo the white bear w/ halo &
wings 9/30/98 (1st religious
bear)
35-1999 Signature Bear (heather
w/ "1999 Ty" insignia) 1/1/99
36-Fuzz the brown, silky napped
bear 1/1/99 (2nd napped bear)
37-Germania the brown, thick
napped bear w/ German flag
1/1/99 (4th international bear)
(3rd napped bear)
38-Hope the butterscotch praying
bear 1/1/99 (2nd religious
bear)
39-Kicks the lime green soccer
bear 1/1/99 (1st sports bear)
40-Millennium the magenta bear
w/ globe insignia 1/1/99
41-Sammy the tie-dyed bear
1/1/99 (2nd bear to commemorate a person) (2nd sports
bear) (4th tie-dyed bear) (6th
lay-down bear)
42-Valentina the hot pink bear w/
white heart 1/1/99 (5th holiday bear) (companion to
Valentino)
43-Almond the almond heather
bear 4/19/99 (3rd stand-up
bear)
44-Eucalyptus the blue-green
heather koala 4/8/99 (2nd
koala) (1st stand-up bear)
45-Osito the red bear w/ Mexican
flag 4/17/99 (5th international
bear)
46-Pecan the pecan heather bear
4/8/99 (2nd stand-up bear)

47-Spangle the Flag Day bear
4/24/99 (3rd American bear)
48-Clubby II the orchid heather
BBOC mascot, spring '99 (2nd
BBOC mascot)

Birds
1-Caw the crow 6/3/95
2-Kiwi the toucan 6/3/95
3-Hoot the owl 1/7/96
4-Scoop the pelican 6/15/96
5-Gracie the swan 1/1/97
6-Baldy the eagle 5/11/97
7-Strut the rooster 7/12/97
8-Stretch the ostrich 12/31/97
9-Early the robin 5/30/98
10-Jabber the parrot 5/30/98
11-Jake the mallard 5/30/98
12-Kuku the cockatoo 5/30/98
13-Rocket the blue jay 5/30/98
14-Wise the owl 5/30/98
15-Beak the kiwi 9/30/98
16-Loosy the Canadian goose
9/30/98
17-Eggbert the chick 1/1/99
18-Mac the cardinal 1/1/99
19-Stilts the stork 1/1/99
20-Wiser the owl 4/22/99 (Class of
'99)

Bulls
1-Tabasco the red bull (w/o
hooves) 6/3/95
2-renamed Snort (w/ hooves)
1/1/97

Bunnies
1-Ears the brown lay-down bunny
1/7/96
2-Floppity the lavender sit-up
bunny 1/1/97
3-Hippity the mint green sit-up
bunny 1/1/97
4-Hoppity the pink sit-up bunny
1/1/97

5-Hippie the tie-dyed sit-up bunny
1/1/99
6-Nibbler the cream bunny 1/1/99
7-Nibbly the heather bunny 1/1/99

Cats
1-Nip the gold cat 3/10/96
2-Zip the black cat 3/10/96
3-Flip the white cat 1/7/96
4-Chip the calico cat 5/11/97
5-Snip the Siamese cat 1/1/97
6-Pounce the brown cat 12/31/97
7-Prance the tiger cat 12/31/97
8-Scat the heather cat 1/1/99
9-Amber the gold striped cat
4/19/99
10-Silver the gray striped cat
4/21/99

Chameleons
1-Rainbow the chameleon w/ blue
tie-dyed fabric 12/31/97
2-replaced by Rainbow the
chameleon w/ rainbow tie-
dyed fabric 5/30/98

Clubby
1-Clubby the royal blue BBOC mascot, summer '98 (1st BBOC
mascot)
2-Clubby II the orchid heather
BBOC mascot, spring '99 (2nd
BBOC mascot)

Crabs
1-Digger the orange crab 6/25/94
2-replaced by Digger the red crab
6/3/95
3-Claude the tie-dyed crab
5/11/97

Dalmatians
1-Sparky 6/15/96
2-renamed Dotty 5/11/97

Derby the brown horse
1-w/ fine yarn mane & tail, '95
2-w/ coarse yarn mane & tail, '95-
'97
3-w/ coarse yarn mane & tail +
white diamond on forehead,
'98
4-w/ hairy mane & tail + white
diamond on forehead, '99

Dinosaurs
1-Bronty the brontosaurus 6/3/95
2-Rex the tyrannosaurus 6/3/95
3-Steg the stegosaurus 6/3/95

Dogs
1-Spot the dog w/o spot 1/8/94
2-replaced by Spot the dog w/ spot
4/13/94
3-Bones the brown hound 6/25/94
4-Weenie the dachshund 1/7/96
5-Sparky the dalmatian 6/15/96
6-replaced by Dottie the dalmatian
5/11/97
7-Rover the red hound 6/15/96
8-Wrinkles the bulldog 6/15/96
9-Scottie the napped terrier
6/15/96
10-Bernie the St. Bernard 1/1/97
11-Doby the doberman 1/1/97
12-Nanook the husky 5/11/97
13-Pugsly the pug 5/11/97
14-Tuffy the napped terrier 5/11/97
15-Bruno the bull terrier 12/31/97
16-Spunky the cockerspaniel
12/31/97
17-Fetch the golden lab 5/30/98
18-Gigi the poodle 5/30/98
19-Tracker the basset hound
5/30/98
20-Butch the bull terrier 1/1/99
21-Luke the black lab 1/1/99
22-Tiny the chihuahua 1/1/99

Dolphins
1-Flash the gray dolphin 1/8/94
2-Echo the marine blue dolphin
   5/11/97

Dragons
1-Magic the white dragon 6/3/95
2-Scorch the brown dragon
   9/30/98

Elephants
1-Peanut the royal blue elephant
   6/3/95
2-replaced by Peanut the light blue
   elephant 10/2/95
3-Righty the gray Republican elephant w/ U.S. flag 6/15/96

Fish
1-Goldie the goldfish 6/25/94
2-Coral the tie-dyed fish 6/3/95
3-Bubbles the yellow fish w/ black
   stripes 6/3/95
4-Goochy the tie-dyed jellyfish
   1/1/99

Frogs
1-Legs the green frog 1/8/94
2-Smoochy the green & gold frog
   12/31/97

Happy the Hippo
1-Gray 6/25/94
2-replaced by purple Happy
   6/3/95

Iguanas
1-Iggy the iguana w/ rainbow tie-
   dyed fabric 12/31/97
2-Iggy the iguana w/ tongue,
   spring '98
3-replaced by Iggy the iguana w/
   blue tie-dyed fabric 5/30/98

Inch the multi-colored inchworm
1-w/ felt antennae 6/3/95
2-replaced by Inch w/ yarn
   antennae 10/15/97

Inky the octopus
1-Tan w/o mouth 6/25/94
2-replaced by tan Inky w/ mouth
   9/12/94
3-replaced by pink Inky w/ mouth
   6/3/95

Lambs
1-Chops the cream-colored lamb
   1/7/96
2-Fleece the white lamb 1/1/97
3-Ewey the cream-colored lamb
   1/1/99

Lizzy the lizard
1-Tie-dyed 6/3/95
2-replaced by blue Lizzy 1/7/96

Lobsters
1-Punchers 1/8/94
2-renamed Pinchers, '94

Lucky the red ladybug
1-w/ felt spots 6/25/94
2-replaced by Lucky w/ printed
   spots 2/27/96

Magic the white dragon
1-w/ hot pink thread, '96-'97
2-w/ pale pink thread, '95-'97

Maple the white bear w/ Canadian flag
1-w/ "Pride" tush tag, '97
2-w/ "Maple" tush tag, '97

Mice
1-Trap the gray mouse 6/25/94
2-Tiptoe the brown mouse 4/16/99

Monkeys
1-Nana the brown monkey w/ tan tail
2-renamed Bongo the brown monkey w/ tan tail 6/3/95
3-Bongo the brown monkey w/ brown tail 2/6/96
4-Mooch the black spider monkey 1/1/99
5-Schweetheart the red orang-utan 4/11/99
6-Cheeks the brown heather baboon 4/17/99

Mystic the white unicorn
1-w/ fine yarn mane & tail + gold horn, '94-'95
2-w/ coarse yarn mane & tail + gold horn, '95-'97
3-w/ coarse yarn mane & tail + iridescent horn, '97-'98
4-w/ rainbow-colored hairy mane & tail + iridescent horn, '99

Nip the gold cat
1-w/ white face 1/7/95
2-replaced by all gold Nip 1/7/96
3-replaced by Nip w/ white socks 3/10/96

Owls
1-Hoot the brown & tan owl 1/7/96
2-Wise the brown owl/Class of '98 5/30/98 (1st graduation owl)
3-Wiser the gray striped owl/Class of '99 4/22/99 (2nd graduation owl)

Patti the platypus
1-Maroon 1/8/94
2-replaced by magenta Patti 2/28/95

Peanut the elephant
1-Royal blue 6/3/95
2-replaced by light blue Peanut 10/2/95

Penguins
1-Waddles 6/3/95
2-Zero w/ red cap 9/30/98

Pigs
1-Squealer the pink pig 1/8/94
2-Knuckles the flesh-colored pig 4/14/99

Princess the royal purple bear
1-w/ PVC filling, '97
2-w/ PE filling, '98

Quackers the yellow duck
1-w/o wings 6/25/94
2-replaced by Quackers w/ wings 1/7/95

Roosters
1-Doodles the tie-dyed rooster
2-renamed Strut 7/12/97

Sly the fox
1-w/ brown belly 6/15/96
2-replaced by Sly w/ white belly 8/6/96

Snakes
1-Slither the green long snake 6/25/94
2-Hissy the blue coiled snake 12/31/97

Spiders
1-Web the black spider 6/25/94
2-Spinner the black & brown spider 10/1/97

Spooky the white ghost
1-w/ "Spook" tag, '95
2-w/ "Spooky" tag, '95-'97

Spot the white dog
1-w/o a spot 1/8/94
2-replaced by Spot w/ a spot
    4/13/94

Stripes the gold tiger
1-w/ thin stripes 1/7/96
2-replaced by Stripes w/ wide
    stripes 6/3/96

Tank the armadillo
1-w/o shell 1/7/95
2-replaced by Tank w/ shell
    1/7/96

Tigers
1-Stripes the gold tiger w/ thin
    stripes 1/7/96
2-replaced by Stripes the gold tiger
    w/ wide stripes 6/3/96
3-Blizzard the white tiger 5/11/97

Walruses
1-Tusk the brown walrus 1/7/95
2-Jolly the brown bearded walrus
    5/11/97
3-Paul the brown walrus w/ tusks
    & beard 4/12/99

Whales
1-Splash the black & white whale
    1/8/94
2-Waves the black & white whale
    5/11/97

Zip the black cat
1-w/ white face 1/7/95
2-replaced by all black Zip 1/7/96
3-replaced by Zip w/ white socks
    3/10/96

List #5:

Beanie Baby™ birthdays
As of 5/30/99

Some collectors like to know which Beanie Babies® were born on their birthday (or on the birthdays of family members and friends), hence, following is a list of all Beanie Babies® with birthdays to date, for your information and shopping/collecting convenience.

January
1 Millennium, Spot
2 Zero
5 Kuku
6 Patti
8 Tiptoe
13 Crunch
14 Spunky
15 Mel
17 Slippery
18 Bones
21 Nuts
23 Schweetheart
25 Peanut
26 Chip

February
1 Peace
3 Beak
4 Fetch
5 Osito
11 Silver
13 Pinky, Stinky
14 Valentina, Valentino
17 Baldy
19 Prickles
20 Roary
21 Amber
22 Tank
23 Paul
25 Happy
27 Sparky
28 Flip

March
1 Ewey

2 Coral
6 Nip
8 Strut
10 Swirly
12 Rocket
14 Ally
17 Erin
19 Seaweed
20 Early
21 Fleece
23 Hope
25 Knuckles
28 Zip
29 Loosy

April
1 Neon
3 Hoppity
4 Hissy
5 Whisper
6 Nibbler
7 Gigi
10 Eggbert
12 Curly
14 Almond
15 Pecan
16 Jake
18 Ears
19 Quackers
23 Squealer
25 Legs
27 Chocolate
28 Eucalyptus

May
1 Lucky, Wrinkles

2 Pugsly
3 Chops
4 Hippie
7 Nibbly
10 Daisy
11 Lizzy
13 Flash
15 Tabasco, Snort
18 Cheeks
19 Twigs
21 Mystic
27 Scat
28 Floppity
29 Canyon
30 Rover
31 Wise

June
1 Hippity
3 Freckles
4 Wiser
5 Tracker
8 Manny, Bucky
10 Mac
11 Stripes
14 Spangle
15 Luke, Scottie
16 Stilts
17 Gracie
19 Pinchers
23 Sammy
27 Bessie

July
1 Maple, Scoop
2 Bubbles

4 Lefty, Righty, Glory
8 Splash
14 Ringo
15 Blackie
19 Grunt
20 Weenie
23 Fuzz
31 Scorch

August
1 Garcia, Mooch
9 Hoot
12 Iggy
13 Spike
14 Speedy
16 Kicks
17 Bongo
23 Digger
27 Sting
28 Pounce
31 Halo

September
3 Inch, Claude
5 Magic
8 Tiny
9 Bruno
12 Sly
16 Kiwi, Derby
18 Tusk
21 Stretch
27 Roam
29 Stinger

October
1 Smoochy
2 Butch
3 Bernie, Germania
9 Doby
10 Jabber
12 Tuffy
14 Rainbow
17 Dotty
22 Snip
28 Spinner

29 Batty
30 Radar
31 Pumkin, Spooky

November
3 Puffer
4 Goatee
6 Pouch
7 Ants
9 Congo
14 Cubbie, Goldie
18 Goochy
20 Prance
21 Nanook
27 Gobbles
28 Teddy Brown (new)
29 Inky

December
2 Jolly
6 Fortune, Santa
8 Waves
12 Blizzard
14 Seamore
15 Britannia
16 Velvet
19 Waddle
21 Echo
22 Snowball
24 Ziggy
25 1997 Holiday Teddy,
   1998 Holiday Teddy